The
Quiet Conquest
THE HUGUENOTS
1685 TO 1985

A Museum of London exhibition in association with the Huguenot Society of London
15 May to 31 October 1985

Catalogue compiled by Tessa Murdoch

MUSEUM OF LONDON *in association with* A H Jolly (Editorial) Limited

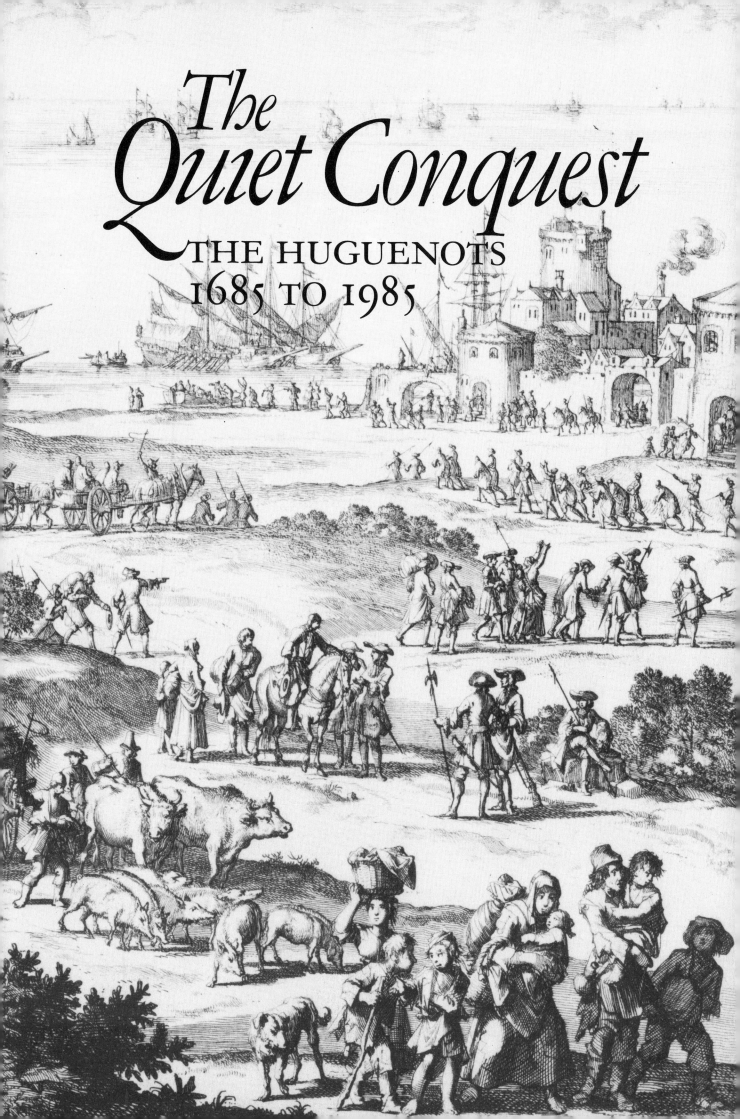

The Quiet Conquest

THE HUGUENOTS
1685 TO 1985

Catalogue contributors

Tessa Murdoch
Tudor & Stuart Department, Museum of London

Rosemary Weinstein
Tudor & Stuart Department, Museum of London

Natalie Rothstein
Department of Textiles, Victoria & Albert Museum

Robin Gwynn
Director of Huguenot Heritage

Chris Ellmers
Modern Department, Museum of London

Celina Fox
Paintings, Prints & Drawings Department, Museum of London

Mireille Galinou
Paintings, Prints & Drawings Department, Museum of London

Marjorie Trusted
Department of Sculpture, Victoria & Albert Museum

Wendy Evans
Modern Department, Museum of London

Robert Baldwin
Modern Department, Museum of London

Amanda Herries
Modern Department, Museum of London

Anne Jones
Tudor & Stuart Department, Museum of London

Julian Litten
Department of Prints & Drawings, Victoria & Albert Museum

Contributors' catalogue entries are listed on page 18

EXHIBITION DESIGN
Christopher Hutton
Hancock Hutton and Wilcher

CATALOGUE PRODUCTION
PHOTOGRAPHERS
John Edwards and Barrington Gray
MAP ILLUSTRATOR
Brian Elkins
DESIGNERS
David Challis and Tony Waugh
EDITORIAL ADVISERS
Valerie Cumming, Robin Gwynn, Charles Marmoy and Randolph Vigne
PUBLISHER
Alec Jolly

Set in Monophoto Garamond

Filmset, originated and printed in England by Jolly & Barber Ltd, Rugby

ISBN 0 904818 14 4

TITLE SPREAD ILLUSTRATION
The flight of the Huguenots, a contemporary Dutch engraving by Jan Luyken, 1696

RIJKSMUSEUM, AMSTERDAM

FRONT COVER ILLUSTRATION
Huguenots emerging from worship at the conformist French church, Les Grecs, Hog Lane, Soho. The kite, above, is a symbol of their past flight. Oil on canvas, William Hogarth, c.1736

THE GRIMSTHORPE AND DRUMMOND CASTLE TRUSTEES

BACK COVER ILLUSTRATION
Paul Crespin (1694–1770), Huguenot goldsmith resident in Soho. Crespin worked for the King of Portugal, the Empress Catherine of Russia, and Frederick, Prince of Wales. Oil on canvas, attributed to Pierre Subleyras, c.1726

PRIVATE COLLECTION

FOREWORD

The Quiet Conquest: the Huguenots 1685 to 1985 is the result of a happy and fruitful collaboration between the Museum of London and the Huguenot Society of London. Since the earliest discussions regarding this exhibition in the late 1970s, the Huguenot Society has demonstrated admirable enthusiasm and support for every stage of the project. The Museum is pleased to have this opportunity to present the first major exhibition to examine the Huguenot contribution to British life, and it is appropriate that this should take place in 1985 which is designated *Huguenot Heritage Year*, the tercentenary of the Revocation of the Edict of Nantes.

In 1685 Louis XIV revoked the Edict of Nantes, signed by Henry IV in 1598, which had guaranteed religious toleration to the Protestants in France. Huguenots (French Protestants) first settled in Britain in the 1550s. During the late seventeenth century, large numbers of Huguenot refugees joined Britain's established Huguenot communities. Their quiet integration into our society during the subsequent centuries has passed almost unnoticed. It is the intention of both the Museum and the Society that, by the time 1985 draws to its close, everyone will have had an opportunity to discover who the Huguenots were and what they achieved. The exhibition celebrates their rich contribution to all aspects of the nation's life: the arts, crafts, commerce, science and industry.

Her Majesty the Queen and a great many private, public and institutional lenders in Britain and abroad, have generously agreed to our request for loans. Many private lenders are allowing us to exhibit material which is an integral element in their family's Huguenot ancestry. The Huguenot connection is reinforced by invaluable help given by the French Hospital and the Huguenot Library. The Huguenot Society have helped in every sphere of the exhibition's preparation, with loans, specialist advice and the co-ordination of sponsorship.

Within the Museum, the determination and tireless energy of the Keeper of the Tudor and Stuart Department, Rosemary Weinstein, has ensured the production of an exhibition which allies scholarship to presentation in a manner which befits the subject matter. She has been ably assisted by her colleague, Tessa Murdoch, who has compiled the catalogue and drawn unstintingly upon her own unpublished researches into Huguenot history and craftsmanship to strengthen many sections of the exhibition. Anne Jones and Anne Middleton of the Tudor and Stuart Department and other colleagues within the Museum have contributed expertise, and co-operated with their usual wholehearted enthusiasm during the whole of the project. Outside the Museum, we extend our thanks to colleagues who contributed catalogue entries, and to the many people who commented on the text for both the exhibition and catalogue. The design of the exhibition by Christopher Hutton, provides an excellent example of the manner in which widely varied material can be brought together in a fruitful and complementary way. The catalogue, designed by David Challis in close collaboration with Tony Waugh, has been made possible through the generous support of Alec Jolly.

Max Hebditch
Director

Acknowledgments

A great many people have contributed towards the exhibition and catalogue, but particular thanks are due to the Honorary Librarian of the Huguenot Society of London, Mr Charles Marmoy and the Honorary Secretary, Miss Irene Scouloudi, Mr Stephen de Crespigny, Secretary of the French Hospital, Dr Robin Gwynn, Director of Huguenot Heritage, Mr Yves Jaulmes, Treasurer of the French Church, Soho Square and Mrs Jaulmes, the Lady Monson, Chairman of Huguenot Heritage, Mr Jonathan Ouvry, Mrs Jean Tsushima, Mr Randolph Vigne, President of the Huguenot Society of London and Miss Yvette Williams have all been particularly generous with their knowledge and time. We are grateful to His Excellency M Emmanuel and Mme de Margerie for their encouragement during the early days of the project.

Dr Charles Avery, Mr Malcom Baker, Mr David Beasley, Mr Frank Britton, Miss Mireille Galinou, Miss Susan Hare and Miss Natalie Rothstein have kindly read sections of the catalogue and made invaluable suggestions. Mrs Valerie Cumming, Dr Robin Gwynn, Mr Charles Marmoy and Mr Randolph Vigne have read the full catalogue and have made many helpful comments. Particular thanks are due to Dr Robin Gwynn who has often drawn on his own unpublished research to add important new information where appropriate.

Other curators, librarians, scholars, private owners and friends who have been particularly helpful include Mr Brian Allen, Miss Judith Bannister, Mr Howard Blackmore, Mr Melvyn Barnes, Mrs Elaine Barr, Mr David Beasley, Dr Sarah Bevan, Dr David Bindman, Mr Tony Bingham, Mr Richard Broyd, Mrs Pat Buchanan, Mr Ian Burgoyne, Miss Marion Campbell, Miss Frances Carey, Miss Joan Chowdry, Mr Peter Day, Mr C Downey, Mrs Marie Draper, Pasteur Dubois, Mr Charles Du Cane, Dr Terry Friedman, Mr Richard Garnier, Mrs Madeleine Ginsberg, Dr Mark Girouard, Mrs Philippa Glanville, Mr J W Gledhill, Miss Francesca Gostling, Mr Irvine Gray, Mr Edwin Green, Mr Arthur Grimwade, Mr John Hardy, Miss Avril Hart, Mr Ian Haslam, Miss Wendy Hefford, Captain David Horn, Sir Westrow Hulse, Mr Ralph Hyde, Mr Gervase Jackson-Stops, Mr Cedric Jagger, Mr Mark Jones, Mr John Kerslake, Mr John Keyworth, Mr Alastair Laing, Mr Christopher Lloyd, Mr John Lord, Mr Tony Mackle, Mr John Mallet, Mr James de la Mare, Mr Peter Miall, Mr James Miller, Mr Jeremy Montagu, Mr David Murdoch, Mr Patrick Noon, Miss Sheila O'Connell, Major Charles O'Leary, Miss Elaine Paintin, Miss Frances Palmer, Mr Richard Parsons, Miss Julia Pilkington, Mr William Place, Mrs Clare Prince, Mr Tony Radcliffe, Dr Robert Raines, Miss Rosemary Ransome-Wallis, Mrs Florence Roper, Miss Natalie Rothstein, Mr Michael Snodin, Mr Hugh Tait, Mme Odette Tessier du Cros, Dr Christian Theuerkauff, Mr F H Thompson, Mr Martyn Tillier, Mr David Tooth, Mr Charles Truman, Miss Marjorie Trusted, Mrs Sheila Tull, Dr William Vaughan, Dr J J Vogel, Mrs Eve Walch, Miss Patricia Want, Mr Anthony Wells-Cole, Sir Richard Wheeler, Mr D E Wickham, Colonel P Willing, Mr Tim Wilson, Miss Sarah Wimbush.

We are grateful to Mr Julian Brigstocke for proof-reading, Mrs Jill Ford for compiling the index, and Mrs Jean Duke for typesetting the catalogue, Mr Desmond Taylor for photograph origination, and the rest of the staff at Jolly & Barber Ltd who printed the catalogue.

CONTENTS

By the King and Queen,

A DECLARATION

For the Encouraging of French *Proteſtants to Tranſport themſelves into this Kingdom.*

William R.

Hereas it hath pleaſed Almighty God to Deliver Our Realm of *England,* and the Subjects thereof, from the Perſecution lately threatning them for their Religion, and from the Oppreſſion and Deſtruction which the Subverſion of their Laws, and the Arbitrary Exerciſe of Power and Dominion over them had very near introduced; We finding in Our Subjects a True and Juſt Senſe hereof, and of the Miſeries and Oppreſſions the *French* Proteſtants lye under; For their Relief, and to Encourage them that ſhall be willing to Tranſport themſelves, their Families and Eſtates, into this Our Kingdom, We do hereby Declare, That all *French* Proteſtants that ſhall ſeek their Refuge in, and Tranſport themſelves into this Our Kingdom, ſhall not only have Our Royal Protection for themſelves, Families and Eſtates, within this Our Realm, But We will alſo do Our Endeavour in all reaſonable Ways and Means ſo to Support, Aid and Aſſiſt them in their ſeveral and reſpective Trades and Ways of Livelyhood, as that their living and being in this Realm may be comfortable and eaſie to them.

Given at Our Court at Whitehall *this Twenty fifth Day of* April, 1689, *In the Firſt Year of Our Reign.*

God ſave the King and Queen.

L O N D O N,

Printed by *Charles Bill* and *Thomas Newcomb,* Printers to the King and Queen's moſt Excellent Majeſties. 1689.

INTRODUCTION

A Declaration of William and Mary encouraging French Protestant Refugees to settle in England, 1689 (left)

In November 1738, Philip Stanhope, 4th Earl of Chesterfield, commented on the eagerness with which the fashion for French taste was pursued and pointed out that those in search of the same would find 'a much shorter, less expensive and more effectual method of travelling and frenchifying themselves ... if they would but travel to Old Soho and stay two or three months in le quartier des Grecs. Lodgings and legumes are very cheap there, and the people very civil to strangers. There too, they might possibly get acquainted with some French people which they never do at Paris, and it may be learn a little French which they never do in France neither, and I appeal to anyone who has seen these venerable persons of both sexes, of the refugees, if they are not infinitely more genteel, easier, and better dressed in the French manner, than any of their modern English mimics'.[1]

1. Matthew Maty, *The Miscellaneous Works of the late Philip Dormer Stanhope, Earl of Chesterfield*, 1777, Vol. I, pp. 99–104.

Fifty-three years after the Revocation of the Edict of Nantes, the Huguenot immigrants who had settled in England, and their descendants, were still identified as a separate community, speaking their own language, and recognizable for their culture. This Huguenot presence inspired William Hogarth's painting 'Noon', which contrasts the soberly dressed members of the Huguenot community emerging from their worship at the Eglise des Grecs, with the disorderly natives on the other side of the gutter. The elaborately dressed group in the immediate foreground are probably English fops, identifying with the Huguenot community in their eagerness to pursue the French taste.

L'Eglise des Grecs was the meeting place of one of the two original Huguenot congregations in London's West End. Their service conformed to the Anglican liturgy. By 1700 there were fourteen Huguenot 'temples' in the Soho area.[2] The refugees who worshipped there were attracted to the area by its proximity to the Court at St. James's and the Palace of Westminster, the seat of government, law and patronage. They specialised in trades which served the upper and growing middle classes. Many worked in the fashion trade as tailors or wigmakers. Andrew Regnier, with premises in Pall Mall and Leicester Fields in the 1750s, was Lord Chesterfield's tailor. By 1733, a letter from a London wigmaker in the 'Gentleman's Magazine' complained, 'Now, is it not a cruel case that a Tradesman shall not be employed merely because he is an Englishman'. The Huguenot dominance in the fashion trade included the manufacture of shoes, gloves and hats.

2. Robin D. Gwynn, *The Distribution of Huguenot Refugees in England, II, London and its Environs*, Proceedings of the Huguenot Society of London, Vol. 22 (1971–76), pp. 509–568.

From the 1680s Soho became the home of skilled craftsmen who supplied the gentry with luxury goods, silver, furniture, watches and jewellery. When William III's Huguenot architect, Daniel Marot, was based in England in the 1680s, he lived in the Leicester Fields area. One of the first refugee goldsmiths to be admitted to the Freedom of the Goldsmiths' Company in 1682, Pierre Harache, from Rouen, lived in Suffolk Street, near Charing Cross. Furniture makers included the skilled Pelletier family who were patronised by the Duke of Montagu, formerly ambassador to the Court of Louis XIV at Versailles. These craftsmen handed on their skills to the next generation and in the 1730s the Huguenots still dominated their respective fields, and the demand for work in London even attracted refugees who had initially settled elsewhere on the continent, such as the engineer Charles Labelye.

Francis Perigal, a third generation Huguenot craftsman, who achieved recognition in his own right, became watchmaker to George III. His family originally came from Dieppe and an account of their exodus from France is contained in a remarkable manuscript entitled 'Histoire des Antiquitez, et de la Reformation de la Ville de Dieppe et de ce qui s'est passé de plus remarquable dans L'Eglise et dans la Ville', which was compiled in 1723 by Jean Perigal, an ivory turner who settled in London.[3]

3. Frederick Perigal, *Story of Jean Perigal of Dieppe*, Proceedings of the Huguenot Society of London, Vol. 2 (1886–8), pp. 14–42.

Denis Papin (1647–1712)
Huguenot scientist, holding
a copy of his account of
the 'New Digester of
Bones'; artist unknown,
c.1688
(far left)

Thomas Papillon
(1623–1702) Huguenot
merchant, Director of the
East India Company, and
politician, Sir Godfrey
Kneller, 1698
(left)

Henry Guinand
(1686–1755) Huguenot
merchant, Director of the
French Hospital, 1721,
and Deputy Governor,
1739; artist unknown
c.1721
(far left)

Sir Richard Houblon
(1672–1724) Huguenot
merchant and Director of
the Bank of England
1713–20; after Kneller,
c.1715
(left)

4. A.F.W. Papillon, Thomas
Papillon of London, Merchant,
1623–1702, 1887.

In October 1685, Perigal noted, 'Tous Paris était plein d'une nouvelle c'était la Révocation de L'Edit de Nantes, avec order aux Ministres de sortir du Roiaume quinze jours après la publication sous peine des Galères avec promesse de laisser les Protestants en repos chez eux, jusques à ce qu'il plut à Dieu de les illuminer'.

Far from being left to their own devices, the Protestants were harassed by the 'dragoons', soldiers who were billeted on private homes, and encouraged to maltreat their hosts. In Dieppe, these troops, who entered the town in early November 1685, were responsible for the conversion of over 4,000 Protestants, but some one hundred and forty families managed to escape, and fifty citizens who refused to abjure their faith were imprisoned. Jean Perigal was one of the latter, arrested on 6 December 1685 in Dieppe, taken to a prison at Aumale on 19 December, and returned to Dieppe in March 1688. This return was in response to an 'Ordre du Roi ... de faire sortir de mon Roiaume le petit nombre de mes sujets qui ont persisté jusques à présent dans l'obstination à ne pas abjurer la Religion Prétendue Réformée'. Thus prisoners from Rouen, Neuchatel, Aumale and Caudebec were transferred to the Château at Dieppe to await embarkation. Jean Perigal had been in the same prison as his mother, but at Dieppe was reunited with his father, although his two brothers and a sister were already 'hors du Roiaume'. In April 1688, ninety-three prisoners from the Château at Dieppe left France in a forty-ton vessel and landed at Dover, where their first reaction was to seek out the minister of the French congregation and give thanks for their deliverance. The Perigal family then made for London via Canterbury, Rochester and Gravesend, where they were reunited with Jean's sister. She had also been imprisoned at Dieppe, but had escaped and had lived for some time in London, with her husband and one of her brothers, who had also escaped at the time of the dragonnades without having abjured.

This account of the Perigal family is one of the happiest and most exceptional stories of the exodus. Such ardent Protestants, who refused to abjure their faith after three years of persecution and imprisonment, were an embarrassment to the French establishment, and the problem was best solved by arranging their removal. Other refugees were less fortunate. If caught attempting to leave France, Protestants were liable to be sentenced to the galleys for a lifetime's penal servitude. Children were smuggled out in wine barrels or panniers of bread; perhaps it was the fear of losing their children, who from the age of seven onwards might be taken and put into convents, that persuaded the greater number of the refugees to emigrate.

Why did they come to England? Many settled in Holland, Prussia and Switzerland. For those who already had trading contacts with England, for example, the Rouen merchant Isaac Caillouel, it was probably relatively straightforward to transfer property in kind and arrange personal transport. Ships also offered capacity for concealing the refugees, although after October 1685, they were liable to be searched by the authorities. The refugees were attracted to Britain as they would be joining a settled community of Huguenots who had come to London and the South East, Canterbury, Southampton and Norwich, from the latter half of the sixteenth century onwards. The first Huguenot church in London was founded in 1550.

Furthermore, the descendants of many of these earlier refugees were by then in a strong position to assist their compatriots. Sir John Houblon, one of the founders of the Bank of England and its first Governor, was a member of a Walloon family that was well established in the City of London by the mid-seventeenth century. The des Bouveries were another eminent family, and by the 1690s pillars of the Levant Company. Thomas Papillon, Member of Parliament for the City of London, 1695–1700, was the son of David Papillon, who emigrated to England in 1588.[4]

On 28 July 1681, Charles II issued a proclamation offering England as a place of refuge. The refugees would receive letters patent of denization under the Great Seal, free of expense, and their possessions and stock in trade were to be landed duty free. Despite this encouragement, many fled to Holland instead. Amsterdam was particularly charitable. One contemporary reported

William De La Cour (d.1767) Huguenot designer and drawing master, self portrait, 1765 (far left)

Louis François Roubiliac (1702/5–1762) Huguenot sculptor, with a model for David Garrick's statue of Shakespeare; Adrien Carpentiers, c.1762 (left)

5. *An Accurate Description of the United Netherlands,* 1691, pp. 27,111.

6. Robin D. Gwynn, *James II: His Treatment of Huguenot Refugees 1685–1686,* Proceedings of the Huguenot Society of London, Vol. 23 (1980), pp. 212–224.

7. Abel Boyer, *History of the Life and Reign of Queen Anne,* 1722, p. 369.

8. Georgia Harkness, *John Calvin, The Man and his Ethics,* 1931, p.164.

Louisa Perina Courtauld (1729–1807) Huguenot goldsmith, attributed to Nathaniel Dance, c.1770 (far left)

Smart Lethieullier (1701–1760) Huguenot scholar and collector, George Knapton, c.1725 (left)

9. William Chapman Waller, *Early Huguenot Friendly Societies,* Proceedings of the Huguenot Society of London, Vol. 6 (1898–1901), pp. 201–236.

10. C.F.A. Marmoy, *La Soupe: La Maison de Charité de Spittlefields,* Proceedings of the Huguenot Society of London, Vol. 23 (1977–82), pp. 134–147.

11. C.F.A. Marmoy, *La Providence: the French Hospital during two and a half centuries,* Proceedings of the Huguenot Society of London, Vol. 21 (1967–68), pp. 335–354.

that the city authorities lent sums of money without interest for the refugees to buy tools and materials for their work. By contrast, it was rumoured that in England refugees were being persecuted, the Bank at London was broke, aliens could not purchase land, and that the English were restless and quarrelsome, contriving and plotting against their lawful sovereign and the government.[5] This was probably the result of the ambivalence of the Catholic James II's attitude towards the Huguenots, and with the Protestant William III's accession to the English throne, such rumours were dispelled.[6]

Why were the Huguenots encouraged to settle in Great Britain? When Edward Wortley Montagu proposed in 1708 the motion for the naturalisation of French Protestants, he showed the advantages that would accrue to the Nation by such an Act 'Alledging amongst other particulars the example of the King of Prussia, who had not only invited but furnished abundance of French Refugees with Means to settle in his Dominions, whereby he had fertilised an almost barren country, improved Trade and vastly increased his Revenue, and added that if foreigners were induced to settle under a Despotick Government, where they found protection and encouragement, they would undoubtedly be the more inclined to bring their effects and their Industry into Great Britain, where they would share the priveleges of a Free Nation'.[7]

Furthermore, the Huguenots had established a reputation for their industry and hard work. This was the result of their Calvinistic ethic which assigned a high value to work, regarding it as 'the practical exercise of a calling appointed by God' and therefore as Divine Worship. Work was an appropriate method of self-discipline, and a means of averting temptation. The distinctive feature of Calvin's creed was the belief in election by grace. This dictated an absolute duty to consider oneself chosen and to combat all doubts as temptations, in order to continue in God's grace.[8] Another distinctive feature of the Huguenot way of life was the democratic organisation of their church; all churches and pastors were considered equal, and preachers were chosen by ballot. Huguenot social life was organised in much the same way; the individual responsibility to fulfil the daily task was used to achieve a rational organisation of their social environment. Ultimately the Huguenot was responsible for working out his own salvation, and this individual responsibility, common to large groups of refugees, produced the Huguenot traits of reverence, chastity, sobriety, frugality, industry and honesty.

Many of the poorer refugees were weavers and settled in Spitalfields, to the east of the City of London, which became a centre of the silk trade. Jean Perigal, transported from prison in Dieppe, arrived without any possessions, and is recorded ten years later as living in Artillery Ground, Fore Street, Spitalfields. The attractions of this area included its proximity to the City and the original Huguenot congregation, founded in 1550, at the Threadneedle Street church, although by 1700 there were nine Huguenot churches in Spitalfields, none of which conformed to the Anglican Liturgy. The less prosperous refugees were probably also attracted to the East End by the presence there of Friendly Societies, such as the Society of Parisians, founded in 1687, or the Society of the Province of Normandy, founded in 1703, to maintain mutual friendship amongst refugees from Normandy and to provide financial assistance in case of sickness and death.[9] In case of dire need, there was also the Spitalfields 'Soupe' which was founded in the winter of 1689.[10] There was an equivalent in Soho, and the poorer refugees relied to a certain extent on donations from the backdoors of great houses, such as those recorded in the archives of the Bedford family.

By 1718, the need for assistance in case of sickness was relieved by the foundation of the French Hospital, originally housed in Old Street, Clerkenwell, and then moved to Victoria Park, Hackney in the 1860s; it is now still functioning in Rochester, Kent.[11] It was founded by Jacques de Gastigny, an officer in William III's army, and many of its directors in the eighteenth century were Huguenot descendants with strong and useful connections in the City, Army, Law or Trade.

Even the well-established Huguenot refugees in Soho built up their own support groups, such as the Huguenot Masonic Lodge recorded in Hemmings

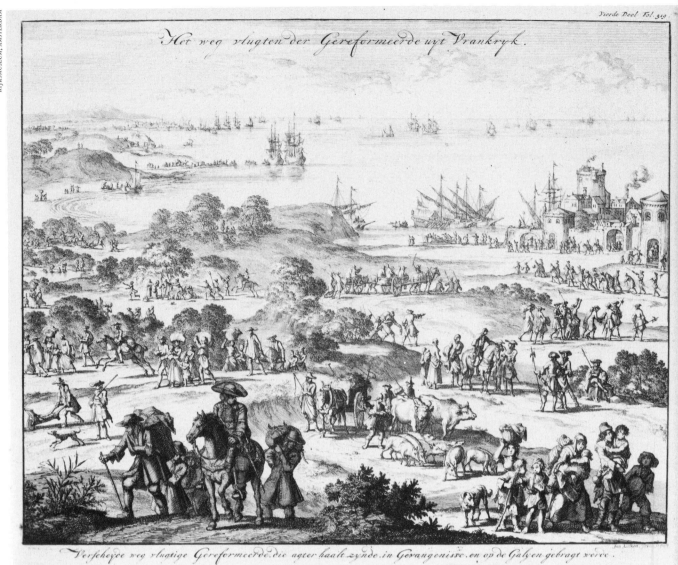

Het weg vlugten der Gereformeerde uyt Vrankryk.

Verscheyde weg vlugtige Gereformeerde die agter haalt zynde in Gevangenisse en op de Galyen gebragt werde.

Row, off St. Martin's Lane *c.*1725, which included amongst its membership, the scientist John Theophilus Desaguliers, the engineer Charles Labelye, and watchmaker Daniel Grignion.[12]

In 1747, Huguenot descendants founded the French Protestant School at Westminster, which also survives in the form of a charity today, giving grants for educational purposes.[13]

These support groups, Friendly Societies, Huguenot Masonic Lodges, and primarily the French Hospital, helped to arouse the interest with which the memory of the Huguenots who settled in this country is revered today. In 1885, the Huguenot Society of London was founded by Directors of the French Hospital to further research and interest in 'these venerable persons', as a commemoration of the bicentenary of the Revocation of the Edict of Nantes. The tercentenary is appropriately marked in England by a major international exhibition (the first to examine the wide Huguenot contribution to British culture, industry and finance), a nation-wide Huguenot Heritage Trail and a Historical Conference at the Royal Society. These activities, co-ordinated under the title 'Huguenot Heritage' have been organised by the descendants of those original refugees who made England their home as a result of the persecution which culminated in the Revocation of the Edict of Nantes.

Tessa Murdoch

The Flight of the Huguenots, engraving; Jan Luyken, 1696 (above)

12. Information kindly supplied by Mr. J. Hammill, Librarian, United Grand Lodge.

13. Susan Minet, *The French Protestant School, Westminster*, Proceedings of the Huguenot Society of London, Vol. 12 (1917–23), pp. 91–117; Vol. 13 (1923–29), pp. 374–392.

Sir John Ligonier (1680–1770) Huguenot soldier, Colonel of the Royal Regiment of Horse Guards; Sir Joshua Reynolds, 1755 (right)

Financial supporters

The Huguenot Society of London and the
Museum of London are indebted to the
following who have contributed financial
support to the exhibition.

Baddeley Bros.
Bankers Trust Company
The Bank of England
Barclays Bank PLC
The Baring Foundation
The Brewers' Company
The Butchers' Company
Cazenove & Company
The Clothworkers' Company
The Augustine Courtauld Trust
Dollond and Aitchison Group Limited
De Clermont Charitable Company Limited
The Du Boulay Charitable Trust
The Drapers' Company
The Dyers' Company
The Fanmakers' Company
The Goldsmiths' Company
The Grocers' Company
The Members of Lloyd's and Lloyd's Brokers
The Mercers' Company
The Idlewild Trust
The McLaren Foundation
Paul Minet Esq
The Peter Minet Trust
N.J.H. Minet Esq
J.H. Minet & Company Limited
National Westminster Bank
G.S. Panchaud
Portals Holdings PLC
S C O R (UK) Reinsurance Company Limited
The Siddons Trust
The 27 Foundation
The Vintners' Company
The Weavers' Company
Willis Faber & Dumas Limited
The Woolmen's Company

*The Museum of London is funded by the
Office of Arts and Libraries, the
Greater London Council and the
Corporation of the City of London*

Colour plates

John Calvin (1509–1564) oil on card,
German School, 1535
Catalogue number 1

Edward VI Giving John à Lasco and his
Congregation a charter, oil on canvas, English
School, early seventeenth century
Catalogue number 52

The French Hospital, Victoria Park, Hackney
watercolour, attributed to R.L. Roumieu,
c.1870

Catalogue number 101

Jacques de Gastigny (d.1708), founder of the
French Hospital, oil on canvas, attributed to
Thomas Murray, c.1690

Catalogue number 90

L.ᵗGeneral De Jean

*Lieutenant-General de Jean (d.1764) oil on
canvas, attributed to Philip Mercier, c.1740*

Catalogue number 141

Noon, L'Eglise des Grecs, Hog Lane, Soho,
oil on canvas, William Hogarth, c.1736

See catalogue number 149

Mr and Mrs David Garrick outside the Temple of Shakespeare at Hampton, oil on canvas, Johann Zoffany, 1762
Catalogue number 204

Suit worn by David Garrick, brown velvet, c.1763/4
Catalogue number 202

Sir Theodore de Mayerne (1573–1655) oil and black chalk on paper, Sir Peter Paul Rubens, c.1635 (left)
Catalogue number 169

Anthony Chamier (1725–1780) oil on canvas,
Sir Joshua Reynolds, 1777

Catalogue number 217

Tankard, amber, mounted in silver-gilt,
German, c.1650–60, formerly belonging to
Smart Lethieullier (1701–1760)
Catalogue number 225

Mulberry (Morus nigra) watercolour and bodycolour,
Jacques Le Moyne de Morgues, c.1566

Catalogue number 250

Paul Vaillant (1716–1803), his second wife Theodosia Whichcote,
and his daughters Letitia and Frances Vaillant, miniatures,
attributed to Joseph Daniels, c.1790

Catalogue number 254

The Fourdrinier family, oil on metal, attributed to John Downman, c.1785

Catalogue number 259

Wall panel, oil on canvas, one from a set of five,
designed by Daniel Marot for Montagu House,
London, c.1690
Catalogue number 271

State Coach for William III designed by
Daniel Marot, c.1698 (left)
Catalogue number 268

*Circular dish, earthenware, Bernard Palissy or his school, France,
late sixteenth century*

Catalogue number 399

*Group representing Taste, porcelain, Derby,
attributed to the modeller Andrew Planché, c.1750–55*

Catalogue number 407

*Side table, carved and gilt walnut, Jean
Pelletier, c.1695. Detail of top showing monogram and coronet of Ralph, Earl of Montagu*

Catalogue number 285

Frame, carved and gilt wood, Paul Petit, 1740

Catalogue number 291

*Paul Crespin (1694–1770), oil on canvas, attributed
to Pierre Subleyras, c.1726*

Catalogue number 344

Design for woven silk, pen, ink and watercolour, Anne Maria Garthwaite for Simon Julins, 1752

Catalogue number 439

Dress (detail) silk, woven by Simon Julins, Spitalfields, to Anna Maria Garthwaite's design (above left), mid-eighteenth century

Catalogue number 440

Waistcoat, figured satin, woven by Maze & Steer, Spitalfields, 1787

Catalogue number 449

Design for woven silk, pencil, ink and watercolour, James Leman, 1718 (left)

Catalogue number 436

Historical background

List of contributors' entries

CONTRIBUTOR	CATALOGUE NUMBER
Robert Baldwin	41
Chris Ellmers	356, 362, 368, 452
Wendy Evans	397, 398
Celina Fox	393, 394, 395, 396
Mirielle Galinou	64, 129, 226, 227
Robin Gwynn	54, 55, 56, 57, 59, 60, 61, 62, 66, 68, 69, 70, 71, 75, 80, 130, 132, 435
Amanda Herries	145
Anne Jones	53
Julian Litten	166
Tessa Murdoch	1, 2, 3, 4, 5, 6, 7, 8, 9, 10, 11, 12, 14, 15, 16, 17, 18, 19, 20, 21, 22, 23, 24, 25, 26, 27, 28, 29, 30, 31, 32, 33, 34, 35, 36, 37, 38, 39, 40, 41, 42, 43, 44, 45, 46, 47, 48, 49, 50, 51, 52, 58, 62, 63, 65, 66, 67, 72, 73, 75, 76, 77, 78, 79, 80, 81, 82, 83, 104, 110, 116, 121, 125, 126, 129, 131, 133, 134, 135, 136, 138, 140, 141, 142, 143, 144, 145, 146, 147, 148, 149, 150, 151, 152, 153, 154, 155, 156, 157, 158, 159, 160, 161, 162, 163, 164, 165, 194, 195, 196, 197, 201, 202, 203, 204, 205, 206, 207, 208, 209, 210, 211, 212, 214, 215, 229, 230, 231, 232, 233, 234, 235, 236, 237, 238, 239, 240, 241, 242, 243, 244, 245, 246, 247, 248, 249, 250, 251, 252, 253, 254, 255, 256, 257, 258, 259, 260, 261, 262, 263, 264, 265, 266, 267, 268, 269, 270, 271, 272, 273, 274, 275, 276, 277, 278, 279, 280, 281, 282, 283, 284, 285, 286, 287, 288, 289, 290, 291, 292, 293, 294, 295, 296, 297, 298, 299, 300, 301, 302, 303, 304, 305, 306, 307, 308, 309, 310, 311, 312, 313, 314, 315, 316, 317, 318, 319, 320, 321, 322, 323, 324, 325, 326, 328, 329, 330, 331, 332, 333, 334, 335, 336, 337, 338, 339, 340, 341, 342, 343, 344, 345, 346, 347, 348, 349, 350, 351, 352, 353, 354, 355, 356, 357, 358, 359, 360, 361, 362, 363, 364, 365, 366, 367, 368, 369, 370, 371, 372, 373, 374, 375, 376, 377, 378, 379, 380, 381, 382, 383, 384, 385, 386, 387, 388, 389, 390, 391, 392, 399, 400, 401, 402, 403, 404, 405, 406, 407, 408, 409, 410, 411, 417, 422, 431, 457, 458, 459, 460, 461, 462, 463, 464, 466, 468, 469
Marjorie Trusted	222, 223, 224, 225
Natalie Rothstein	435, 436, 437, 438, 439, 440, 441, 442, 443, 444, 445, 446, 447, 448, 449, 450, 453
Rosemary Weinstein	9, 13, 74, 83, 84, 85, 86, 87, 88, 89, 90, 91, 92, 93, 94, 95, 96, 97, 98, 99, 100, 101, 102, 103, 105, 106, 107, 108, 109, 110, 111, 112, 113, 114, 115, 117, 118, 119, 120, 122, 123, 124, 125, 126, 127, 128, 133, 137, 139, 167, 168, 169, 170, 171, 172, 173, 174, 175, 176, 177, 178, 179, 180, 181, 182, 183, 184, 185, 186, 187, 188, 189, 190, 191, 192, 193, 198, 199, 200, 213, 216, 217, 218, 219, 220, 221, 228, 327, 412, 413, 414, 415, 416, 418, 419, 420, 421, 423, 424, 425, 426, 427, 428, 429, 430, 431, 432, 433, 434, 435, 451, 454, 455, 456, 465, 467, 470, 471, 472, 473, 474, 475

THE HUGUENOTS

'Huguenot' is the popular name for the French Protestants, followers of John Calvin (1509–1564). The term is of disputed origin but may derive from 'Eidgenoss' meaning 'confederate', a word used in Geneva where Calvin and many Huguenots settled. The Genevan Church provided the model for Huguenot congregations in France. These congregations met secretly at first, and they attracted members of most of the social classes, including noblemen.

In 1559, the first General Synod of the Reformed Church in France was attended by representatives of seventy-two churches, who came mainly from Languedoc, Normandy, Ile de France, Guyenne and Gascony. As a result of the Synod, over one hundred ministers were trained in Geneva and took up formal duties at the new French churches. Thus French Protestantism, which had existed since the early 1520s, took on the character of the Calvinist Church. The period which saw the Calvinist Church established in France also saw in 1562 the beginning of the Wars of Religion, and the persecution of the Huguenots. Their hopes were placed in Henry of Navarre, a Protestant leader from his youth. Although Henry had to abjure his faith in order to ascend the throne, in 1598 he signed the Edict of Nantes, which guaranteed the Huguenots freedom of worship in France.

Reformed churches in France in the sixteenth century

- • Congregations established in the sixteenth century
- o Congregations which may or may not have been fully established
- ■ Congregations which had several pastors

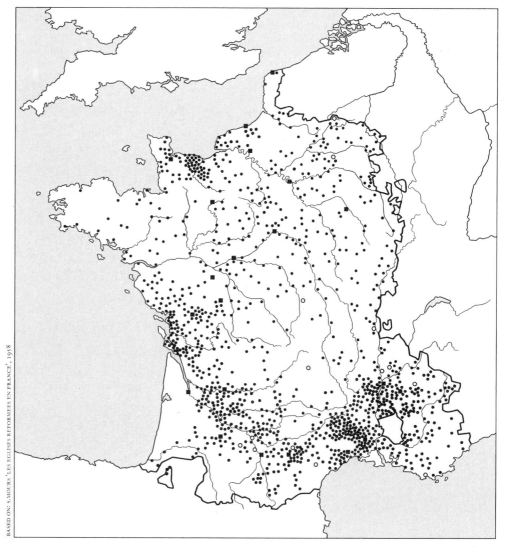

BASED ON: S.MOURS 'LES EGLISES RÉFORMÉES EN FRANCE', 1958

1 *John Calvin (1509–1564)*

PORTRAIT, OIL ON CARD, GERMAN SCHOOL, 1535; INSCRIBED: IEAN CALVIN 1535.

Head and shoulders in profile to the right.

John Calvin or Cauvin was born at Noyon, 10 July 1509, the son of a notary apostolic. He trained initially for the priesthood, but abandoned theology to study law at Orléans and Bourges. He attacked Catholicism in Paris, and had to take refuge in Basle where he associated with the Swiss Reformers and published the 'Institutes of the Christian Religion'. After visiting the Court of Ferrara, he came in 1536 to Geneva, where he remained, with one short absence, until his death on 27 May 1564.

Calvin became the leading figure of the Protestant world. His theology, based on successive editions of the 'Institutes', was distinguished by the doctrine of predestination, 'God hath once for all determined both whom he would admit to salvation and whom he would condemn to destruction'. The church in Geneva was governed by a Consistory consisting of six ministers and twelve laymen. Its business was to enforce a discipline of life, so that God would be worshipped through the citizens' occupations, dress and social customs. The Genevan church dictated the character of the Huguenot congregations in France and later in those countries that welcomed the refugees.

This portrait was included in an inventory of the Radnor collection in 1814, but may have been in family ownership since the sixteenth century, when their ancestor Laurens Desbouveries settled in Sandwich.

COLOUR PLATE: *page 2.*

DIMENSIONS: *102 × 90mm.*

PROVENANCE: *By descent to the present owner, The Rt. Hon. The Earl of Radnor.*

LITERATURE: *Helen Matilda Radnor, Catalogue of the Earl of Radnor's Collection of Pictures, 1909, Vol.I, no.154, p.99.*

2 *Clément Marot (1496–1544)*

ENGRAVING, SIXTEENTH CENTURY.

INSCRIBED: LA MORT NY MORD CLEMENS MAROTIUS POETA GALLICUS.

Marot was born at Cahors, the son of a poet who enjoyed the patronage of the Queen, Anne de Bretagne (Consort of Charles VIII and later Louis XII). On his father's death in 1527, Marot succeeded to his position as court poet. His first volume of poems was published in 1532. Later in the same decade Marot began his translation of the Psalms, which were published by 1542. This excellent version was used and constantly sung by the Huguenots and earned these lines from Théodore de Bèze, 'des Psaumes saincts, tes riches versions te couronnent Marot, d'une éternelle gloire'.

Marot had already spent one period of exile at Ferrara in the 1530s. In 1542, he was forced to flee to Geneva, where although he was welcomed by Calvin, he did not find a livelihood and eventually left for Turin where he died.

Clément Marot was the first to protest publicly in France against torture and censorship and to extol freedom of conscience.

DIMENSIONS: *170 × 125mm.*

PROVENANCE: *Musée du Protestantisme, Paris.*

LITERATURE: *C.A. Mayer, Clement Marot, 1964.*

3 *Théodore de Bèze (1519–1605)*

ENGRAVING, C. MEYER, 1675.

The theologian is shown here seated in his study at Geneva.

De Bèze was born at Vézelay and brought up by his uncle, who was a councillor at the Parlement of Paris. He studied law at Orléans and then practised in Paris. In 1548, he broke away from the Catholic Church, and left Paris for Geneva. He then accepted the Chair of Greek at the Lausanne Academy.

He translated the New Testament into Latin in 1556, and his translation of the Psalms appeared between 1553 and 1561.

In 1559 he became Rector and a Professor of the new Academy in Geneva. He was also one of the city's pastors.

After the massacre at Vassy (*Catalogue number* 11) de Bèze attempted to gain support for the Huguenot cause from the French Court, the Swiss Cantons and the German Protestant princes.

In 1564 on the death of Calvin, de Bèze succeeded him as President of the Company of Pastors of Geneva.

In 1571, he attended the Synod at La Rochelle, where the Confession of Faith of the Reformed Church was formed, which is still used today.

De Bèze also wrote a biography of Calvin and an ecclesiastical history of the Reformed Church.

PROVENANCE: *Musée du Protestantisme, Paris.*

LITERATURE: *P.F. Geisendorf, Théodore de Bèze, 1949.*

4 *Henri IV [Henry of Navarre] (1553–1610)*

ENGRAVING, HENDRICK GOLTZIUS; INSCRIBED: CE GRAND ROY QUE TU VOYS EST REMPLY DE LA GRACE DE MARS ET DE PALLAS DE CES NOBLES AYEUXS IL FUIT DE PAS A PAS LES SENTIERS VERTUEUX QUI LA DEDANS LE CIEL LUY PROMETTENT UNE PLACE H. GOLTZIUS SCULP AVEC PRIVIL DU ROY PAUL DE LA HOUVE EXCUDEBAT AU PALAIS.

The King is shown wearing the collars of the Order of St. Esprit and the Order of St. Michael.

Henry IV was the son of Antony, Duke of Bourbon, a descendant of the greatest of the old feudal families of France, and Jeanne d'Albret, the Queen of Navarre, a Calvinist, who converted her husband. In 1568, Henry was placed under the protection of the Huguenots in

DIMENSIONS: *352 × 250mm.*

PROVENANCE: *Slade Collection; Department of Prints and Drawings, British Museum.*

LITERATURE: *O. Hirschmann, Verzeichnes des graphischen Werks von Hendrick Goltzius, 1558–1617, 1921, no.193.*

1

CLEMENS · MAROTIVS ·
POETA GALLICVS ·
· B ·

R.D. N° 111.

2

THEODORUS BEZA,
PASTOR ECCLESIÆ GENEVENSIS, NATUS VEZELIS
VETUSTO HEDUORUM OPPIDO, 1519. 24 JUNII,
Denatus 13 Octobr. 1605. Æt. 86.
BEZA Reformator, præcoq; saluber, et acer
    Hoc, olim vultu conspiciendus erat:
Quo vero fructu divinum paverit agmen
    Scriptarum illius lectio abunde docet.
Delitiis autem cœli nunc pascitur ipse
    Qui sedet in solio pascit enim agnus eum.

Corn: Meyer fecit A° 1675.

3

4

La Rochelle. In 1572, he married the Catholic Margaret of Valois, sister of Henry III, King of France, last of the Valois line, but the marriage celebrations were marred by the ensuing Massacre of St. Bartholomew (*Catalogue number* 14). On the King's assassination in 1589, Henry of Navarre was the obvious heir to the throne provided he was prepared to abjure his Calvinist faith. This he did in the Cathedral of St. Denis, in July 1593. It was only in 1594 that the city of Paris opened her gates to the new monarch.

The Huguenots now regarded their former leader in the Wars of Religion with suspicion. However, the Peace of Bergerac in 1577 had given them permission to worship in only one town in each district or in the houses of great nobility. The Huguenots used their efficient organisation to negotiate further mutual concessions and compromises which resulted in the Edict of Nantes, 1598 (*Catalogue number* 5).

5 *Edict of Nantes, 1598*
FACSIMILE, NINETEENTH CENTURY.

The 'perpetual and irrevocable' Edict of Nantes was signed by King Henry IV in Nantes on 13 April, 1598. The Huguenots were granted complete freedom of conscience and freedom to worship in any 'temples' already established, and in noblemen's houses. The document also promised complete civil equality, guarantees for the administration of justice, and a large state subsidy for the maintenance of Huguenot troops and ministers.

This, the first Edict proper, contained ninety-two articles, but was followed by fifty-six secret articles, which allowed meetings for religious purposes, with the condition 'by the permission of His Majesty'. Interpretation of the Edict was thus dependent on the sympathy of the reigning monarch, and under Louis XIV, the Huguenots found themselves at the mercy of a dogmatic Catholic King.

PROVENANCE: *Sir Henry W. Peek; Arthur Giraud Browning; Huguenot Library.*

LITERATURE: *M. Favier, La France du VIIe au XXe Siècles à travers soixante et onze documents, Paris, Archives Nationales, 1980, p.45.*

Henry by the Grace of God King of France and Navarre. To all present and to come, Greeteth. Among the infinite mercies that God hath pleased to bestow upon us, that most signal and remarkable is, his having given us power and strength not to yield to the dreadful Troubles, Confusions and Disorders, which were found at our coming to this Kingdom, divided into so many Parties and Factions, that the most legitimate was almost the least, enabling us with constancy, in such manner to oppose the storm, as in the end to surmount it, reducing this Estate to peace and rest for which to Him alone be given the honour and glory; and us the grace to acknowledge our obligation, in having our labours made use of for the accomplishing so good a work, in which it has been visible to all, that we have not only done what was our duty, and in our power, but something more than at another time, would (peradventure) have been agreeable to the Dignity we now hold; as in not having had more care, than to have many times so freely exposed our own life. And in this great concurrence of weighty and perillous Affairs, not being able to compose all at one and the same time, we have chosen this Order. First to undertake those who were not to be suppressed but by force, and rather to remit and suspend others for some time, who might be dealt with by reason and justice: for for the general differences among our good Subjects, and the particular evils of the soundest parts of the State, we judged might be easily cured, after the principal cause, (the continuation of the Civil Wars) was taken away, in which we have, by the blessing of God, well and happily succeeded, all Hostility and Wars through the Kingdom being now ceased, and we hope he will also prosper us in our other affairs which remain to be composed, and that by this means we shall arrive at the Establishment of a good Peace, with tranquillity and rest, (which hath ever been the end of all our vows and intentions) as all the reward we desire or expect for so much pain and trouble, as we have taken in the whole course of our life. Amongst our said affairs (towards which it behoves us to have patience) one of the principal hath been, the many complaints we have received from divers of our Provinces and Catholick Cities, for that the exercise of the Catholick Religion was not universally re-established, as is provided by Edicts or Statutes heretofore made for the Pacification of the trouble arising from Religion: as also the Supplications and Remonstrances which have been made to us by our Subjects of the Reformed Religion, the liberty of their consciences, and the security of their Persons and Fortunes . . .

TRANSCRIPTION: *Taken from 'The Last Famous Siege of the City of Rochel: together with the Edict of Nantes', 1680. Written in French by Peter Meruault, printed for John Wickins, London.*

. . . We do require our Procurators General to pursue immediately and without delay the said Publication hereof. We give in Command to the said People of our Courts of Parliaments, Chambers of our Courts, and Courts of our Aids, Bailiffs, Chief Justices, Provosts, and other our Justices and Officers to whom it appertains, and to their Lieutenants, that they cause to be read, published, and inregistered this our present Edict and Ordinance in their Courts and Jurisdictions, and the same keep and observe punctually, and the Contents of the same to cause to be injoyed and used fully and peaceably by all those to whom it shall belong, ceasing and making to cease all troubles and obstructions to the contrary. For such is our pleasure: And in witness hereof we have signed these Presents with our own Hand; and to the end to make it a thing firm and stable for ever, we have caused to put and indorse our Seal to the same. Given at Nantes in the month of April, in the Year of Grace 1598 and of our Reign the ninth.

Signed: HENRY
And underneath, the King being in Council

FORGET   *VISA*
And on the side,

This Visa signifies the Lord Chancellor's perusal.
Sealed with the Great Seal of Green Wax upon a red and green String of silk.
Read, published, and registred, the Kings Procurator or Atturney General hearing and consenting to it, in the Parliament of Paris, the 25th of February, 1599.

Signed, VOYSIN

Read, published, and inregistred in the Chamber of Accompts, the Kings Procurator General hearing and consenting to it, the last day of March, 1599.

Signed, DE LA FONTAINE

Read, published, and registred, the King's Procurator General hearing and consenting, at Paris in the Court of Aids, the 30th April 1599.

Signed, BERNARD

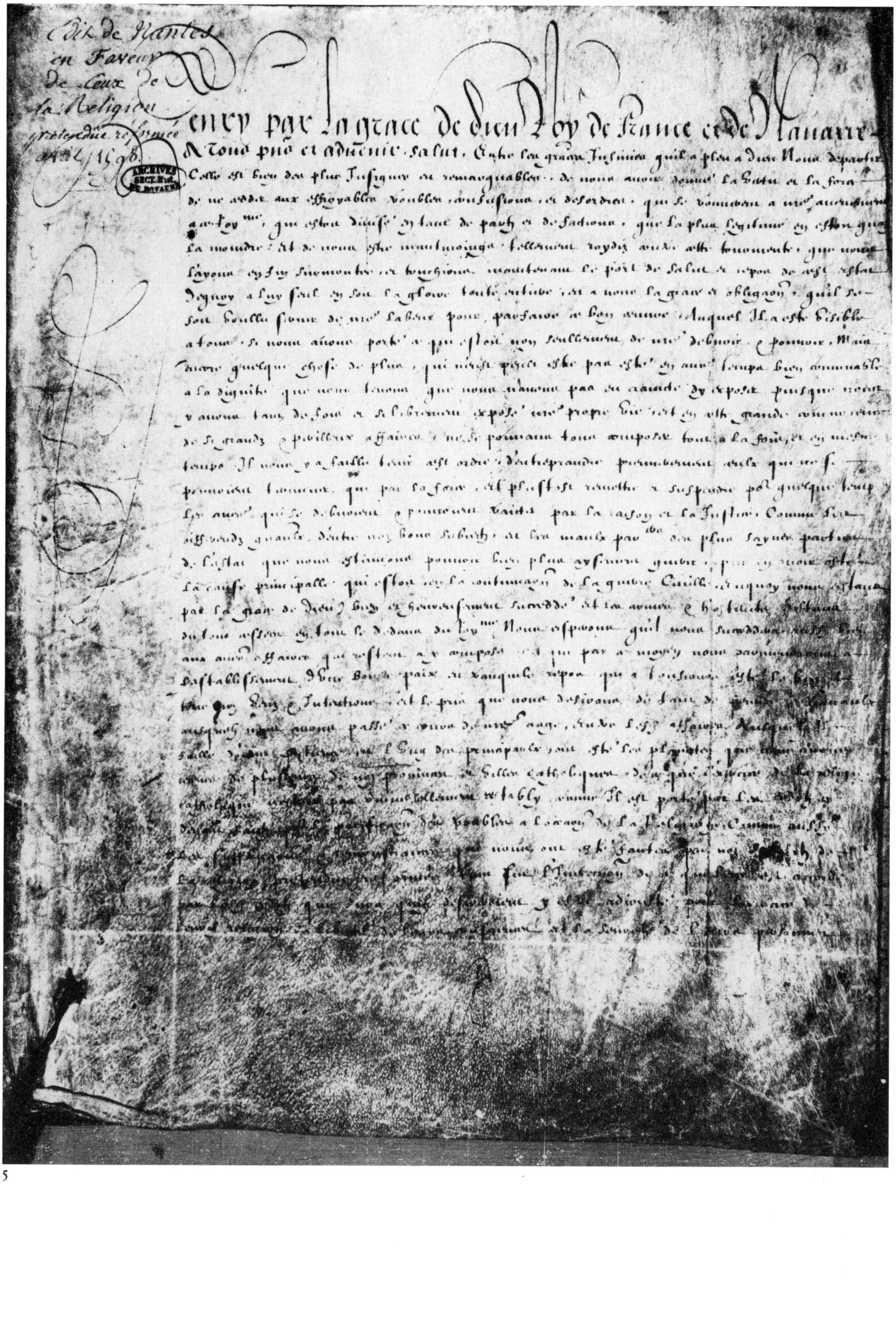
Edit de Nantes en Faveur de ceux de la Religion pretendue reformée Avril 1598

Henry par la grace de dieu Roy de France et de Navarre A tous presens et advenir salut.

5

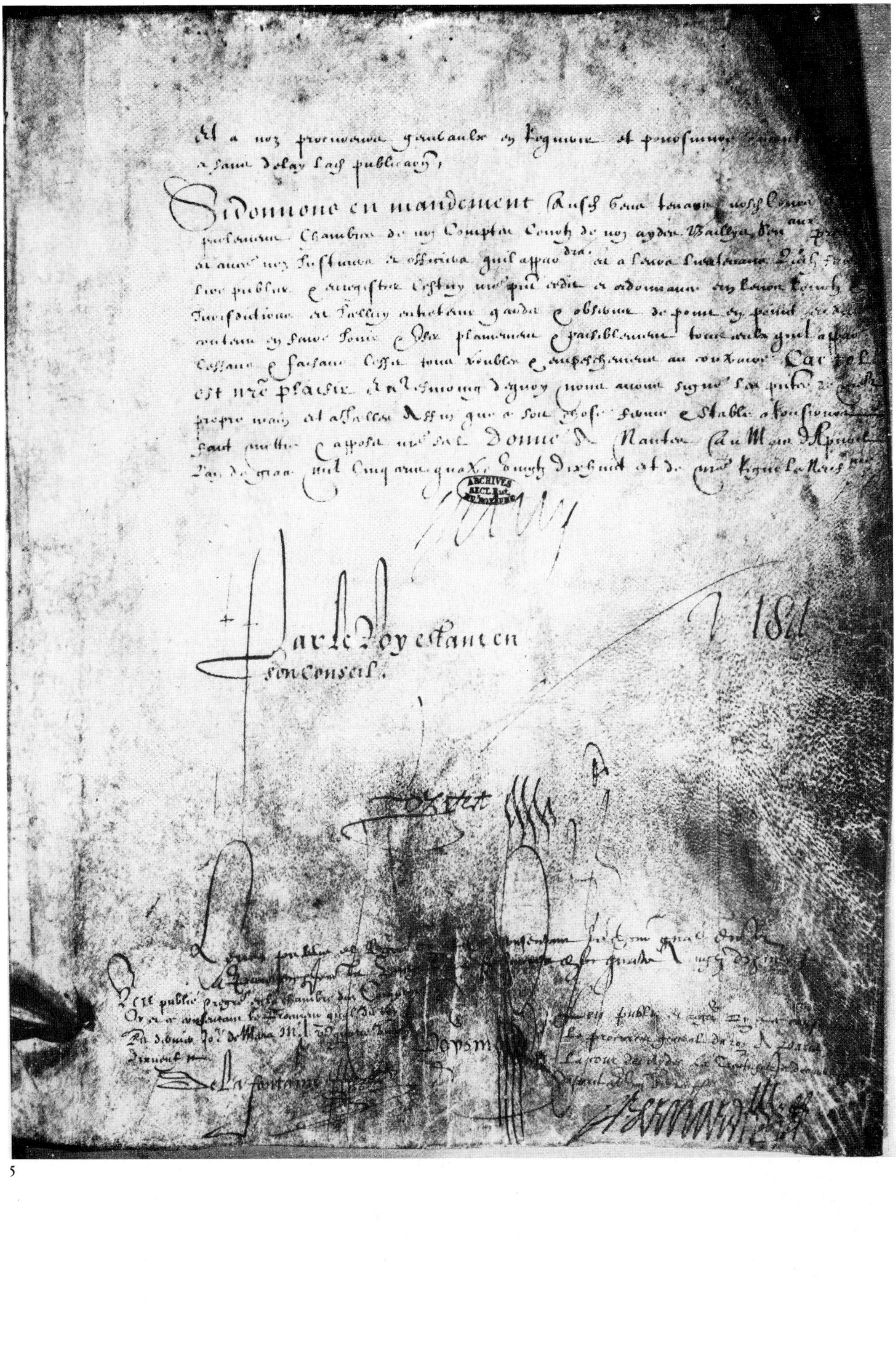
Si donnons en mandement
Car tel est nre plaisir
Donne a Nantes
Par le Roy estant en son Conseil.

5

WORSHIP IN FRANCE

By the late sixteenth century, the Huguenots probably accounted for some 10 per cent of the total population in France. The Reformed Faith attracted members of the Catholic clergy, noblemen, businessmen with international contacts and small traders, teachers, goldsmiths, apothecaries, grocers, artisans and weavers.

Initially, the Huguenots worshipped secretly, outside their towns, or in the homes of the nobility, but the Edict of Nantes, 1598, established their freedom to worship openly, and permanent temples were built, such as that at Charenton, outside Paris. The congregations were governed by a Consistory, made up of ministers and elected laymen, who were responsible for the supervision and education of the faithful. The Consistory usually met on Sunday in the temple after the sermon, or whenever necessary, to run the church, to resolve family quarrels or to examine a member of the congregation who had sinned. The congregation were issued with tokens which were required to be shown before taking Communion in order to prevent the admission of impostors. Apart from the weekly sermon and Communion which was received four times a year, an important part of weekly worship was the singing of psalms translated into French by Clément Marot and Théodore de Bèze.

Interior of the Temple at Charenton, watercolour, 1623

6 *The Temple at Lyons*

PHOTOGRAPH OF A PAINTING ATTRIBUTED TO JEAN PERRISIN.
INSCRIBED: TEMPLE DE LYON NOMME PARADIS.

This, the second Huguenot temple in Lyons, was situated in the Quartier St. Nizier, near the Town Hall. It was built on a site acquired by the Huguenot community in 1564, when it accommodated 'une maison haute, moyenne et basse, jardin et establerye appelée de Paradis'. The temple, retaining the name 'Paradis', remained the property of the Huguenot congregation until the Revocation, when it was destroyed.

The Municipal Archives of Lyons house two drawings of the exterior and interior of the temple by Jean Perrisin. It has been suggested that the latter was responsible for the design of the building.

Perrisin (1536–1611), a native of Lyons, worked for the local authorities undertaking the interior decoration of the Town Hall in 1583, and the Triumphal Entries for the visits of Mme. de Nemours and Henry IV to the city in 1566, 1595 and 1600.

The painting may have been taken to Geneva by a Huguenot refugee at the same time as three volumes of registers of the Lyons temple (1573–1685).

The building, of circular plan, with three entrances at ground level and a gallery running round the inside which was reached by a double staircase on the exterior, was lit by four oval windows. The pulpit occupied a central position, and the congregation sat on plain wooden benches. On this occasion, the rather sparse congregation indicates that the service was a wedding or baptism. As was customary the men retained their hats during the service and were seated apart from the women.

PROVENANCE: *Given to the Bibliothèque Publique et Universitaire of Geneva by Professor Jean Picot, 1827.*

LITERATURE: *Bulletin Historique et Littéraire; Société de l'histoire du Protestantisme français, 1890, pp.286–288; Natalis Rondot, Les Protestants à Lyon au dix-huitième siècle, 1891, pp. 172–3; André Steyart, Nouvelle histoire de Lyon, 1899, vol.3, p.143.*

7 *Two Méreaux (lead communion tokens)*

FROM THE HUGUENOT TEMPLES LA MOTHE AND ST. HERAYE AT SAINTE MAIXANTE, POITOU.
INSCRIBED: *a* S.M. (FOR SAINTE MAIXANTE);
b. DIEU (AND DECORATED WITH A COMMUNION CUP).

In 1560, Jean Calvin recommended to the Council of Geneva that tokens should be issued in advance to those who wished to receive communion in order to exclude those who might profane the service. He later repeated this instruction in a letter to the faithful in France.

Communion services were held only four times a year; Easter, Whitsun, early September and Christmas. The tokens were usually made by the elders of the Church in lead, pewter or copper, hence their rather crude appearance. These 'méreaux' are mostly found in the south-west of France and include two principal symbols; the shepherd, typical of Saintonge and Agenais, and the communion cup, characteristic of Poitou and Melle.

Such tokens are known to have been used by the Huguenot congregations at Canterbury, Dover and London.

DIMENSIONS: *a. 21mm diameter, b. 19mm diameter.*

PROVENANCE: *William Minet; presented to the French Hospital, 1898; Huguenot Library.*

LITERATURE: *Charles Delormeau, Les Méreaux de Communion des Eglises Protestantes de France et du Refuge; Musée du Désert, 1983. A similar example to a. is illustrated in Fig.12.*

8 *The Temple at Charenton near Paris*

ENGRAVING, REPRINTED, LONDON, 1708.
INSCRIBED:
Le Temple de Charenton proche de PARIS Ma Maison sera appellée Maison d'Oraison.

Ce Temple a été rebati par la permissn. de Louis XIII l'An 1624. Et démoli par l'Ordre de Louis XIV. 22 Oct. 1685. Et r'imprimé sur l'Original, par les M^rs. de la Société des Parisiens, l'An 1708.

O Dieu, la Gloire qui t'est deue
T'attend dedans Sion:
En ce leiu (sic) te sera rendue
De voeux Oblation.
Et d'autant que la voix entend^re,
De tiens il te plaira,
Tout droit â toy se venir rend^re
Toutes Gens on verra.
Heureux celuy que veux eslire
Et pres de toy loger
Afin que chez toy se retire
Pour jamais n'en bouger.   Ps: 65

DIMENSIONS: *210 × 205mm.*

PROVENANCE: *Society of Parisians; Huguenot Library.*

LITERATURE: *E.J. Ciprut, Le Premier Grand Temple de Charenton, Bulletin de la Société de l'Histoire du Protestantisme français, Jan–Mar, 1968, pp.106–113; Rosalys Coope, Salomon de Brosse, 1972, pp.6,183–7,201,212–13; William Chapman Waller, Early Huguenot Friendly Societies, Proceedings of the Huguenot Society of London, Vol.6 (1898–1901), pp.201–236.*

These words are taken from Marot and Bèze's version of Psalm 65. Charenton was a village on the outskirts of Paris at the confluence of the Marne and Seine, on the edges of the Bois de Vincennes. After the St. Bartholomew's Day Massacre, 1572, the Protestants left the centre of Paris for the outskirts. After the Edict of Nantes in 1598 had guaranteed freedom of worship, the first temple at Charenton was built to the designs of Salomon de Brosse in 1606. In 1621 it was burnt by an angry Catholic mob, but was rebuilt five years later by the same architect. In 1685, the destruction of the temple at Charenton was one of the main actions against the Huguenots immediately after the Revocation of the Edict of Nantes.

The Société des Parisiens was probably founded in London in 1687. The total number of members was limited to sixty-one; in order to qualify for membership, the Protestant should be between eighteen and forty-one years, of reliable character, sound in mind and body, and living within three miles of Christ Church, Spitalfields.

6

MEREAVX OF THE CHVRCHES AT
LA MOTHE S. HERAYE · SAINT MAIXANT
IN POITOV.
PRESENTED BY WILLIAM MINET. DIRECTOR.
1898

7

Le Temple de Charenton proche de PARIS.

Ma Maison sera appellée
Maison d'Oraison.

O Dieu la Gloire qui t'est deue Et d'autaut que la voix entend. Heureux celuy que veux eslire
T'attend dedans Sion : De tiens il te plaira . Et pres de toy loger Ps:65
En ce leiu te sera rendue Tout droit à toy se venir rend. Afin que chez toy se retire
De vœux Oblation . Toutes Gens on verra . Pour jamais n'en bouger.
Ce Temple a été rebati par la permiss." de Louis XIII l'An 1624. Et démoli par l'Ordre de Louis XIV. 22 Oct. 1685.
Et rimprimé sur l'Original par les M". de la Societé des Parisiens. l'An 1708.

8

In 1882, a 'Memorandum of the Origin of this Society' included in the printed rules, explains, 'Whereas in the reign of Louis XIV, King of France, the Protestants in his dominions were cruelly persecuted, and many obliged to take refuge in this country . . . when all the Protestant Churches in France were demolished; in particular the Temple of Charenton near Paris. About two years after which a number of Parisians, late members of the said Temple, being refugees in London, formed the laudable resolution to raise a society in order to establish a fund for the mutual relief of each other, which they did under the title of "Society of Parisians".'

9 *Raymond Gaches*

PORTRAIT, OIL ON CANVAS, FRENCH SCHOOL, 1666.
INSCRIBED: RAYMOND GACHES AN AET: 46. 1666.

The sitter is shown here in a black cloak and white lawn collar. Judging by contemporary portraits, this is the usual dress worn by Huguenot ministers, although no rules of dress were formally laid down by the Calvinist doctrine.

Gaches came from Albi in Languedoc, and was the son of a judge of the Court of Appeal in the province. Raymond Gaches was Huguenot minister at Charenton from 1654–1660.

As minister at Charenton, his duties involved the reception of English and other Protestants residing in France. Sir William Lockhart records his public reception at Charenton on 3 November 1656, 'by the Ministers and Elders, Monsr. Gaches making the welcoming speech in the name of the rest'. In 1654, Gaches preached a sermon at the Dutch Embassy in Paris on the declaration of peace between England and Holland.

As a result of his familiarity with the episcopal tradition he was able to assist the French Protestant community in England in overcoming their scruples about submitting to episcopal ordination and adopting the Anglican Liturgy in their French Church at the Savoy.

Gaches' sermons delivered at Charenton were published at Saumur in 1670.

Gaches settled in England and became vicar of Barking, Essex. He died in 1682 and was survived by his widow Marie.

DIMENSIONS: *760 × 630mm.*

PROVENANCE: *Louis Gaches; presented to the French Hospital.*

LITERATURE: *Louis Gaches, Raymond Gaches: A Huguenot, Fenland Notes and Queries, 1901; Guildhall Library Ms.25625/4, f.55.*

10 *Order regarding singing of psalms*

ORDONNANCE PORTANT DEFFENCES A TOUS CEUX DE LA RELIGION PRETENDUE REFORMEE, DE CHANTER LEURS PSEAUMES SUR LA RIVIERE ET GRANDS CHEMINS, ALLANS ET VENANS DE CHARENTON, ET AUTRES LIEUX, PARIS, 1681.

The Order complains that members of the Religion Prétendue Réformée living in Paris are to be heard singing psalms and debating on matters of their creed whilst travelling to and from their temple at Charenton. The order cites article XII of the Edict of Nantes to the effect that such worship is only permitted within the approved locations. It is not permitted to sing psalms composed and translated by Clément Marot and Théodore de Bèze in public places, or even in private houses, unless they are sung so softly that they cannot be heard by passers-by or neighbours. The document cites five different decisions of the King's Council to this effect, ranging in date from 1659 to 1666.

DIMENSIONS: *250 × 180mm.*

PROVENANCE: *Musée du Protestantisme, Paris.*

9

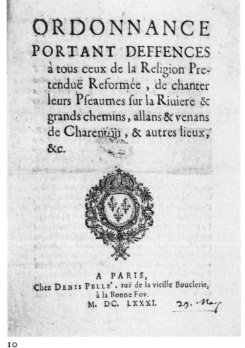

10

PERSECUTION

The means of converting the heretics to the Catholic Faith

Lithograph by G. Engelmann, based on a drawing of 1686

The new missionaries, the 'dragons'

Lithograph by G. Engelmann, based on a drawing of 1686

Massacre of St Bartholomew's Day

John Calvin dedicated the 'Institutes of the Christian Religion', 1536 to Francis I, but official French policy would not accept Protestantism. By 1547, Henry II set up a 'Chambre Ardente' in Paris at which more than five hundred 'heretics' were condemned to death for their Protestant beliefs. Within three years of the first General Synod in 1559, the opening of the Wars of Religion was marked by the Massacre at Vassy, 1562. Ten years later, at the Massacre of St. Bartholomew in Paris, several thousand Protestants lost their lives, including members of the nobility. Despite a short lull in persecution after the Edict of Nantes, 1598, during which the Huguenots enjoyed the right to garrison four towns, La Rochelle, Montauban, Cognac and La Cité, they lost their military status as a result of the Siege of La Rochelle, 1628.

11 *Massacre at Vassy*
ENGRAVING, BASED ON A CONTEMPORARY PRINT.

The engraving shows (b) the Duke of Guise leading the Massacre; (c) the Huguenot minister who remained in the pulpit in prayer; (d) the minister outside the building who would have been killed if the sword had not broken in two; (e) Cardinal Guise leaning on the church wall; (f) and (g) members of the congregation taking refuge on the roof, or throwing themselves over the wall of the town.

On 1 March 1562, Francis, Duke of Guise, one of the leaders of the Catholic faction, was travelling through Vassy and found a Huguenot service in progress there. In January of that year the Queen Mother, Catherine de Medici, had been instrumental in furthering the publication of an Edict which gave the Huguenots permission to worship outside towns, provided that they were prepared to admit royal officials to their gatherings and that they preached in accordance with the Nicene Creed and the Scriptures. However, on this occasion the service was taking place inside the town of Vassy, so the Duke sent his soldiers to protest. They were resisted and as a result many of the congregation of 1,200 lost their lives.

This event marked the beginning of the Wars of Religion.

DIMENSIONS: *460 × 620mm.*

PROVENANCE: *The French Church, Soho Square.*

LITERATURE: *A.J. Grant, The Huguenots, 1934, p.33; Histoire des Protestants en France, ed. Privat, 1977, pp.86–7.*

12 *Gaspard de Coligny, Admiral of France (1519–1572)*
ENGRAVING JOST AMMAN, NUREMBERG, 1573; INSCRIBED: EFFIGIES GASPARIS DE COLIGNI D. DE CASTILIONE AMIRALI FRANCIAE FECIT NUREMBERGAEHOF AMMAN FIGURUTTE.

Gaspard de Coligny was one of three brothers who played a vital part in the formation of Huguenot policy in the third quarter of the sixteenth century. His elder brother, Odet, Cardinal de Châtillon and Bishop of Beauvais (1515–1571) abandoned his bishopric as a result of his adherence to the Huguenot cause and took refuge in England. Their uncle, Anne de Montmorency, was Constable of France.

Gaspard de Coligny had commanded the armies of France before he professed his new faith, but later led the Protestant campaigns during the Second War of Religion (1567–1570). His skilled leadership was largely responsible for securing the Treaty of St. Germain in 1570, which gave the Huguenots freedom of conscience and the right to garrison four towns, La Rochelle, Montauban, Cognac and La Cité.

The engraving shows at the base a vignette of the assassination of Gaspard de Coligny which occurred two days before the Massacre of St. Bartholomew, 22 August 1572, and which was supervised in person by Henry, Duke of Guise.

DIMENSIONS: *365 × 275mm.*

PROVENANCE: *Huguenot Library.*

LITERATURE: *A.J. Grant, op.cit., 1934, pp.24–6,37,40; Histoire des Protestants en France, ed. Privat, 1977, pp.89–92,104,109–10,445.*

13 *Massacre of St Bartholomew's Day*
MEDAL, 1572 GIANFEDERIGO BONZAGNA; INSCRIBED: OBVERSE: GREGORIVS.XIII.PONT.MAX.AN.I – FP.REVERSE: VGONOTTORVM.STRAGES.1572.

The medal shows on the obverse, a bust of Gregory XIII to the left, bearded and wearing a calotte and hood; on the reverse, an angel, armed with a sword and cross who smites the Huguenots. This medal applauds the event.

DIMENSIONS: *30mm diameter.*

PROVENANCE: *British Museum, Department of Coins and Medals.*

LITERATURE: *A. Armand, Les Médailleurs Italiens des Quinzième et Seizième Siècles, 1883, Vol.1, p.226, no.37.*

13

11

12

14 *Massacre of St Bartholomew's Day*

ENGRAVING, GASPARD BOUTTATS, ANTWERP.

INSCRIBED:

Massacre des Huguenots fait a Paris le 24 Aoust 1572 Jour de S. Barthelemi au moins de
dix mille d'entre eux, entrautres de Gaspar de Coligni Amiral de France, et de plus de 500
Seigneurs ou Gentils-Homes.

Que ce jour fut rempli d'abomination;
On devoit bien le rayer de l'histoire,
Et pour jamais en ôter la mémoire
Pour l'honneur de la Nation.
O mortels insensés, O profane vulgaire,
Vils, mais terribles instrumens
Des passions de ceux que l'on appelle Grands,
Qui serves leur orgueil, leur jalouse colère.

Oui, c'est ainsi qu'on vit Chrétiens contre Chrétiens
Rompre les plus sacrés liens,
Le Frère armé contre son propre Frére,
Le Fils meme égorger le Pere
On les vit se couvrir du nom de Piété
Pour mieux se depouiller de toute Humanité
Barbares, cruels homicides
Hommes exécrables, perfides.

Et qui prenez leurs intérests
Particuliers et secrets
Pour une affaire général,
Quittés pour un moment votre fureur brutale;
Dites-moi, qu'avoient fait l'Amiral Coligni
Et tant de milliers de noble personnages
Généreux vertueux et sages,
Qu'on rendoit odieux sous le nom de Parti.

Si vous eussiez été sous un Gouvernement
Tel que celui qui fleurit à présent,
Pleins d'une Juste obéissance
(Pre)nants les Loix d'un aimable devoir
Certes vous n'auriez pas fait voir
Tant de rage et de violence.

A Paris chez Jean, rue Jean de Beauvais, no.32.

Dans le Massacre afreux que l'on vous en fit faire,
Dans cet événement terrible, sanguinaire,
Je pense voir les vents faire combattre entre eux
De toutes parts les flots impétueux,
Et par un effroyable orage
Enveloper Vieillards, Jeunes Garçons
Et les scélérats et les bons
Dans un commun et funeste Naufrage.

Paris was full of Huguenots who had come to attend the wedding of Henry of Navarre and
Margaret of Valois. The Parisians hated the Protestants and could not understand how God
could allow such an execrable union to take place. The Pope had to give his assent to the
marriage, and the papal permission only arrived after the event. Furthermore, as a Protestant,
Henry of Navarre was not prepared to enter Notre Dame and attend Catholic Mass, so the
marriage took place outside the Cathedral in the open air.

On Friday 22 August 1572, as he was returning to his apartment, Admiral Coligny was
wounded in the hand and arm by a shot fired from a window in the Louvre. There followed
three days of massacre, during which the gates of the city were closed, and the Catholic mob
ran wild. It is estimated that between two and three thousand Protestants perished of which
five hundred were members of the nobility. Subsequently, repetitions of the Massacre occurred
in other French cities like Bordeaux and Lyons, claiming a further 10,000 Huguenot lives.

DIMENSIONS: *475 × 360mm.*

PROVENANCE: *French Hospital.*

LITERATURE: *A.J. Grant, The
Huguenots, 1934, pp. 40–46; Histoire
des Protestants en France, ed. Privat,
1977, pp. 90–94.*

15 *Siege of La Rochelle*

ENGRAVING AFTER CALLOT, 1628 (PHOTOGRAPH).

La Rochelle had officially been a Huguenot stronghold since the Treaty of St. Germain, 1570,
although Henry of Navarre spent part of his youth with the Protestants there in the 1560s.
After the Massacre of St. Bartholomew, there was another wave of civil war; the Huguenots
held on behind the water defences of La Rochelle, until the Peace of La Rochelle which
conceded freedom of conscience and a restricted right of worship to the Protestants. From
1619 the Council of the Huguenots sat regularly at La Rochelle.

In 1626, England declared war on France, ostensibly in support of the French Protestants.
In July, an English fleet under the Duke of Buckingham landed on the Ile de Ré, one of the
two islands in the mouth of the estuary of La Rochelle. However, the Catholic-held Fort of
St. Martin on the Ile de Ré resisted the English attack and Buckingham was forced to withdraw
his troops. As a result, La Rochelle was besieged by the Catholic army under Cardinal
Richelieu, and the estuary was blockaded by a breakwater of masonry and a guard of French
ships. An English fleet under Lord Denbigh attempted to break through before the works
were completed, but failed to do so. On 18 September 1628, another English fleet sailed
under Lord Lindsay but this attack was equally unsuccessful.

The siege continued for more than fourteen months, and under the leadership of their
Mayor, Jean Guiton, the citizens held out or died of starvation, but did not surrender. In
October, 1628, on All Saints Day, the King, Louis XIII, entered the city. The streets were
covered with dead and the living were too few and too weak to bury them. Of a population
of 25,000 at least 10,000 had perished.

At the Peace of Alais in 1629 the Huguenots lost their garrison towns and were forced to
destroy all their fortifications. But the Edict of Nantes was reaffirmed, and the Huguenots
still enjoyed freedom of worship and civil equality.

PROVENANCE: *H. Roger Viollet,
Paris.*

LITERATURE: *A.J. Grant, The
Huguenots, 1934, pp.36, 46, 101, 110,
111, 112, 116, 121.*

14

MASSACRE DES HUGUENOTS FAIT A PARIS LE 24 AOUST 1572 JOUR DE S. BARTHELEMI AU MOINS DE DIX MILLE D'ENTRE EUX ENTRAUTRES DE GASPAR DE COLIGNI AMIRAL DE FRANCE, ET DE PLUS DE 500. SEIGNEURS OU GENTILS-HOMES.

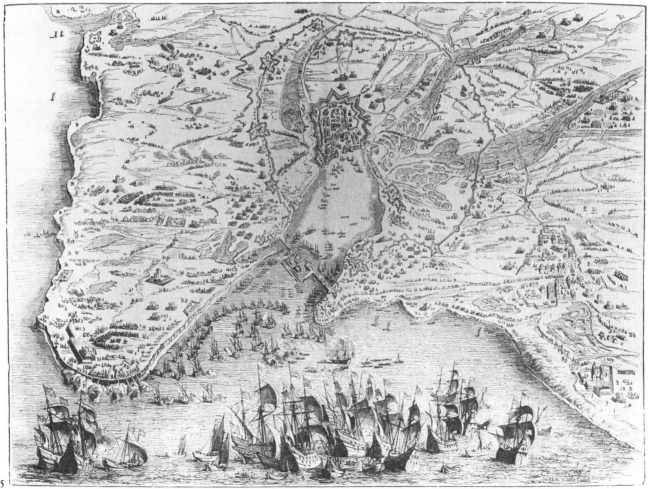

15

Revocation of the Edict of Nantes

In the half century after the fall of La Rochelle in 1628, the Huguenots showed devoted loyalty to the Crown, and at the beginning of his reign in 1652, Louis XIV declared his intention to maintain the Edict of Nantes for the benefit of his Protestant subjects. A Catholic revival in France was probably largely responsible for Louis XIV's change of heart; moreover, it was believed that the State would be more secure if all the king's subjects shared the same religion. By 1678, a campaign to convert the Huguenots was under way.

In 1681, in the province of Poitou, many Protestants were forcibly converted by the 'dragonnades', the billeting on the Protestant population of troops, who harassed their hosts. In the same year, an Edict encouraged children aged seven and above to abjure their faith, leave home and demand an allowance from their parents. By 1685, over three hundred Protestant temples had been demolished. The Revocation of the Edict of Nantes gave Protestant ministers a fortnight in which to leave France, on pain of death or imprisonment if they delayed. Any other Protestant subjects caught attempting to leave the country would be condemned to the galleys, if men, or confined to a convent, if women.

16 *Louis XIV (1638–1715)*

ENGRAVING, EDELINCK AFTER A PAINTING BY JEAN DE LA HAYE.

INSCRIBED: VICIT INACCESSIS CONSISAS RUPIBUS ARCES MIRARIS PER RHENUM HIC SIBI FECIT ITER SANTOLIUS VICTORINUS.

The engraving shows the King three-quarter length in armour.

Nine years after he had acceded to the throne of France, at the age of fourteen, the young Louis XIV declared, 'Inasmuch as our subjects of the so-called Reformed Religion have given us proof of their affection and fidelity, we wish them to understand for this reason they will be maintained and kept in the full enjoyment of the Edict of Nantes'. This declaration was greeted with enthusiasm by the Huguenots. As Louis XIV's Catholic faith strengthened, he realised that the extirpation of heresy was the best way by which he could show his repentance. It would also guarantee the political and religious unity of France.

Persecution of members of the Religion Prétendue Réformée was renewed as early as 1661, after the death of Cardinal Mazarin, who had acknowledged the loyalty and good services of the Huguenots and had acted as their protector in France. From that year, the King sanctioned a series of proclamations which reinterpreted the Edict of Nantes culminating, twenty-four years later, in the Revocation. Ironically, the years of renewed persecution for the Huguenots were the most prosperous of Louis XIV's reign. It is probable that Louis XIV did not realise how strongly the Huguenots held their Protestant faith, or how numerous they were.

DIMENSIONS: *530 × 380mm.*

PROVENANCE: *Cracheron Collection: Department of Prints and Drawings, British Museum.*

LITERATURE: *A.J. Grant, The Huguenots, 1934, pp.127,142,146, 152,214.*

17 *Madame de Maintenon (1635–1719)*

ENGRAVING, P. GIFFART; INSCRIBED: PAR SON TRES HUMBLE ET TRES OBEISSANT SERVITEUR, LE BLANC DE NEAUVILLE AUTANT MODESTE QU'ESTEUEE, JE NE PAROIS QUE POUR FAIRE DU BIEN, PAR MES RESPECTS J'ATTIRE SES REGARDS, MA VERTU ME FAIT ESTIMER. FAIT PAR P. GIFFART GRAVEUR DU ROY AVEC PRIVIL RUE ST. JACQUES A STE THERESE.

Madame de Maintenon is shown, half length, facing to the left, with four emblematic medallions in the corners.

Françoise d'Aubigné, as she was born, was the grand-daughter of the Huguenot poet Agrippa d'Aubigné, and was brought up in the Huguenot faith. At seventeen she married the dramatist Paul Scarron, and was widowed in 1660. In 1669, at the age of thirty-four, she became governess to Louis XIV's illegitimate children by her friend Madame de Montespan. Although she was initially disliked by the King, in 1674, he gave her the estate and title of Maintenon, and he eventually fell in love with her. They were married secretly, probably in the autumn of 1683, after the death of the Queen, Marie Thérèse.

In 1679 Madame de Maintenon had written of the King, 'He is thinking seriously of the conversion of the heretics, and will soon set to work at it earnestly'. In 1681, she wrote, 'The King is beginning to think seriously of his salvation, and if God preserves him to us, there will soon be only one religion in the kingdom'.

Madame de Maintenon has often been blamed for the Revocation. However, she grieved quietly at the persecutions the Protestants had to endure, and she even sheltered several Huguenots in her own household.

DIMENSIONS: *380 × 315mm.*

PROVENANCE: *Cracheron Collection; Department of Prints and Drawings, British Museum.*

LITERATURE: *A.J. Grant, The Huguenots, 1934, pp.160–1; Nancy Mitford, The Sun King, 1966, pp.18,39,61,69,109,132,134.*

16

17

21

20

18

(1)

The Humble

PETITION

OF THE

Proteſtants of France,

Lately preſented to

His Moſt Chriſtian Majeſty,

By the Mareſchal *Schomberg*, and the Marquis of *Ruvigny*.

A *true Copy in* Engliſh.

SIR,

WE your Subjects of that Religion (which we call the Reformed) do, with moſt profound Reverence, caſt our ſelves at the
feet of your Majeſty, that ſo we may repreſent the many aggrievances
which have been heaped upon us, one after another, and may moſt
humbly beg ſome effectual reſentments of the ſame, from your juſtice
and goodneſs.

The Edicts of the Kings your Predeceſſors, and particularly thoſe
of *Henry* the Great, and *Lewis* the Juſt, which your Majeſty moſt au-
thentically confirmed at your happy Inauguration, and ſince, by divers
and ſundry Declarations have always had regard to thoſe of the ſaid Religion, which conſiſts of a conſiderable part of thoſe people which God
hath committed to your charge: And as ſuch, they have not only been
permitted to exerciſe their Employments, and Arts, and Trades, whereby they gain their Livelihood, but alſo have been promoted to Places of
Truſt and Honour, as effects of their Merit and Vertue; They have
alſo enjoyed a Liberty of Conſcience, by a free exerciſe of their Religion and Diſcipline in all places priviledged by the aforeſaid Edicts, and
Commiſſioners alſo have been appointed to take care, that there ſhould
be no infringements or violations thereof.

There have been alſo Courts of Juſtice conſiſting of men of both Religion; that at all times the Proteſtants might be aſſured of impartial juſtice both as to their Perſons, and Eſtates. And the Gentlemen particularly had right, to place in their Fee-Farms thoſe of one or the other Religion, without any difference: In ſhort, your Petitioners enjoyed
almoſt the ſame freedom and advantages, as the other Subjects of your
Majeſty:

A   It

18 *The Humble Petition of the Protestants of France*

PRESENTED TO LOUIS XIV BY MARESCHAL SCHOMBERG AND THE MARQUIS OF RUVIGNY, 1685:
ENGLISH TRANSLATION.

The Petition states that in the last few years Protestants have been refused admission to
Public Office, and have also been dismissed from positions of authority in which they had
served with honour and fidelity.

Within ten years at least 300 Protestant Temples had been demolished.

Protestant children were often taken away from their homes. They were only allowed one
schoolmaster in each town, even when there were more than two hundred children in the
school.

As a result many Protestants had been forced to leave their homes and seek refuge abroad.

The petitioners suggest that the King had been distracted by war, and as a result, through
neglect, the persecution of the Protestants had increased. They plead for a return to the
observance of the Edict of Nantes.

Ruvigny and Schomberg were both eminent soldiers. Ruvigny had served as French
Ambassador in England in the 1670s. He eventually took refuge there in 1686 and lived at
Greenwich till his death in 1689. Mareschal Schomberg led William III's troops in Ireland,
and was killed in action at the Battle of the Boyne in 1690.

ILLUSTRATED: *page 35.*

DIMENSIONS: *Folio.*

PROVENANCE: *British Library.*

LITERATURE: *Rev. D.C. Agnew,
Protestant Exiles from France, Vol.1,
1871, p.141.*

19 *Document listing expenses caused by the Dragonnades, Rouen*

MANUSCRIPT, ROUEN, 1686.

This document lists expenses 'caused by the dragoons at my house because of the said
Mme Gansel, and money paid to them'. The house in question belonged to Isaac Caillouel, a
prosperous merchant, whose business included trade in cloth with London. In October 1686
he was still in Rouen, but by November had emigrated to England. Madame Gansel was a
relative, and the Caillouel papers also include letters from David Gansel, a cousin who was
based in London.

By 1681 the billeting of troops on the Protestant population was being used as a means of
conversion. In that year the Intendant of the province of Poitou obtained 30,000 conversions
as a result. The soldiers or 'dragoons' as they were known, were encouraged to ill-treat their
hosts, and the financial burden of supporting them was considerable.

PROVENANCE: *Mrs. Soley; Presented
to the Huguenot Library, 1942.*

LITERATURE: *Irvine R. Gray, Huguenot
Manuscripts, Huguenot Society Quarto
Series, Vol.LVI (1983), p.140;
Winifred Turner, Proceedings of the
Huguenot Society of London, Vol.17
(1942–46), pp.152–153. For the Gansel
family, see Randolph Vigne, David
Gansel of Leyton Grange, Proceedings
of the Huguenot Society of London,
Vol.23 (1977–82), pp.358–375.*

20 *Sword*

IRON, FRENCH, *c.*1660.

An iron sword with a pear-shaped metal pommel surmounted by a button, with a quillion
and hilt covered in cabled filigree wire. The blade is rounded and channelled at the point.

This example is typical of the swords used by the French cavalry and dragoons of the late
seventeenth century.

ILLUSTRATED: *page 35.*

DIMENSIONS: *800mm long.*

PROVENANCE: *Koechlin Collection;
bought by the Musée de L'Armée,
Paris, 1954.*

21 *Pair of spurs*

IRON, FRENCH, EARLY EIGHTEENTH CENTURY.

The dragoons, known as the 'new missionaries', were mounted infantry. They wore special
boots with separate shoe sections, enabling the soldier to dismount with ease. A unique pair
of these boots can be seen in the Musée de L'Armée, Paris. The spurs were worn over the
boots.

The iron spurs have broad straight shanks, with four holes to take straphooks, and a
straight neck set with a seven-pointed star-rowel.

ILLUSTRATED: *page 35.*

DIMENSIONS: *70mm spread.*

PROVENANCE: *Musée de L'Armée,
Paris.*

22 *The London Gazette*

11–14 DECEMBER, 1682.

'Paris Dec.19

The 14th Instant the Council of State made an Order forbidding the Exercise of the
Protestant Religion at Lenquais and Badesou, in the Diocess of Sarlatte, and commanding,
That the Protestant Churches there should be forthwith Demolished. And from Mompellier
we have an account, That the Duke de Nouailles, the King's Lieutenant in Languedoc, had,
upon the Orders he received from Court, executed the Decree of the Parliament of Toulouse
for the Demolishing the Protestant Church at Mompellier.'

The effect of repeated reports of this kind in British newspapers had all the more impact on
contemporary readers because the heir to the throne, the future James II, was a Catholic.

PROVENANCE: *Museum of London.*

Numb. 1781

The London Gazette.

Published by Authority.

From Monday December 11. to Thursday December 14. 1682.

Warfaw, Nov. 20.

The Advices that come from all hands of the great Preparations which the Turks are making for War, are received at the Polish Court with much Concern, and it has been confidently reported, That the King of Poland had resolved to enter into strict Engagements with the motest parts of the Empire, and that the Horses Tail had been sent to the Bassa of *Aleppo*, and other Bassa's, who are accounted their best Commanders, which signifies a Command to them to repair forthwith to the Army; That the Grand-Vizier, as was said, intended to go as far as *Belgrade* to give the necessary Orders, and to return to *Adrianople* against the time that the Grand-Signior has done

good Prize. There was a long conceit upon the matter, but the French would not part with their Prize.

Paris, Dec. 19. The 14th Instant the Council of State made an Order forbidding the Exercise of the Protestant Religion at *Lenquais* and *Badefou*, in the Diocess of *Sarlatte*, and commanding, That the Protestant Churches there should be forthwith Demolished. And from *Mompellier* we have an account, That the Duke *de Novailles*, the King's Lieutenant in *Languedoc*, had, upon the Orders he received from Court, executed the Decree of the Parliament of *Toulouse* for the Demolishing the Protestant Church at *Mompelier*. The Letters we receive from *Rome* tell us, That the Endeavours that have been used to accommodate the differences between that Court and this, and par...

S. *Easter-day*, Lord Almoner.

ARLINGTON.

The Sheriffs for

Stafford — *Mathew Flawyer of Iuce* Esq;
Essex — Sir *William Glascocke* Kt.

London, Dec. 11. At the Sessions held the last Week at the Old-Baily, several Apprentices and others were Indicted of having Committed a Ryot within this City on the sixth of *November* at night, of which being Convicted, they were Fined 20 Marks each, and ordered to stand on the Pillory at the several places where they committed the Ryot, which was Executed accordingly on Saturday last.

Advertisements.

ON the 20th of this Instant December, will be exposed to Sale (by Inch of Candle) several Houshold Goods...

22

3

DECLARATION DU ROY,

Portant que les enfans dont les peres feront morts dans la R. P. R. & dont les meres feront Catholiques, feront élevez en la Religion Catholique, avec défenses de leur donner des Tuteurs de la R. P. R.

LOUIS par la grace de Dieu, Roy de France & de Navarre; A tous ceux qui ces presentes Lettres verront, SALUT. Ayant esté informez que plusieurs femmes Catholiques, veuves de marys qui faisoient profession de la Religion Pretenduë Reformée font inquietées en la conduite & éducation de leurs enfans par les parens de leurs marys, qui leur font à cet effet establir des Tuteurs ou Subrogez Tuteurs, faisant profession de la R. P. R. Nous avons voulu donner ausdites veuves dans la perte de leurs marys cette consolation, de pouvoir en veillant aux biens & à l'avantage de leurs enfans, leur procurer celuy d'estre élevez & instruits dans la veritable Religion. A CES CAUSES, Nous avons dit & declaré, disons & declarons par ces Presentes signées de nostre main, Voulons & nous plaist que les enfans âgez de quatorze ans & au dessous, dont les peres font morts faisant profession de la R.P.R. & qui auront leurs meres Catholiques, soient instruits & élevez à la Religion Catholique, & qu'à cet effet il ne puisse leur estre donné pour Tuteurs, Subrogez Tuteurs ou Curateurs d'autres que des

23

23 *Declaration relating to the children of the Huguenots*

PARIS 12 JULY 1685.

This declaration affected children whose fathers, members of the Religion Prétendue Réformée, had died, and whose mothers were Catholic. These children were apparently being brought up in the Protestant faith under the guidance of Protestant teachers.

The document explains that as a consolation to the widows, their children would be brought up in the true faith. The mother of a child of fourteen years or under who was not being brought up in the true faith would be fined and banished for nine years.

It was the fear of losing their children, if they remained in France, that made many Protestants decide to emigrate.

The Declaration is bound in a collection of 'Reglemens concernant les Religionnaires depuis l'année 1685 jusques & compris 1734'.

PROVENANCE: *Musée du Protestantisme, Paris.*

24 *Revocation of the Edict of Nantes, 1685*

FACSIMILE

The document explains that Henry IV had granted the Edict of Nantes 'to the end that he might be in a better condition for the taking some effectual course to re-unite these again to the Church, who upon so slight occasions had withdrawn themselves from it'. Like his father and grandfather before him, this was also Louis XIV's intention.

The detailed clauses of the document declare that all temples are to be immediately destroyed. No Huguenot services are to be allowed in any public place or private house. Ministers who will not abjure their faith must leave the kingdom within a fortnight or be condemned to the galleys if they are found in France thereafter. Ministers who accept conversion will receive a pension one-third larger than their former stipend. Children born to Huguenot parents are to be baptised by Catholic priests and brought up as Catholics. The property of those Huguenots who have left the country will be confiscated if they do not return.

Huguenots who attempt to leave France or to send out their property will be sentenced to the galleys.

French Protestants will be allowed to live freely in France provided they do not meet for any religious purpose.

The Revocation of the Edict of Nantes was signed by Louis XIV at Fontainebleau on 18 October 1685.

The original document is in the Archives Nationales, Paris.

ILLUSTRATED: *page 39.*

PROVENANCE: *Sir Henry W. Peek; Arthur Giraud Browning; Huguenot Library.*

LITERATURE: *A.J. Grant, The Huguenots, 1934, pp.172–174.*

Transcription overleaf is taken from 'An Edict of the French King Prohibiting all Publick Exercise of the Pretended Reformed Religion in his Kingdom, Translated out of the French, second edition, 1686.

Lewes, by the Grace of God, King of France and of Navarre, to all present and to come, Greeting. King Henry the Great, Our Grand-Father of Glorious Memory, desiring to prevent, that the Peace which he had procured for his Subjects, after the great Losses they had sustained, by the long Continuance of Civil and Foreign Wars, might not be disturbed by occasion of the Pretended Reformed Religion, as it had been during the reign of the Kings, his Predecessors; had, by his Edict given at Nantes, in the Month of April, 1598, regulated the Conduct which was to be observed, with Respect to those of the said Religion, the Places where they might publickly exercise the same, appointed extraordinary Judges, to administer Justice to them: And lastly, also by several distinct Articles, provided for everything, which he judged needful for the maintenance of Peace and Tranquility in his Kingdom, and to diminish the Aversion which was between these of the One and Other Religion: and this, to the end that he might be in a better condition for the taking some effectual Course (which he was resolved to do) and re-unite those again to the Church, who upon so slight occasions had with drawn themselves from it. And forasmuch as this Intention of the King, our said Grand-Father, could not be effected, by reason of his suddain and precipitated Death; and that the Execution of the fore-said Edict was interrupted during the Minority of the late King, our most Honoured Lord and Father, of Glorious Memory, by reason of some new Enterprizes of those of the Pretended Reformed Religion, whereby they gave occasion for their being deprived of several Advantages, which had been granted to them, by the afore-said Edict: notwithstanding, the King, our said late Lord and Father, according to his wonted Clemency, granted them another Edict at Nismes, in the Month of July, 1629, by means of which the Spirit and Zeal for Religion, as the King Our Said Grand-Father was, resolved to make good use of this Pious Design in Execution; but Wars abroad, coming on a few Years after, so that from the Year 1635 to the Truce which was concluded with the Princes of Europe, in 1684, the Kingdom having been only for some short Intervals, altogether free from Troubles, it was not possible to do any other thing for the Advantage of Religion, save only to diminish the number of Places permitted for the Exercise of the Pretended Reformed Religion, as well as by the Interdiction of those which were found Erected, in prejudice to the Disposal made in the said Edict, as by suppressing the Mixt Chambers of Judicature, which were composed of an equal number of Papists and Protestants; the Erecting of which was only done by Provision, and to serve the present Exigency.

Whereas therefore, at length, it hath pleased God to grant, that Our Subjects enjoying a perfect Peace, and We Our Selves being no longer taken up with the Cares of Protecting them against Our Enemies, are now in a Condition to make good Use of the said Truce, which we have on purpose facilitated in order to the applying ourselves entirely to the searching out of Means, which might successfully effect and accomplish the Design of the Kings, Our Said Grand-Father and Father, and which also hath been our Intention ever since we came to the Crown; We see, at present (not without a Just Acknowledgement of what We owe to God on that Account) that Our Endeavours have attained the End we propos'd to Our selves, forasmuch as the greater and better Part of Our Subjects of the said Pretended Reformed Religion, have already Embraced the Catholick; and since, by Means thereof, the Execution of the Edict of Nantes, and of all other Ordinances in favour of the said Pretended Reformed Religion, is become useless, We judge that We can do nothing better towards the entire effacing of the Memory of those Troubles, Confusions, and Mischief, which the Progress of that false Religion hath been the cause of in Our Kingdom, and which have given Occasion to the said Edict, and to so many other Edicts and Declarations which went before it, or were made since with reference thereto, than by a Total Revocation of the said Edict of Nantes, and the particular Articles and Concessions granted therein, and whatsoever also hath been Enacted since, in favour of the said Religion.

I

We made known, that We, for these and other Reasons Us thereto moving, and of Our certain Knowledge, full Power and Authority Royal, have by the present Perpetual and Irrevocable Edict, Suppressed and Annulled, do Suppress and Annull the Edict of the King, Our said Grand-Father, given at Nantes, in April 1598 in its whole extent, together with the particular Articles ratified the Second of May, next following, and Letters Patent granted thereupon; as likewise, the Edict given at Nismes, in July 1629, declaring them null and void, as if they had never been Enacted; together with all the concessions granted in them, as well as other Declarations, Edicts and Arrests, to those of the Pretended Reformed Religion, of what nature soever they may be, which shall all continue as if they never had been. And in pursuance hereof, We Will, and it is our Pleasure, That all the Churches of those of the Pretended Reformed Religion, situate in our Kingdom, Countries, Lands, and Dominions belonging to Us, be forthwith demolished.

II

We forbid our Subjects of the Pretended Reformed Religion, to Assemble themselves, for time to come, in order to the Exercise of their Religion in any Place or House, under what pretext so ever, whether the said Places have been granted by the Crown, or permitted by the Judges of particular places; any Arrests of our Council, for Authorizing and Establishing of the said places for Exercise, notwithstanding.

III

We likewise Prohibit all Lords, of what condition soever they may be, to have any Publick Exercise in their Houses and Fiefs, of what quality soever the said Fiefs may be, upon penalty to all our said Subjects, who shall have the said Exercises performed in their Houses or otherwise, of Confiscation of Body and Goods.

IV

We do strictly Charge and Commend all Ministers of the said Pretended Reformed Religion, who are not willing to be Converted, and to embrace the Catholick, Apostolick and Roman Religion, to depart out of our Kingdom and Countries under our Obedience, 15 days after the Publication hereof, so as not to continue there beyond the said term, or within the same, to Preach, Exhort, or perform any other Ministerial Function, upon pain of being sent to the Galleys.

V

Our Will and Pleasure is, That those Ministers who shall be Converted, do continue to enjoy during their Lives, and their Widows after their Decease, as long as they continue to do so, the same Exemptions from Payments and Quartering of Souldiers, which they did enjoy during the time of their Exercise of the Ministerial Function. Moreover, We will cause to be paid to the said Ministers, during their Lives, a Pension, which by a third part shall exceed the appointed Allowance to them as Ministers; the half of which Pension, shall be continued to their Wives, after their Decease, as long as they shall continue in the state of widow-hood.

VI

And in case any of the said Ministers shall be willing to become Advocates, or to take the Degree of Doctors in Law, we Will and Understand that they be dispensed with, as to the three Years of Study, which are prescribed by our Declarations, as requisite, in order to the taking of the said Degree; and that, after they have pass'd the ordinary Examinations, they be forthwith received as Doctors, paying only the Moiety of those dues, which are usually paid upon that account in every University.

VII

We prohibit any particular schools for Instructing the Children of those of the Pretended Reformed Religion; and in general, all other things whatsoever, which may Import a Concession, of what kind soever, in favour of the said Religion.

VIII

And as to the Children which shall for the future be Born of those of the said Pretended Reformed Religion, Our Will and Pleasure is, That henceforward they be Bab(sic)tized by the Curates of our Parishes; strictly charging their representative Fathers and Mothers to take care they be sent to Church in order thereto, upon Forfeiture of 500 livres or more, as it shall happen. Furthermore, Our Will is that the said Children be afterwards Educated and brought up in the Catholick Apostolick and Roman Religion, and give an express Charge to all Our Justices, to take care the same be performed accordingly.

IX

And for a Mark of our Clemency towards those of our Subjects of the said Pretended Reformed Religion, who have retired themselves out of our Kingdom, Countries and Territories, before the Publication of this our present Edict, Our Will and Meaning is, That in case they return hither again, within the time of Four Months, from the time of the Publication hereof, they may, and it shall be lawful for them, to Re-enter upon the Possession of their Goods and Estates, and enjoy the same in like manner, as they might have done in case they had always continued upon the place. And on the contrary, that the Goods of all those, who within the said time of four Months, shall not return into our Kingdom, Countries or Territories under our Obedience, which they have forsaken, remain and be Confiscated in pursuance of our Declaration of the 20th of August last.

X

We most expresly and strictly forbid all our Subjects of the said Pretended Reformed Religion, them, their Wives or Children, to depart out of our said Kingdom, Countries or Territories under our Obedience, or to Transport thence their Goods or Effects, upon Penalty of the Gally(sic), for Men, and of Confiscation of Body and Goods for Women.

XI

Our Will and Meaning is, That the Declaration made against those who shall relapse, be Executed upon them according to their Form and Tenor.

Moreover, those of the said Pretended Reformed Religion, in the meantime, till it shall Please God to enlighten them, as well as others, may abide in the several respective Cities and Places of our Kingdoms, Countries and Territories under our Obedience, and their continue their Commerce, and enjoy their Goods and Estates, without being any way molested upon account of the said Pretended Reformed Religion; upon condition nevertheless, as forementioned, that they do not use any publick Religious Exercise, nor assemble themselves upon the account of Prayer or Worship of the said Religion, of what kind soever the same may be, upon forfeiture above specified of Body and Goods.

Accordingly, We Will and Command our Trusty and Beloved Counsellors, the people holding our Courts of Aids at Paris, Bayliffs, Chief Justices, Provosts, and other our Justices and Officers to whom it appertains, and to their Lieutenants, that they cause to be Read, Published, and Registered, this Our present Edict in their Courts and Jurisdictions, even in Vacation time, and the same keep punctually, without contrevening or suffering the same to be contrevened; for such is Our Will and Pleasure. And to the end to make it a thing firm and stable, we have caused Our Seal to be put to the same. Given at Fontainebleau, in the Month of October, in the Year of Grace 1685, and of Our Reign the XLIII.

Signed LEWES

This signifies the Lord Chancellor's Perusal *VISA* *Le Tellier*

Sealed with the Great Seal of Green-Wax, upon a Red and Green string of silk. Registred and Published, the Kings Attorney General requiring it in order to their being Executed according to Form and Tenor; and the Copies being Examined and Compared, sent to the Several Courts of Justice, Bailywicks, and Sheriffs Courts of each District, to be there Entred and Registred in like manner; and Charge given to the Deputies of the said Attorney General, to take care to see the same Executed, and put in Force; and to certify the Court thereof. At Paris, in the Court of Vacations, the 22th of Octob. 1685

Signed De la Baune

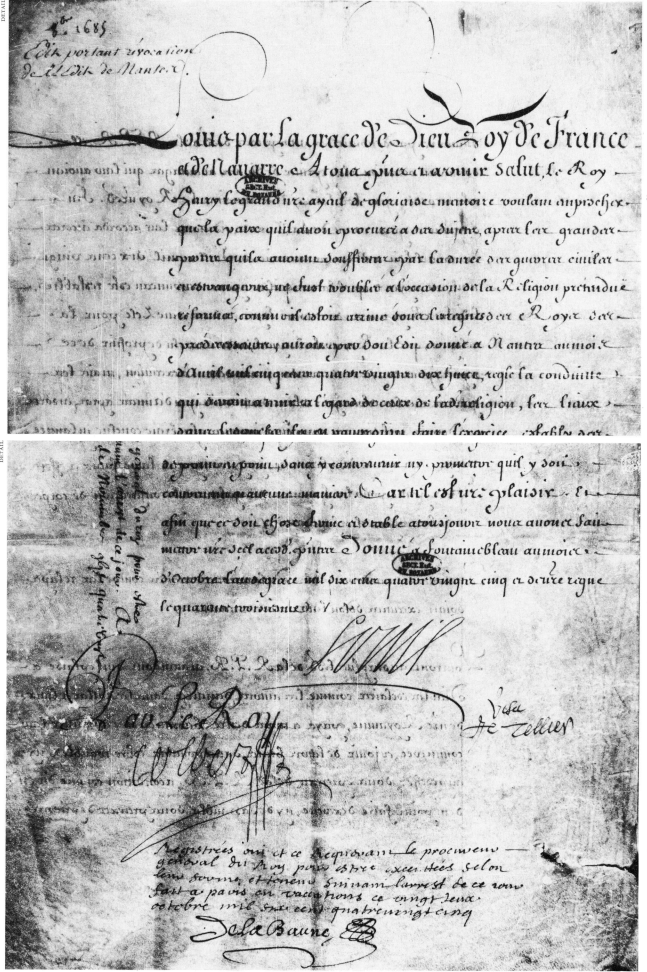

8bre 1685
Edit portant révocation
de l'Edit de Nantes.

Louis par la grace de Dieu Roy de France
et de Navarre. A tous presens et avenir Salut, Le Roy
Henry le grand nre ayeul de glorieuse memoire voulant empescher
que la paix quil auoit procurée a ses subjets, aprés les grandes
pertes quils auoient soufferts par la durée des guerres ciuiles
et estrangeres, ne fust troublée à l'occasion de la Religion prétendue
reformée, comme il estoit arriué sous les regnes des Roys ses
prédécesseurs, auroit par son Edit donné a Nantes au mois
d'Auril cinq cent quatre vingts dix huict, reglé sa conduitte
qui deuoit estre à l'égard de ceux de ladicte Religion, les lieux
ou ils pourroient faire l'exercice establis...

24

25 *Demolition of the Temple at Charenton*
ENGRAVING, SEBASTIEN LE CLERC, PARIS, 1685.

The destruction of the temple at Charenton was regarded by the authorities as a most significant development in the campaign against heresy. To commemorate the event, a medal was produced entitled 'The demolition of Calvinist Temples'. The official description of the medal explained that the Revocation document had declared that all Huguenot temples were to be destroyed, and particularly the one at Charenton, which was regarded as the principal seat of heresy. The temple at Charenton was destroyed by the fury of the mob on 29 October 1685. According to the official account, within two days, no trace of the temple was to be seen.

DIMENSIONS: *240 × 300mm.*

PROVENANCE: *Musée du Protestantisme, Paris.*

LITERATURE: *Médailles sur les principaux événements du règne de Louis Le Grand, avec les explications historiques par L'Académie Royale des Inscriptions et Médailles, 1702.*

26 *The Complaints of the Protestants cruelly persecuted in the Kingdom of France*
JEAN CLAUDE, 1686.

Jean Claude (1619–1687) was the son of a French pastor. He studied for the ministry at Montauban, was ordained in 1645, and worked at Nîmes (1654), Montauban (1662), and Charenton (1666). An eloquent defender of the Huguenot faith, he presented petitions to the King after the Edict of 17 June 1681, in which Protestant children of seven were encouraged to abjure their faith, demand an allowance from their parents, and leave home to practise as Catholics, and again early in 1685. Four days after the Revocation document was signed, Claude received an order to leave Paris within twenty-four hours. He fled to the Hague where he joined members of his family.

This volume was written as a protest against the injustice and violence of the persecution of the Protestants in France and as a witness to the suffering the Huguenots had undergone in defence of their rights and their conscience. Needless to say it was regarded as an incitement to war by the French ambassador at The Hague. The book was banned in France, and although translated into English in the same year, was burnt by order of James II by the public hangman at the London Exchange and elsewhere; its translators were arrested.

PROVENANCE: *G.B. Beeman; presented to the Huguenot Library, 1948.*

LITERATURE: *Jean Claude, Les Plaintes des Protestants, 1885, ed. F. Puaux; R.S. Faber, Catalogue of the Library of the French Hospital, Victoria Park Road, London, 1890, pp.33–4; A.J. Grant, The Huguenots, 1934, pp.130,156, 168,186,190. Robin Gwynn, Huguenot Heritage, 1985, p.135.*

27 *History of the Edict of Nantes*
ELIE BENOIT, LONDON, 1694.

This history contains 'an Account of all the Persecutions That have been in France From its First Publication to this Present Time Faithfully Extracted from all the Publick and Private Memoirs that could possibly be procured'. The volumes were printed initially in French by the authority of the States of Holland and West Friesland. The English translation is dedicated to Queen Mary, and pays tribute to 'the tender Compassion and Charity' she showed to 'multitudes of French Refugiez of all Ranks and Degrees who have been forced to fly hither for your Glorious Protection and Relief.'

The term 'refugee', derived from the French, was first used in English in the 1680s in reference to the Huguenots.

DIMENSIONS: *Quarto.*

PROVENANCE: *British Library.*

28 *L'Ecole de la Vérité pour les nouveaux convertis*
PHOTOGRAPH

This board game is representative of the considerable effort made to convert Protestant children to Catholicism. It was published in Paris, probably in the 1680s.

PROVENANCE: *Purchased by Charles Marmoy in La Rochelle, 1969; Huguenot Library.*

29 *Certificate of abjuration granted to a Huguenot*
PARIS, 1733

This certificate was granted to Anthony Lauzy, born into the Huguenot faith, who at 27 decided to abjure, by Charles Gaspard William de Vintimille, Archbishop of Paris, in the Episcopal Palace, Paris, 1733. It is headed by the coat of arms of the Archbishop.

In order to receive a certificate of abjuration, the person concerned had to 'Swear upon the Book of the Gospel' and declare, 'I Promise, Vow and Swear, and most constantly Profess, by God's Assistance, to keep entirely and inviolably unto Death, this self same Catholick and Apostolick Faith, out of which no Person can be saved'. The oath was preceded by a catechism in which the person concerned had to acknowledge the seven sacraments, transubstantiation, the existence of Purgatory, the veneration of the Saints and images of Christ, the Blessed Virgin and the Saints, and also 'that the power of indulgence was left to the Church by Christ Jesus, and that the use thereof is very beneficial to Christians'. He also had to profess and swear true obedience to the Pope of Rome.

DIMENSIONS: *197 × 203mm.*

PROVENANCE: *Bequeathed to the French Hospital by Charles Poyntz Stewart F.S.A.*

LITERATURE: *Winifred Turner, Ms. Catalogue of the French Hospital Collection.*

25

THE
HISTORY
Of the Famous
Edict of Nantes:
CONTAINING AN
ACCOUNT
OF THE
PERSECUTIONS,
That have been in
FRANCE
From its First Publication to this Present Time.

Faithfully Extracted from all the Publick and Private Memoirs, that could possibly be procured.

VOL. I.

Printed first in *French*, by the Authority of the States of *Holland* and *West-Friezland*. And now Translated into English.

With Her Majesties Royal Priviledge.

LONDON,
Printed for JOHN DUNTON, at the *Raven* in the Poultry. MDCXCIV.

27

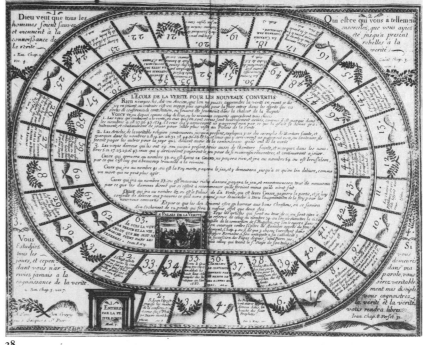

28

29

Church of the Désert

Officially Protestantism no longer existed in France as an organised religion after 1685. However, the Huguenots continued to meet for worship in secret. Pulpits, pastors' hats, communion cups and bibles had to be concealed from the authorities. These illegal gatherings were known as 'Les Déserts' by reference to the trials of the people of Israel in the Old Testament.

Ministers returned from exile to preach to the faithful and often lost their lives as a result. Those Protestants who were caught worshipping or assisting their ministers were imprisoned or condemned to the galleys. By 1775, over three thousand Huguenots had been sentenced in this way.

30 Bonnet worn by a Huguenot
SILK, FRENCH, EIGHTEENTH CENTURY.

During the years of persecution, women were largely responsible for the fervour with which the Protestant faith was handed down to the next generation.

This traditional bonnet, worn by the women at worship, is of black quilted silk, with long ear pieces, and is lined with blue silk and gathered with blue silk ribbons at the back and silk ties in front.

The bonnet belonged to the Piollenc family who were based in Nîmes, where they worked as lawyers.

DIMENSIONS: *570mm long, 325mm wide.*
PROVENANCE: *Madame Rosin.*

31 Three lamps
ONE BRASS, TWO IRON, FRENCH, SEVENTEETH CENTURY.

These oil lamps, originally used by miners, were carried by the faithful in order to light their way to the secret assemblies in the désert, which were usually held after dark. The well-to-do members of the congregation would have carried brass lamps.

DIMENSIONS: *242, 274, 258mm high.*
PROVENANCE: *Comte Nicolas César de Magnin; by family descent to Madame Jaulmes.*

32 Bible
FRENCH VERSION, GENEVA, c.1588–90.

The title page has been removed, so that the identity of the printer could remain secret. There is a record of births, marriages and deaths in the Fasquest family dating back to 1625. According to family tradition, during a search of the home, this bible was concealed by being baked in a loaf of bread. The family concerned lived in the Drôme.

This French version of the bible was first published in Geneva in 1560. It was based on the Olivetan edition produced by the Ministers of Geneva.

DIMENSIONS: *255 × 215 × 110mm.*
PROVENANCE: *Fasquest family till c.1800; Rambaud family, given to Suzanne Magnin, c.1900; by descent to Madame Jaulmes.*

33 Milk churn concealing pastor's hat
IRON, USED IN THE DESERT, LATE SEVENTEENTH CENTURY ONWARDS.

The Huguenot pastor traditionally wore a hat whilst preaching. Such a hat was probably a rarity among such simple folk, and had to be concealed when not in use in order to avoid suspicion.

DIMENSIONS: *300mm high 230mm diameter at base.*
PROVENANCE: *Musée du Protestantisme, Paris.*

34 Communion cup dividing into a candlestick and a goblet
PEWTER, USED IN THE DESERT, LATE SEVENTEENTH CENTURY ONWARDS.

Communion was only received four times a year. In the interim, the cup could be divided into a candlestick and a goblet in order to conceal its real purpose.

DIMENSIONS: *275mm high. 100m diameter at base.*
PROVENANCE: *Musée du Protestantisme, Paris.*

35 Pulpit
WOOD AND IRON, WITH HANGINGS, FRENCH, EIGHTEENTH CENTURY, USED IN THE DESERT.

Folding pulpits were used for clandestine worship in the désert, after the Edict of Nantes was revoked in 1685, and until the Edict of Toleration was passed in 1787.

This particular example was used in the woods of Saint-Benezit, to the north of Nîmes. In the early nineteenth century, it served as a pulpit in the temporary building in St. Benezit which was used for Protestant worship, and the hangings probably date from this period. Its continued use in the nineteenth century explains its remarkably good state of preservation, by comparison with the other surviving folding pulpits in the Musée du Désert, the Musée du Protestantisme, Paris and the Musée du Protestantisme, La Rochelle.

NOT EXHIBITED.
DIMENSIONS: *2600 × 850mm.*
PROVENANCE: *Given to the Musée du Désert by the Labouchère family, 1911.*

30

31

32

33

33

34

34

36 The Church of the Désert

ENGRAVING, L.L. BELLOTTI AFTER J.J. STORNI, 1775; INSCRIBED: BIENHEUREUX SONT CEUX
QUI ECOUTENT LA PAROLE DE DIEU ET QUI LA PRATIQUE J.C. EN S. LUC CHAPITRE XI VERSET
28 ASSEMBLEE DANS LE DESERT.

Officially Protestantism no longer existed in France after 1685. However, in the South East
and in the Cévennes and Bas-Languedoc, the Huguenots met secretly, choosing suitable
venues such as a cave, rocky valley, or farm, that provided seclusion and a potential hide-out.
With the exception of a short period when worship was dominated by 'prophets' and
unqualified preachers, worship conformed to the traditional liturgy. Men and women gathered
in separate groups. Passages of scripture were read, psalms sung and a general confession was
followed by a sermon. The service closed with a blessing and a collection for the poor. Elders
were elected, psalters distributed, and baptisms or marriages celebrated.

Gradually pastors, trained in Lausanne, became attached to particular areas. By 1740
Consistories were meeting regularly. The years 1717, 1726, 1745 and 1750 marked a temporary
increase in persecution. In the reign of Louis XV (1715–1774) two hundred Protestants were
condemned to the galleys.

DIMENSIONS: *836 × 614mm.*
PROVENANCE: *French Hospital.*
LITERATURE: *Histoire des Protestants en France, 1977, pp.192,212.*

37 Sermons of the Désert

CLAUDE BROUSSON (1647–1698) AMSTERDAM, 1695; ENTITLED: PRONONCEZ EN FRANCE
DANS LES DESERTS ET DANS LES CAVERNES DURANT LES TENEBRES DE LA NUIT & DE
L'AFFLICTION LES ANNEES 1689, 1690, 1691, 1692 & 1693.

Claude Brousson was a lawyer at Nîmes. During the 1680s he played a significant part in the
organisation of the persecuted church in the Midi and West of France. In Toulouse in 1683,
he drew up a petition stating that there were still Protestants in France and that to uproot the
Protestant church in France was not as simple as it might seem. This was sent to Louis XIV.

As a preacher, Brousson's legal training gave him a prestigious following. Most of those
who attended secret worship were peasants or artisans, many of whom worked in the textile
trade. Brousson left France and trained for the ministry in Switzerland. He was ordained at
the French Church in The Hague. In 1695, he returned to France and visited Picardy,
Champagne, Brie and Normandy. In Holland again he tried to persuade Protestant leaders to
insert a clause in the Treaty of Ryswick, 1697, guaranteeing freedom of worship for the
Protestants in France. Discouraged by his failure to do so, he returned to France, visiting
Lyon, Vivarais, Dauphiné, Cévennes and Béarn, where he was arrested in 1698. He was transferred to Montpellier and executed there by being broken on the wheel on 3 November 1698.

PROVENANCE: *R.C. Critchett; Huguenot Library.*
LITERATURE: *Histoire des Protestants en France, 1977, pp.117,132,148,189, 194–5,197,199,204,206; Leopold Nègre, Vie et Ministère de Claude Brousson, 1647–1698, 1878.*

38 Monument to the six Protestant Martyrs, Fort Real, Ile St Marguerite

PHOTOGRAPH; INSCRIBED: A LA MEMOIRE DES PASTEURS PAUL GARDEL, PIERRE DE SALVE,
GABRIEL MATHURIN, MATHIEU MALZAC, ELISEE GIRAUD, GARDIEN GIVRY. EXILES DE
FRANCE A LA REVOCATION DE L'EDIT DE NANTES RENTRES CLANDESTINEMENT POUR SERVIR
LES EGLISES SOUS LA CROIX. ENFERMES A VIE A VINCENNES ET A SAINTE MARGUERITE DE
1689 A 1725 AYANT PREFERE LA PRISON A L'ABJURATION. (THE MONUMENT IS ENGRAVED
WITH A HUGUENOT CROSS).

The Fort, occupied by the Spanish in 1633, and situated on an island in the Bay of Cannes,
was used as a prison for Protestant pastors from 1689. The monument records six names of
pastors who left France on the Revocation and returned several years later to minister to the
faithful. Of these, Gardien Givry spent five years as pastor to the conformist French
congregation in Plymouth. (The Bounty papers in the Huguenot Library refer to him as Jean
Givry, de Loudun.) In 1691, he returned to France, and was arrested in Paris in 1692. Paul
Gardel fled to England on the Revocation. He became Pastor of the French congregation at
Harlem before returning to Paris, where he was caught and imprisoned in the Bastille before
being transferred to Sainte Marguerite. Gabriel Mathurin was also arrested in Paris in April,
1690. He was the only survivor in 1715, after twenty-five years in secret confinement. He
joined his wife and family in Ireland, where he died in 1718.

PROVENANCE: *H. Roger Viollet, Paris.*

39 Prisoner's verses

JEREMIE DUPUY, 1686.

Sombres et tristes lieux, témoins de ma souffrance
Hideux et noirs cachots, image des enfers
Si le Dieu que je sers n'appuyait ma constance
Sans doute je mourrais accablé de vos fers

Mon unique Sauveur m'assiste et me console
Répand dans mon esprit sa divine clarté
Et m'instruit tous les jours, dans sa sainte parole
De souffrir constamment tout pour sa vérité

Je chéris dans mon coeur les peines que j'endure
Et bénis les tourments que je souffre en ce lieu.
Et malgré les ennuis d'une prison si dure
Je sens que tout est doux quand on souffre pour Dieu.

These verses were written by Jérémie Dupuy, a member of the Consistoire de L'Eglise de
Caraman (Haute-Garonne) in prison at Puymirol, near D'Agen in 1686.

36

A LA MEMOIRE DES PASTEVRS
PAVL GARDEL
PIERRE DE SALVE
GABRIEL MATHVRIN
MATHIEV MALZAC
ELISEE GIRAVD
GARDIEN GIVRY
EXILES DE FRANCE A LA REVO
CATION DE L'EDIT DE NANTES
RENTRES CLANDESTINEMENT
POVR SERVIR LES EGLISES SOVS
LA CROIX
ENFERMES A VIE A VINCENNES
ET A SAINTE MARGVERITE
DE 1689   A 1725

AYANT   PREFERE

LA PRISON A L'ABJVRATION

38

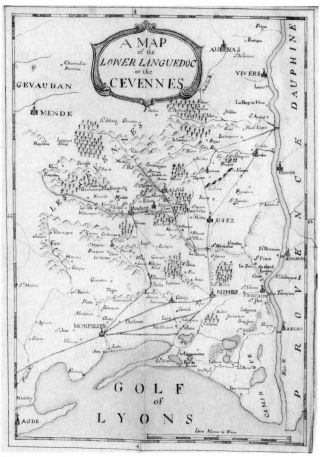

40

40 *Memoirs of the Wars of the Cévennes*

MANUSCRIPT, JEAN CAVALIER, 1726

Jean Cavalier (1681–1740), the son of a Languedoc peasant, led the guerilla war carried on by the Protestants in the Cévennes against the French troops, 1702–4. The war was eventually resolved through diplomatic negotiations with the authorities. Disillusioned, Cavalier fled from France in the summer of 1704. He later commanded a regiment against the French in Spain. Much of his later life was spent in Ireland, with the Huguenot community of veteran soldiers in Portarlington. In 1738, he became Lieutenant-Governor of Jersey and a Major-General in the British Army in 1739.

This manuscript appears to be the fair copy from which the book was first printed in Dublin in 1726. It includes a hand coloured map of the Cévennes.

Sympathy for the Huguenot cause in this guerilla war spread to the refugee community in London, and in 1707, a coffee house in St. Martin's Lane was called the Camisards, the popular name for the guerillas.

ILLUSTRATED: *page 45.*

PROVENANCE: *Rev. Beaver Henry Blacker; Robert Day F.S.A.; R.M. Chirnside; Susan Minet; given to the French Hospital, 1935; Huguenot Library.*

LITERATURE: *Irvine R. Gray, Huguenot Manuscripts, Huguenot Society Quarto Series, Vol. LVI (1983), p.169; R. Hottort, Jean Cavalier, Lieut-Governor de Jersey, Bulletin de La Société Jersiaise, 1931, pp. 326–331; Histoire des Protestants en France, 1977, pp.196,207–8,210; Bryant Lillywhite, London Coffee Houses, 1963, no. 216.*

41 *Model of a 50 oar French galley 'La Réale', c.1670*

This model is based on surviving seventeenth-century plans. The ornamental stern is derived from designs and existing sculpture attributed to the sculptor Pierre Puget. Between 1650 and 1725 several large galleys of this type were kept for the ceremonial use of the Général des Galères, the Admiral in charge of the Galley Fleet of Louis XIV. Substantially larger than most galleys, these vessels lacked the offensive rams of fighting galleys, but carried five or six more thwarts for their ranks of oarsmen. Six or seven men were required for each of these oars, whereas only two or three were normally required on fighting galleys. The cannon carried on this vessel were mainly for ceremonial use, although from the sixteenth century onwards most galleys carried between three and five small cannon to deter pirates operating from the Barbary Coast.

It was the deployment of cannon fire which finally ended the two thousand years' supremacy of the galley in Mediterranean warfare. After 1748, no more galleys were constructed in France, although some saw active service with the French forces during the expedition to Egypt in 1797–8. The last French galley was broken up in 1814.

In 1688 a medal was produced to celebrate the construction of forty galleys at the new Arsenal in Marseilles. These vessels were manned by prisoners, Huguenots sentenced for their faith, and Turkish slaves.

DIMENSIONS: *690mm long.*

PROVENANCE: *Musée de la Marine, Paris.*

42 *Relation des Tourments qu'on fait souffrir aux Protestants qui sont sur les Galeres de France*

JEAN BION, LONDON, 1708

Jean Bion was chaplain aboard the galley 'Superbe'. Deeply moved by the sufferings of the condemned Protestants on board, he was converted to Protestantism and emigrated to England, where he became Pastor of a French Church at Chelsea.

Bion's moving account describes the conditions in which the Protestants worked as slaves. Each oar had five men behind it, and in addition the end of the oar was held by a Turk, as he proved to be stronger than the Christians. Each galley had a crew of five hundred men, three hundred of whom were under sentence of penal servitude.

The men wore two shirts of coarse canvas, a red serge tunic, and a red cap, to cover their head, which was shaven to indicate their subjection. Each prisoner was attached with chains and beaten if he slacked.

Bion described how during the winter of 1703, more than sixty men fell ill off the coast of Italy. They were placed in a room only three foot high in the prow of the boat, with only one hole two foot square for ventilation.

When Bion was writing, eighty-four of the galleys of the fleet were based in Marseilles harbour and only six were at sea.

DIMENSIONS: *Octavo.*

PROVENANCE: *British Library.*

43 *Liste de ceux qui sont arrivez en Galère le 19 de Février & le 11 de Mars 1717, & qui y ont été condamnez pour cause de Religion*

This document lists the names of eighteen Protestants, who, ranging in age from 17 to 60, had been condemned to the galleys, and had taken up their positions between February and March 1717.

Almost all those condemned had been arrested for clandestine worship. The document contains on the reverse another list 'Des confesseurs qui souffrent sur les Galères de France'.

The document was published for circulation in Holland.

A total of over three thousand Protestants had been condemned to the galleys by 1775. A charitable fund established in Holland enabled some to buy their freedom. Funds were also collected amongst the refugees in England for the relief of the *galériens.*

PROVENANCE: *The Walloon Library, Amsterdam.*

44 *List of Protestants condemned to the galleys*

MANUSCRIPT, CORRESPONDENCE OF JACQUES SERCES: LISTE DES PROTESTANTS QUI
SOUFFRENT ACTUELLEMENT POUR CAUSE DE RELIGION SUR LES GALERES DE FRANCE.

Jacques Serces (1695–1762) born in Geneva, was the son of a French Huguenot refugee,
Moïse Serces, from Montmeyran in the Dauphiné. After studying theology in Geneva, Serces
emigrated to England, where he obtained the living of Appleby in Lincolnshire, and from
1738 until 1761 was chaplain of the French Chapel Royal at St. James's Palace. Serces
maintained a voluminous correspondence with Protestant activists in Switzerland.

This list of *galériens* was enclosed with a letter of 1746 from Antoine Court, the pastor who
fled to Lausanne from the Cévennes to save his own life in 1729. It gives the names of forty
galériens, their ages, the name of the vessel in which they were placed, and the reasons for their
sentence. For the most part they had been caught assisting with a secret assembly, but they
were also arrested for circulating books for worship, or for assisting a minister. They came
from the Cévennes, from Dauphiné and the Vivarais. Most of those listed were arrested in the
1740s.

DIMENSIONS: *185 × 235mm.*

PROVENANCE: *William Minet, presented
to the French Hospital; Huguenot
Library.*

LITERATURE: *Irvine R. Gray, Huguenot
Manuscripts, 1983, pp.160–1;
Correspondence de Jacques Serces,
Huguenot Society Quarto Series,
Vols.XLIII, XLIV (1952, 1956).*

41

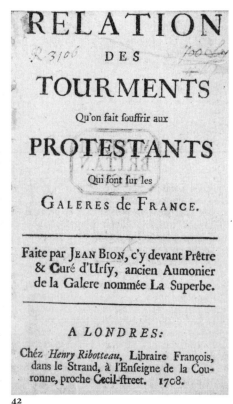

RELATION
DES
TOURMENTS
Qu'on fait souffrir aux
PROTESTANTS
Qui font fur les
GALERES de FRANCE.

Faite par JEAN BION, c'y devant Prêtre
& Curé d'Urfy, ancien Aumonier
de la Galere nommée La Superbe.

A LONDRES:
Chéz *Henry Ribotteau,* Libraire François,
dans le Strand, à l'Enfeigne de la Cou-
ronne, proche Cecil-ftreet. 1708.

42

LISTE
Des Confeffeurs qui fouffrent fur les
Galeres de France.

Noms des Galeres.	Numero	Noms des Confeffeurs	Temps de Souffrance	
Patrone	35871	Jean Chabrier	1710	
Valeur	30792	Jean Malet	1706	
	30902	Ifaac Gouchon	1706	
	32776	Pierre Fonbonne	1708	
	41755	Nicolas Cubuni		
	42922	Jean Niret		condemnés depuis 1713
	38643	Pierre Martin		
	42345	Guillaume Guierdit		
Fiere	29515	Pierre Gautier	1705	
	26129	Jean Marlier	1701	
	26128	Jaques Marlier	1701	
	28204	David Mafre	1704	
	41869	Moyfe de Mardre		depuis 1713
Superbe	28516	Jean Fufie	1704	
Brave	33974	Jean Maurel	1709	
	37991	Arleman Guirinquier	1705	
	37988	Jean Suleman		
Invincible	33978	Anthoine Coulet	1709	
	37562	Paul Dormond	1712	
	37063	Pierre Bariero		depuis 1713
	43083	Pierre Benique		
Fidele	26589	Pierre Chardenon	1702	
	31212	David Maurin		depuis 1713
	39262	Jean Horizon		
Guerriere	30789	Anthoine Claril	1706	
	41788	Charles Guinedy		
	39336	Jean Guillaume		depuis 1713
	36256	Guillaume Arnul		
	26643	Louis Differe		

43

TOLERATION

In France, the Protestants continued to worship in the 'Désert' throughout the eighteenth century. Even in the 1760s, Huguenots were condemned to the galleys. Persecution received renewed publicity abroad as a result of the affair of Jean Calas, a Protestant merchant in Toulouse who was wrongfully accused of murdering his son.

The latter had been prevented from practising his profession as a lawyer because he was a Protestant, and had committed suicide as a result. The injustice revealed by the case was highlighted by Voltaire, and an appeal for the Calas family received international support.

Public opinion was changed by Voltaire's campaign, and the first step towards civil equality and toleration of the Protestants in France was made when Louis XVI signed the Edict of Toleration in 1787.

Edict of Toleration, 1787

45 *La Malheureuse Famille Calas*

ENGRAVING: C. DE CARMONTELLE, 1765; INSCRIBED: LA MERE, LES DEUX FILLES, AVEC JEANNE
VIGUIERE, LEUR BONNE SERVANTE, LE FILS ET SON AMI, LE JEUNE LAVAYSSE. QUALIBUS IN
TENEBRIS VITAE QUANTISQUE PERICLIS REGITUR HOC AEVI QUODCUMQUE EST. LUCRET.

The engraving shows the Calas family, with the exception of their father, the linen merchant,
Jean Calas, in the Conciergerie, Paris, receiving the final judgement on the death of the eldest
son, Marc Antoine, a frustrated scholar of 28, who was unable to be called to the bar because
he was a Protestant. Marc Antoine had committed suicide on 13 October 1761, but in order
to protect the family's reputation, the father claimed that his son had been murdered.

Jean Calas was accused of his son's murder and appeared in Court in November 1761. In
March, 1762, he was condemned to death on the wheel. The public mood of intense anti-
Protestantism in Toulouse had convinced the judges of Calas's guilt. Calas refused to abjure
his faith despite his cruel torture, and as a result redeemed the family honour and prepared the
way for the defenders of the Calas family after the event.

The youngest member of the family, Donat, fled to Geneva, where his presence inspired
Voltaire to take up the cause.

In March 1765, after the case had been heard in the highest court of France, all concerned
were acquitted.

Copies of this engraving, accompanied by the story of the Calas family were sold on the
Continent and in London by the bookseller Paul Vaillant (*Catalogue number* 253 and 254) in
order to raise funds for the Calas family. The actor David Garrick and Dr. Maty, Under-
Librarian at the new British Museum, were amongst those who supported the cause, and
contributions from England were handled by the Protestant bankers, the Mallets, in Paris.
The English were particularly sympathetic as the mother, Anne Rose Calas, was born in
England (baptised at the French Protestant Church in Wheeler Street, Spitalfields, in July
1710). She was the daughter of Peter Cabibel, member of a refugee family from Languedoc.

DIMENSIONS: *423 × 343mm.*

PROVENANCE: *French Hospital.*

LITERATURE: *Uta Janssens, Mathieu
Maty and the Journal Britannique,
1750–1755, 1975, p.33. Edna Nixon,
Voltaire and the Calas Case, 1961,
(frontispiece); Randolph Vigne, The
Killing of Jean Calas, Voltaire's first
Huguenot Cause, Proceedings of the
Huguenot Society of London,
Vol.23 (1977–82), pp.280–294.*

45

46 *A Treatise on Religious Toleration*
VOLTAIRE, ENGLISH TRANSLATION, LONDON, 1764.

Voltaire's Treatise was occasioned by the execution of the unfortunate Jean Calas, 'unjustly condemned and broken upon the wheel at Toulouse, for the supposed Murder of his own Son'.

Voltaire questions the supposition that Toleration is dangerous and cites England as an example of a nation where Toleration prevails to the general benefit of the population.

He points out that, 'the Huguenots have without doubt been intoxicated with fanaticism, and have dipt their hands in blood as well as we: but is the present generation so barbarous as their ancestors? Hath not time, good sense, well-written books, and social complacence, reached those who have the direction of the minds of these people? Nay, do we not perceive a change over the face of all Europe within these fifty years past? The Toleration we contend for ... would permit a quiet people to live at peace ... the rigorous edicts once issued against them, are now become unnecessary.'

Although the book was officially banned in France, it was still circulated and helped to change the opinion of the French authorities. Eventually, in 1787, Louis XVI signed the Edict of Toleration.

PROVENANCE: *British Library*.

LITERATURE: *Edna Nixon, Voltaire and the Calas Case, 1961.*

47 *The Edict of Toleration, 1787*
PHOTOGRAPH

From 1785 the Marquis de Lafayette interceded with Louis XVI on behalf of the French Protestants. Public opinion had already been largely won over by Voltaire's campaign to exonerate the Calas family.

The Huguenot cause was also taken up by the Comte d'Artois, the King's brother. As a result, in November 1787, the King signed an Edict restoring civil equality and freedom of worship to those who did not profess the Catholic faith. Although non-Catholics were permitted to exercise a trade or profession, to contract a legal marriage, and even to bury their dead according to their own rites, they were not permitted to hold public services or to form a recognised church. It was however, the first step towards religious toleration. It was only under Napoleon I in the early years of the nineteenth century that the Protestant Church was officially recognised in France, and its ministers received a state salary.

ILLUSTRATED: *pages 48, 50.*

PROVENANCE: *Archives Nationales, Paris.*

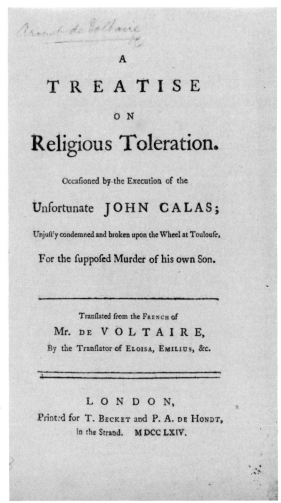

A

TREATISE

ON

Religious Toleration.

Occasioned by the Execution of the

Unfortunate JOHN CALAS;

Unjustly condemned and broken upon the Wheel at Toulouse,

For the supposed Murder of his own Son.

Translated from the FRENCH of
Mr. DE VOLTAIRE,
By the Translator of ELOISA, EMILIUS, &c.

LONDON,
Printed for T. BECKET and P. A. DE HONDT,
in the Strand. MDCCLXIV.

46   47

DISPERSION

It has been estimated that between 200,000 and 250,000 Huguenots left France as a result of the renewed persecution in the late seventeenth century, while the great majority, perhaps 700,000, remained and abjured their faith. They fled over the Swiss and Dutch borders, and by sea, leaving from the main ports, Calais, Dieppe, Nantes, La Rochelle and Bordeaux. They settled mainly in Protestant European countries. Although it is not possible to produce exact figures, the Dutch Republic was the most popular country of refuge, with an estimated 50,000 to 60,000 refugees. Britain followed with between 40,000 to 50,000, Germany with 25,000 to 30,000, and some 10,000 settled in Ireland. A few hundred eventually settled at the Cape of Good Hope and in the American Colonies.

Some popular Huguenot escape routes from France in the 1680s

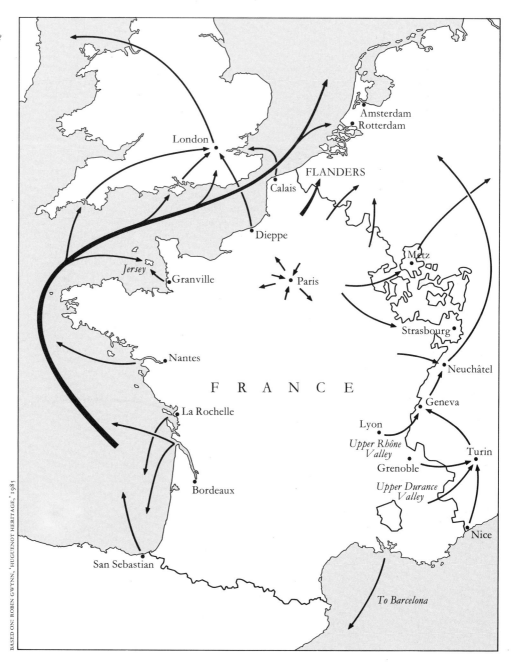

48 Narrative of Isaac Minet's Escape from France

MANUSCRIPT, WRITTEN BY ISAAC MINET, 1737.

Isaac Minet (1660–1745) was the son of a grocer in Calais. In 1674, he was sent to Dover to learn English. He stayed there nearly two years, and returned to Calais to run the family business after his father's death.

In 1685, when the Protestant Church in Calais had been demolished and the dragoons were billeted on the Protestant population, Isaac Minet and his mother left their home and hid in the house of a Dutch shopkeeper for three days. Then, disguised as a porter's wife and a carpenter, they attempted to leave the town. Unfortunately, Isaac's mother was recognised and imprisoned. Isaac was later caught and joined his mother in the same prison. They were taken to a Catholic chapel where they were compelled to sign a form of abjuration. When they returned home they found that their house was still occupied by three soldiers.

Isaac then arranged for his brother Stephen, who was already in England, to send a boat to collect them from a point two miles east of Calais at midnight on Sunday 31 July, 1686. Despite a coast guard of 25 soldiers and patrol vessels from Dunkirk, Isaac, his mother, his brother Ambrose and his sister managed to board the vessel. They landed at Dover on Monday 1 August.

Isaac Minet settled initially in London, where he hired a house in Newport Street and set up a small grocer's shop. In 1690, Isaac returned to Dover where his brother Stephen was dying. (For an account of the Insurance Company founded by the Minet family at Dover *see Catalogue number* 432.)

Isaac kept 1 August as a fast in memory of his escape until his death in April, 1745.

PROVENANCE: *By family descent to Miss Susan Minet; deposited in the Huguenot Library.*

LITERATURE: *William Minet, Isaac Minet's Narrative, Proceedings of the Huguenot Society of London, Vol. 2 (1887–88), p. 428; ibid., The Huguenot Family of Minet, 1892.*

49 Passport signed by Louis XIV

DATED 10 OCTOBER 1685.

This passport signed by Louis XIV at Fontainebleau eight days before the Revocation document, was issued to a M. Morin, a minister of the Reformed Faith at Chateaudun. It gave Morin permission to retire to England with his wife and four children. According to family tradition Madame de Maintenon had interceded with the King on behalf of the Morins as they were distant relatives through connections with the Villette family. The passport was countersigned by Louis XIV's chief minister, Colbert, and endorsed at Calais.

DIMENSIONS: *260 × 350mm.*

PROVENANCE: *By family descent to E.J.V. Hutt; Presented to the British Museum in 1956; British Library, Department of Manuscripts.*

50 Memorials to Henri and Jean François de Portal

MARBLE, EIGHTEENTH CENTURY.

The Portal family came originally from Toulouse and later settled in Bagnols sur Cèze. Jean François de Portal moved to Poitiers where he became Conseiller du Roi. When the dragoons arrived in the town, his two sons Henri and Pierre Guillaume were concealed in a bread oven. They were smuggled to Bordeaux and hidden in empty wine casks in a vessel bound for Southampton. They escaped before the Revocation. After October, 1685, escape by this means was more difficult as the holds of vessels were fumigated in order to stifle refugees who might be concealed there.

Henri de Portal worked initially at the papermill at South Stoneham, a few miles from Southampton, which was run by Gérard de Vaux, another refugee from Languedoc, under the control of the White Paper Makers' Company (*Catalogue number* 256).

In 1711, when he had completed his apprenticeship, he was naturalised at the Winchester Quarter Sessions. In 1712, he set up his own paper manufactory at Bere Mill, employing a number of Huguenot paper makers from South Stoneham.

DIMENSIONS: *Both 2060 × 712mm.*

PROVENANCE: *St. Nicholas, Freefolk; Portals Ltd.*

LITERATURE: *Sir Francis Portal, The Church, The State and The People leading to 250 Years of Papermaking, 1962.*

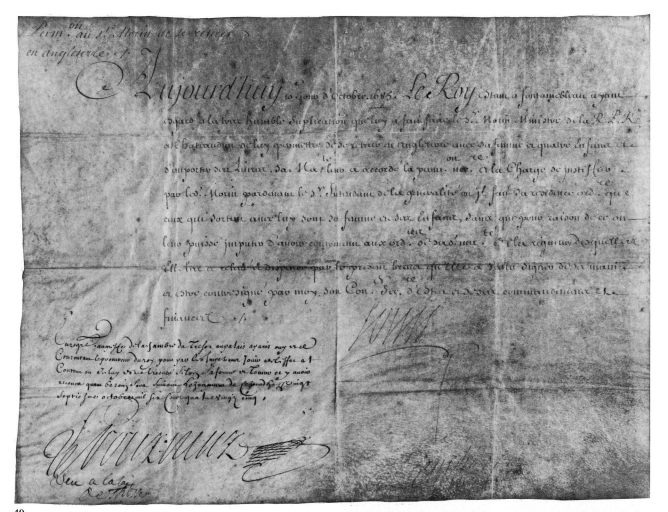

49

50

The French Church des Grecs, Hog Lane, Soho. 'Noon,' oil on canvas, William Hogarth, c.1736

See Catalogue number 149

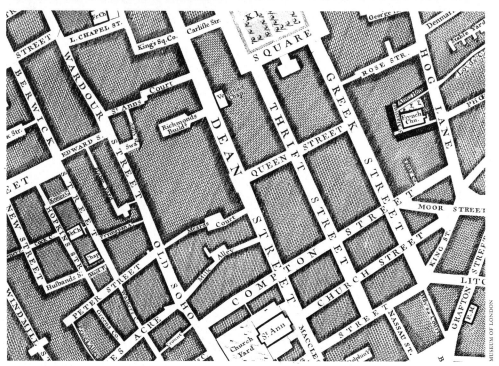

Detail from John Rocque's 'Map of London', 1746, showing the location of the French Church in Hog Lane

Huguenot institutions

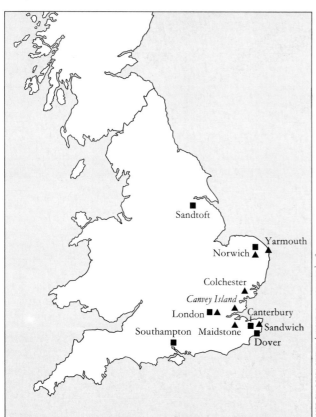

Sandtoft

Yarmouth
Norwich

Colchester
Canvey Island
London   Canterbury
              Sandwich
Southampton Maidstone
              Dover

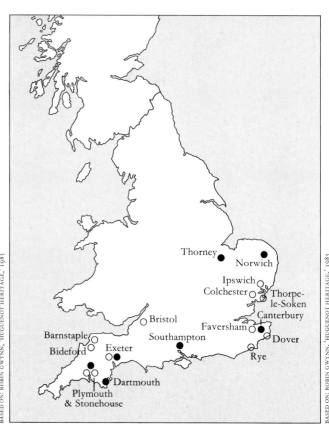

Thorney
        Norwich

Ipswich
Colchester   Thorpe-
              le-Soken
              Canterbury
Bristol   Faversham
        Southampton   Dover
Barnstaple   Rye
Bideford Exeter

        Dartmouth
Plymouth
& Stonehouse

CHURCHES

Communion at a French Church, United Provences from Bernard Picart, from 'The Ceremonies and Religious Customs of the Reformed, commonly called Calvinists,' c.1733

Under Edward VI (1547–53) and his Archbishop of Canterbury, Thomas Cranmer, England committed herself to Protestantism. The French and Dutch Churches of London, which were founded in 1550, may have been intended as models for what the English church was to become; based on the best continental Reformed examples, but with variations to suit local circumstances. The letters patent authorising their existence gave them complete independence from the Bishop of London, but placed them under a 'Superintendent', the Polish nobleman and humanist scholar, John à Lasco.

Because Edward VI died young and was succeeded by the Catholic Queen Mary, the Protestant designs of his reign were never brought to fruition. When Elizabeth I in turn succeeded to the throne in 1559, she allowed the foreign congregations to return. This time they were placed under Episcopal control, but Bishop Grindal of London was sympathetic to European Protestantism, and they developed along Calvinist lines. The Dutch Church met at Austin Friars, the French in Threadneedle Street; the two congregations exchanged buildings once a month, and members of their governing Consistories met together regularly in a body called 'Coetus'.

For nearly a century, the Threadneedle Street congregation was the only French one in London. Then in the early 1640s, Jean d'Espagne drew people to services in the Westminster area. After the Restoration in 1660, Charles II allowed the Westminster group to continue and saw that it was given the use of the chapel at the Savoy, but only with the proviso that it changed its character completely by adopting the Anglican liturgy translated into French. As a result, when large numbers of new Huguenot refugees arrived from Louis XIV's France, they found themselves confronted by a choice: they could worship in London either in traditional French ('non-conformist') or in Anglican ('conformist') style. Both forms were sanctioned by law, even though English dissenters had no legal foundation.

As new French congregations were established to meet the needs of the refugees, they followed either the Threadneedle Street or the Savoy pattern of worship. By 1700, there were some 28 churches in the area that now comprises Greater London. They were concentrated in Spitalfields (where they were all non-conformist), and in Westminster and Soho (where they were equally divided in their form of worship). Others were in the City itself, and in Chelsea, Greenwich and Wandsworth.

Foreign churches in England in the 1640s (far left)

■ French Churches

▲ Dutch Churches

French churches in England (excluding London), 1700 (left)

○ Conformist

● Non-conformist

Church organisation

51 *Letters Patent granting the foundation of the Strangers' Church in London, 1550*

SIGNED BY KING EDWARD VI.

By this charter, dated July 24th, 1550, French and Dutch congregations were established in London. The church of the dissolved monastery, Augustine Friars, was restored for their use, and by December 1550, the Dutch were able to meet there for worship.

In October 1550, the French had obtained a lease for twenty-one years of the church of St. Anthony's Hospital in Threadneedle Street from the Dean and Canons of Windsor. Although they worshipped separately, both congregations shared the same superintendent, John à Lasco. John Utenhove, one of the elders of the Dutch congregation, wrote to Calvin in Geneva about the charter.

'We have actually been given more than we had asked for. In the first place we have the joint use of the church of the Augustine Friars . . . The unadulterated Word may be proclaimed in it and the sacraments administered as instituted by Christ the Lord without "superstitie". We are also permitted to exercise church discipline in accordance with God's Word . . . The Bishop of London and the other Bishops and the Archbishops of the realm, the Mayor, the Sheriffs and aldermen of London, are enjoined and strictly commanded not in any way to interfere with our churches, but to leave it to us to act and organize matters in our own way'.

PROVENANCE: *The Dutch Church, Austin Friars, London.*

LITERATURE: *J.S. Burn, History of the French, Walloon, Dutch and other Foreign Protestant Refugees settled in London, 1846, p.265; J. Lindeboom, Austin Friars, History of the Dutch Reformed Church in London, 1550–1950, pp.7–10 (and appendix, pp.200–203 for full translation of the Charter).*

52 *Edward VI giving John à Lasco and his Congregation a Charter*

OIL ON CANVAS, EARLY SEVENTEENTH CENTURY.

The painting shows King Edward VI granting Letters Patent for the foundation of the Strangers' Church in London to the Polish John à Lasco who came to England in 1548 at the invitation of the Archbishop of Canterbury, Thomas Cranmer. Cranmer is seen to the extreme left, and to the right of John à Lasco are the figures of Bishop Ridley and Bishop Latimer. The figure between à Lasco and the King is Dudley, Duke of Northumberland, who had taken the place of the Duke of Somerset as Regent.

The portraits are all derived from contemporary sources, that of the King from the painting by William Stretes showing Edward VI giving a charter to Bridewell, and those of à Lasco and John Knox from Théodore de Bèze's 'Icones'. It has been suggested that the figure on the extreme right represents John Knox, but the four figures in the background have not been identified.

COLOUR PLATE: *page 2.*

DIMENSIONS: *1830 × 1370 mm.*

PROVENANCE: *W. Jerdone Braikenridge; Christie's 1908; United Reformed Church.*

LITERATURE: *The Foundation of the Strangers' Church in London in 1550, with some remarks upon its earlier title. Proceedings of the Huguenot Society of London, Vol. 4 (1893), pp.330–334; William Carruthers, Edward VI Granting a Charter to the Presbyterians, Journal of the Presbyterian Historical Society of England, May 1914, Volume 1, no.1, pp.14–20.*

53 *Coffee House Token, c.1660*

INSCRIBED: OBVERSE: WM. STONYER.HIS.$\frac{1}{2}$.PENEY = A TURK'S HEAD
REVERSE: AGT.YE.FRENCH.CHURCH.IN.THRED:NEDLE.STREET.

This halfpenny token is typical of the small denomination private currency which was issued by tradespeople to supply the public need for small change in the troubled period between the execution of Charles I in 1648 and Charles II's proclamation of 16 August 1672. This proclamation finally put a stop to the circulation of such tokens, replacing them with the first official issue of base metal coinage bearing the monarch's portrait.

William Stonyer, issuer of this token, was proprietor of a coffee house next door to the French Church in Threadneedle Street. The Turk's head indicated that Turkish coffee was sold on the premises. William Stonyer was the parish clerk for St. Benet Fink, and the churchwardens' accounts record a number of payments made at this establishment. It is probable that members of the congregation of the French church also patronised this coffee house.

DIMENSIONS: *21mm diameter.*

PROVENANCE: *Guildhall Museum; Museum of London.*

LITERATURE: *George C. Williamson, Trade Tokens issued in the Seventeenth Century in England, Wales and Ireland, 1889, p.722, no. 3138; Bryant Lillywhite, London Coffee Houses, 1963, p.607, no.1412.*

54 *Royal Approbation of Jacques Saurin*

SIGNED BY WILLIAM III, 1701.

Although royal endorsement of the choice of ministers made by the French Church of London is a practice which stemmed from its foundation charter, the earliest surviving approbation is that of Marc Michel Michely in 1671.

The approval of Jacques Saurin, whose election in 1701, at a time when the church was at its peak in terms of size and ministerial strength, was not without controversy. When the Consistory decided to proceed to an election, in April, it was agreed that only a full minister, not a *proposant* or trainee pastor, was acceptable: but Saurin had not been received into the ministry. Influential members wanted him considered in view of his outstanding gifts, and a majority vote determined that he would be eligible if received by the time of the election.

ILLUSTRATED: *page 61.*

PROVENANCE: *Library of the French Church, Soho Square.*

LITERATURE: *Library of the French Church, Soho Square, Ms. 8, ff.278–286.*

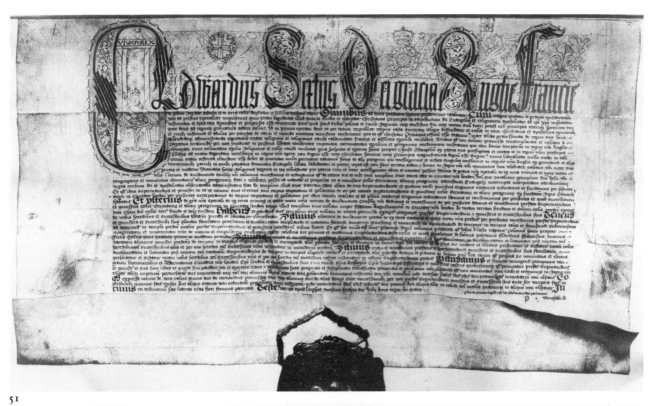

51

53

52

On 2 May he was taken before Bishop Compton of London, who ordained him, waiving the article which would otherwise have compelled him to observe the Anglican liturgy in the churches he served. Later in the month, he was elected a minister of the Threadneedle Street Church, at a salary of £70 per annum.

55 *Jacques Saurin*
PORTRAIT ENGRAVING, TROTTER, 1783. INSCRIBED: SAURIN . . . FROM AN ORIGINAL PICTURE.

Despite the exceptional efforts that had been made in 1701 to secure his election, the French Church of London enjoyed the ministry of Jacques Saurin of Nimes, Languedoc, for only five years. Saurin asked permission to leave pleading grounds of ill health. Although the Consistory was grieved to lose such a talented man, Saurin went on to the Netherlands, where he fulfilled the expectations implied by the references he had brought with him in 1701 from the professors of the Genevan Academy.

DIMENSIONS: *135 × 110mm.*

PROVENANCE: *French Hospital.*

LITERATURE: *Library of the French Church, Soho Square, Ms. 8, pp. 286,488–9.*

56 *The French Church, Threadneedle Street*
SECTION, 1840.

This section was drawn in 1840 by the architect William Grellier when the congregation had to move from the Threadneedle Street Church to St. Martin's Le Grand. The church was rebuilt in the late 1660's after the Fire of London. This drawing does not show the library and two Consistory rooms (one for the ministers and elders, the other for the deacons) at opposite ends of the church. The prominent three-tiered pulpit underlines the Calvinist emphasis on the preaching of God's Word.

William Grellier was of Huguenot origin and his descendant Christopher Grellier is Surveyor to the French Hospital.

DIMENSIONS: *365 × 392mm.*

PROVENANCE: *French Church, Soho Square.*

57 *List of Pews and their Occupants, 1737–1751*
MANUSCRIPT, FRENCH CHURCH, THREADNEEDLE STREET.

The list is displayed at ff 38–9, which records the occupants of the first and second pews 'joignant le Parquet' on the south side. Such a prominent position denoted social status and the list is striking for the wealth of the people named. They include Aubert, the banker Jaques Louis Berchère, the merchant Jean Louis Loubier, Delilers Carbonnel, Antoine Clerimbault, David Godin, Isaac Berthon, Jacques Dargent, Gautier, Le Quesne, Luard, Van Neck and Claude Bosanquet (the benefactor of L'Eglise Neuve, the Spitalfields annexe of the Threadneedle Street Church).

The men and women sat separately.

PROVENANCE: *Library of the French Church, Soho Square.*

LITERATURE: *The Archives of the French Protestant Church of London, 1972, Huguenot Society Quarto Series, Vol. L (1972), p. 35.*

58 *The French Church, St Martin's Le Grand*
INTERIOR, WATERCOLOUR, ATTRIBUTED TO J. CROWTHER NINETEENTH CENTURY.

This watercolour shows the interior of the church that housed the congregation from the original church in Threadneedle Street, from 1841 until 1887, when the site was purchased for the new General Post Office. A blue plaque marks the site today.

An identical watercolour in the Guildhall Library Collection is signed 'J. Crowther del'.

DIMENSIONS: *623 × 535mm.*

PROVENANCE: *French Church, Soho Square.*

59 *New Church, Soho Square*
ENGRAVING, 1893.

After St. Martin's Le Grand was demolished in 1887, the congregation moved into temporary quarters, first at the Athenaeum Hall in Tottenham Court Road, then at a chapel behind 7, Soho Square. A site in Soho was considered most convenient for its current membership.

The architect of the new church was Aston Webb (1849–1930), who had just designed the principal block of the Victoria and Albert Museum. He is said to have been particularly pleased with his design for the French Church of London, which incorporates both Gothic and Romanesque features. The church was built to accommodate a congregation of 400 by Messrs. Higgs and Hill between 1891 and 1893, at a cost of just over £10,000. The building materials consisted of plum coloured brick, light red terracotta tiles and green roof slates.

The church is still used for worship today.

DIMENSIONS: *480 × 387mm.*

PROVENANCE: *French Church, Soho Square.*

LITERATURE: *Dictionary of National Biography under Sir Aston Webb; London County Council, Survey of London, Vol. XXXIII, pp. 62–3.*

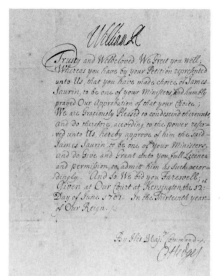

54

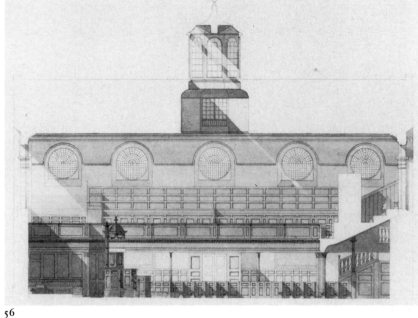

56

55

57

58

59

60 *Order of Service for the Dedication of the New Temple, Soho Square*
SATURDAY 25 MARCH 1893.

At 2 p.m., the architect, Mr. Aston Webb, gave the key of the building to the Rev. Septimus Hansard, the resident pastor, who opened the door. The service that followed included readings, psalms and canticles, and an historical address. The choice of music for the service is rather surprising as it includes only one item from the Genevan Psalter.

It was appropriate that the service was conducted in the presence of the Bishop of London, as his predecessors had so often proved notable protectors of the foreign Protestant churches around the capital.

DIMENSIONS: *260 × 420mm.*
PROVENANCE: *Madame Jaulmes.*

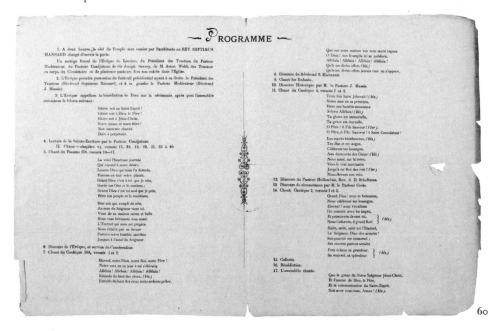

60

61 *Royal Approbation of Pierre Simon, 1982*
SIGNED BY QUEEN ELIZABETH II.

The practice of obtaining royal approbation for ministers elected to the church continues to the present day. The most recent appointment, Pierre Simon, was called from Sète; previously he had been at Majunga in Madagascar.

PROVENANCE: *French Church, Soho Square.*

62 *Plan of an extension to the French Chapel, the Savoy*
SIR CHRISTOPHER WREN, 1685.

As a result of the continued increase in the refugee population, by 1685, the ministers, churchwardens and congregation of the Savoy presented a petition, also exhibited, to the effect 'that their chapelle . . . is much too little for the congregacon, and that intending to inlarge the same they have obtained the Consent of the Master of the Savoy, and the approbation of our Surveyor Generall of our Works, Who hath reported unto us that hee hath viewed the Ground proposed for the inlargement of the said . . . Chapell and finds it is with the allowance of the Master of the Savoy'.

The petition accompanies a plan and section for the extension, which was designed by the Surveyor General, Sir Christopher Wren. It was built at a cost of £1,500. In the early 1730s it was closed 'on account of the danger whereunto the congregation was continually exposed of being suddenly crushed by the falling in of the roof'. The congregation joined its allied churches of des Grecs and Spring Gardens.

PROVENANCE: *Public Record Office.*
LITERATURE: *R. Somerville, The Savoy, 1960, p.229; Robin Gwynn, The Distribution of Huguenot Refugees in England, 2; London and its Environs, Proceedings of the Huguenot Society of London. Vol. 22 (1971–6), pp. 548–549.*

63 *Israel Antoine Aufrère (1677–1758)*
ENGRAVING, PAUL VAN SOMER, *c.*1700.
INSCRIBED: ISRAEL ANTOINE AUFRERE D EN T. MINISTRE DE L'EGLISE FRANCOISE DE LA SAVOYE A LONDRES PVAN SOMER FECIT.

The Aufrère family came originally from Poitou. Their ancestor, on adopting the reformed faith, moved to Toulouse, then Paris, and finally settled in Normandy. Israel Antoine's father, Antoine, a Procureur at the Paris Parlement, took refuge in Holland at the Revocation.

Israel Antoine Aufrère came to London and served as Chaplain to William III at the Chapel Royal, St. James's Palace. He was also minister to the French congregation at the Savoy.

He built himself a house in Charles Street, St. James's Square, which he left to his son Anthony on his death.

Paul van Somer kept a print shop in Newport Street, near Leicesterfields in the 1690s and 1700s.

DIMENSIONS: *171 × 121mm.*
PROVENANCE: *National Portrait Gallery.*
LITERATURE: *Charles Poyntz Stewart, History of the Aufrères, Proceedings of the Huguenot Society of London, Vol. 9 (1909–11), pp.145–160; J. E. Wessely, Paul van Somer, Verzeichness seiner Kupferstiche und Schalskunstblatter, R. Naumunn's Archiv für die Zeichnenden Kunste, Vol. XIV, 1870, pp.39–87.*

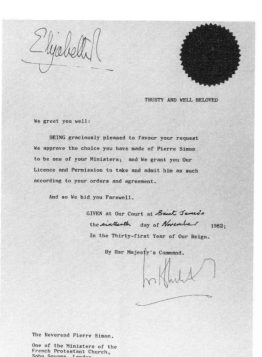

61

ISRAEL ANTOINE AUFRERE
D en T. Ministre de l'Eglise Françoise de la Savoye
a Londres.

63

62

64 *The French Protestant Chapel, Crown Street, Soho*

TWO WATERCOLOURS, R.B. SCHNEBBELIE, 1819.

These two watercolours are the earliest recorded views of the interior of this chapel. They show a typical Protestant meeting house with high panelled pews and a gallery on four sides. The pulpit and the organ dominate the interior, reflecting the importance of preaching and music in the Huguenot service, whereas the altar is not visible. The cleaning ladies and the stove in the centre add a touch of domestic warmth to this otherwise sober setting.

This church was originally built between 1677 and 1680 in Hog Lane, Soho, for the use of a Greek Orthodox congregation. In 1682 it was annexed by the Savoy Chapel which was the first conformist French church in London. When the Savoy closed down in the 1730s the Eglise des Grecs, as this chapel was known, became the leading conformist French church in England. For a view of the exterior see Catalogue no. 149.

DIMENSIONS: *a. 159 × 376mm, b. 100 × 378mm.*

PROVENANCE: *Museum of London.*

LITERATURE: *Robin D. Gwynn, The Distribution of Huguenot Refugees in England, II: London and its Environs, Proceedings of the Huguenot Society of London, Vol. 22 (1971–76), pp. 524; Survey of London, Vol. XXXIV, pl. 17c; ibid, Vol.XXXIII, p. 286.*

65 *Reasons against erecting a French Church, St Martin Orgars*

BROADSIDE, 1700.

This petition presented to the House of Lords by 'several of the Principal Inhabitants of the Parish of St. Martin Orgars' objected to the proposals to erect a church for the French in the churchyard of St. Martin Orgars on the grounds that the erection of such a building would not conform with the Act for Rebuilding the City of London, 1667, which had limited the number of parish churches in the City to fifty-one. Furthermore, a new church on that site would obscure the light from the houses that had been rebuilt round the churchyard. It would also make burial more expensive in that future interments would have to be within the church walls and the present churchyard would have to be cleared of burials.

Perhaps the most pertinent reason for this petition was the suspicion that a new church on the site would 'create a perpetual settlement for Foreigners in the Heart of the City to the prejudice of our own Merchants and Traders'.

In 1686 a congregation of French refugees under Pierre Allix presented a petition to Archbishop Sancroft to establish a new church on the site of St. Martin Orgars, which had been destroyed during the Fire of London. Letters patent were granted in 1686, but the congregation worshipped in various temporary accommodation before a new church was built in 1699, at a cost of £800. It survived until 1823.

DIMENSIONS: *360 × 280mm.*

PROVENANCE: *Guildhall Library.*

LITERATURE: *Robin D. Gwynn, The Distribution of the Huguenot Refugees in England, II: London and its Environs, Proceedings of the Huguenot Society of London, Vol. 22 (1971–76), pp.546–7; William Minet and Susan Minet, Register of the Church of St. Martin Orgars, Huguenot Society Quarto Series, Vol.XXXVII.*

66 *Letters Patent authorising the construction of a new temple in Spitalfields*

SIGNED BY JAMES II, 1687.

This charter, signed by James II on 11 August 1687, and still bearing part of his seal, acknowledges that 'in regard the Church situate in Threadneedle Streete where they meet cannot contayne the multitude of People which cometh thither . . . they may have another place to assemble part of their people therein to serve God after their usuall manner'.
The intended location was Long Hedge Field, in the Hamlet of Spitalfields where 'certain Almes-houses' stood. The alms-houses were to be demolished to make way for one temple, fifty-four feet broad and eighty feet long. The building bordered upon Black Eagle Street and Grey Eagle Street.

This church was built as an annexe of the Threadneedle Street Church as the latter could not be adequately enlarged. Although the building was completed in 1688, further galleries were added later that year to accommodate the 'si grande foule de gens qui arrivent sans cesse'.

PROVENANCE: *French Church, Soho Square.*

LITERATURE: *Robin D. Gwynn, The Distribution of Huguenot Refugees in England, II: London and its Environs, Proceedings of the Huguenot Society of London, Vol. 22 (1971–76), p.526.*

67 *Appointment of Jacques Serces as Chaplain to the Earl of Harrington*

MANUSCRIPT, VELLUM, 1730.

Jacques Serces was appointed Chaplain to William, Earl of Harrington, in September, 1730.
Not all the ministers who left France were able to serve the Huguenot temples in the countries of refuge. They were however eminently suited to becoming chaplains or tutors to noble families. This document bears the seal of the Earl of Harrington and was authorised by the Registrar Deputy, Luthwaite Farrant.

A letter from Jean Sarasin in Geneva, 1731, to Serces refers to the expectations that Serces placed in this new appointment.

DIMENSIONS: *245 × 420mm.*

PROVENANCE: *Huguenot Library.*

LITERATURE: *Correspondance de Jacques Serces, Huguenot Society Quarto Series, Vol.XLIII (1952), p.13.*

64

66

Worship and Liturgy

The church discipline established by John à Lasco was unusual in several ways. It was democratic, emphasising the role of the congregation as a whole. It allowed for a 'superintendency', a kind of Reformed episcopacy, in a way that had no parallel in continental Protestantism. It forcefully encouraged education for the young and 'prophesyings' for the adult. If à Lasco worked along modified Zwinglian lines, it was a more Calvinist influence that prevailed in the London church when it was re-established under Queen Elizabeth I. À Lasco's active 'superintendency' was converted to passive episcopal oversight, his discipline was revised by Nicholas des Gallars and Robert le Maçon de la Fontaine, and the original democratic tendencies were reduced to congregational endorsement of elections managed by the Consistory of ministers and elders that ran the church.

Gradually a Colloquy developed at which all the French-speaking churches of the realm were represented. In 1588, Colloquy made the Discipline of the London church binding on all its members. It was subsequently amended in minor ways, and then in 1641 more extensively revised in the wake of the fall of Archbishop Laud, whose actions had threatened the continued existence of the foreign churches in England, so as to exclude any suggestion of episcopal control. The 1641 Discipline remains the theoretical framework for the French Church of London today. It also long continued to guide the other churches that belonged to the Colloquy: Canterbury, Norwich, Southampton and Thorney. But it did not affect either the conformist refugee churches that worshipped and were to a large degree organised in the Anglican way, or many of the new non-conformist refugee congregations which were given a different sort of authorisation under James II and William III.

68 *Prayer Book*
FRENCH VERSION BY JOHN A LASCO, 1556.

This prayer book was printed for the members of the London congregation in exile in Queen Mary's reign. The printer was Egidius van der Erve, usually called Gellius Ctematius, a member of the Dutch Church of London in 1550 and a printer in London 1551–4 and thereafter at Emden until 1565, after accompanying John à Lasco into exile.

PROVENANCE: *Library of the French Church, Soho Square.*

69 *Psalter of Clément Marot and Théodore de Bèze, 1674*
INSCRIBED: FRANK N. LANDON, OCTOBER 13TH, 1823; ANGELA MARGARET BLOMEFIELD (HIS GREAT GRAND DAUGHTER); THEODORE LANDON, 1983.

This edition of Marot and de Bèze's version of the Psalms, 'mis en rime Françoise' was sold at Charenton, the Huguenot temple outside Paris, and published by Estienne Lucas, Bookseller, at the sign of the Golden Bible in the Rue Chartière.

The clarity of print in this edition of 1674 underlines the importance placed by the Huguenots on the Psalms. They were to French Calvinists what Martin Luther's hymns were to German Lutherans, a source of great spiritual consolation and strength. The last Protestant minister to be hanged for his faith in France, François Rochette, sang on the scaffold in 1762 the verse 'This is the day that the Lord has made; let us rejoice and be glad in it'.

The Landon family settled initially in Rotterdam and then in Spitalfields. The founder of the English family, Samuel Landon, was a silk weaver from Paris.

PROVENANCE: *By descent in the Landon family.*

70 *Police et Discipline, 1641*
MANUSCRIPT, VELLUM, 1739.

The 1641 revision of the Police et Discipline survived as the theoretical code governing the French Church of London even though the Colloquies and Synods it mentions ceased to meet and the appearance of new Huguenot churches in the London area made many of its provisions impracticable.

This copy, on vellum, was made by Abraham Maillet (who came from the Neuchâtel area of Switzerland) in 1739. Bound in gold tooled blue morocco leather, its magnificence bears witness to the continuing importance attached to the origins and royal authorisation of the church. The frontispiece was designed by H. Guinand, and drawn in pen and ink by Maillet; it shows Edward VI, the figures of Faith, Hope and Charity, and the Threadneedle Street Church as it was rebuilt after the Fire of 1666.

After the disciplinary regulations, the volume contains the signatures of the pastors and elders of the church, 1740–1929.

PROVENANCE: *Library of the French Church, Soho Square.*

LITERATURE: *Raymond Smith, Archives of the French Protestant Church of London: a handlist, Huguenot Society Quarto Series, Vol.L (1972), p.20, Ms.18.*

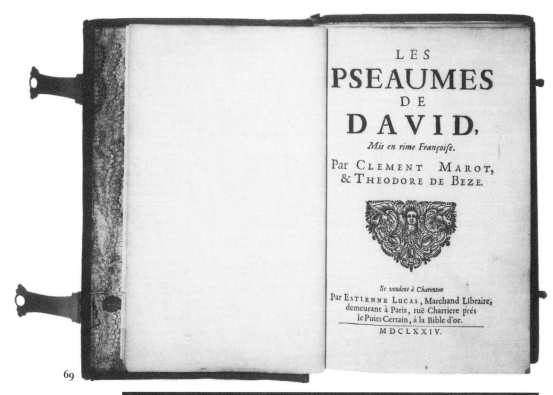

LES
PSEAUMES
DE
DAVID,
Mis en rime Françoise.

PAR CLEMENT MAROT,
& THEODORE DE BEZE.

Se vendent à Charenton
Par ESTIENNE LUCAS, Marchand Libraire,
demeurant à Paris, ruë Charriere prés
le Puits Certain, à la Bible d'or.
MDCLXXIV.

69

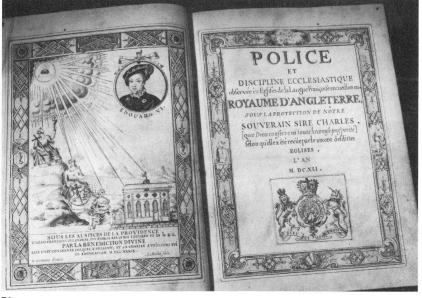

POLICE
ET
DISCIPLINE ECCLESIASTIQUE
observée es Eglises de la Langue Françoise recueillies au
ROYAUME D'ANGLETERRE,
SOUS LA PROTECTION DE NÔTRE
SOUVERAIN SIRE CHARLES,
[que Dieu conserve en toute heureuse prosperité]
selon qu'elle a été reviie par le sixone des dittes
EGLISES,
L'AN
M.DC.XLI.

EDOUARD VI.

SOUS LES AUSPICES DE LA PROVIDENCE

PAR LA BENEDICTION DIVINE

70

LA
LITVRGIE.
C'EST A DIRE,
E FORMVLAIRE DES
RIERES Publiques, de l'Ad-
ministration des SACREMENS;

Et des autres
CEREMONIES
& Coûtumes de l'Eglise, selon l'usage
de l'Eglise ANGLICANE:

VEC LE PSEAVTIER,
ou les PSEAVMES de DAVID,

Ponctuez selon qu'ils doivent estre, ou chantez,
ou leûs dans les EGLISES.

A LONDRES,
our Iean Dunmore & Octavien Pulleyn le Ieune à
l'Enseigne du Roy en la petite Bretagn⹁. 1667.

71

70

71 *Translation of the Anglican Book of Common Prayer*
JEAN DUREL, 1667.

After the Restoration of the monarchy in 1660, Charles II licensed a French congregation in Westminster provided it used the Anglican Liturgy translated into French, and the conformist Savoy church came into being the following year. Its oversight was given to Jean Durel (*c.*1625–83), a royalist clergyman from Jersey who had accompanied the King into exile.

The book is shown open at Charles's order of 1662 that only Durel's translation of the Prayer Book was to be used in the Channel Islands and in all French conformist churches in his dominions. Despite being officially approved in 1663, the translation was criticised in James II's reign, when it was claimed that it was 'not so exactly done as it ought to be, and in many particular offices differs very much from the English'. It was not Durel's own work, but a revision of an earlier translation by a French minister at Norwich, Pierre de Laune.

Worship at the Savoy followed the pattern in the Channel Islands, and contemporary Anglicans would have been struck by departures from normal English practice. For instance, although the clergy accepted the English rather than French custom of preaching bare-headed, they did not wear a surplice or make the sign of the cross.

ILLUSTRATED: *page 67.*

PROVENANCE: *British Library.*

LITERATURE: *D.N. Griffiths, The French Translations of the English Book of Common Prayer, Proceedings of the Huguenot Society of London, Vol. 22 (1971–76), pp.90–114; Robin D. Gwynn, Huguenot Heritage, 1985, Chap.6 and p.134.*

72 *La Liturgie ou Formulaire des Prières Publiques selon l'usage de L'Eglise Anglicane*
PUBLISHED BY N. PREVOST, LONDON 1729.

This volume is a French translation of the Anglican Liturgy and belonged to the Ouvry family. The inside cover is inscribed with the names of John Ouvry (1707–1774), Peter Ouvry (1741–1808), Peter Aimé Ouvry (1766–1830), Peter Thomas Ouvry (1811–1891), Lionel Garnault Ouvry, 1911 and Ernest Carrington Ouvry (1866–1951). It was apparently in continuous use until 1951.

Nicholas Prevost married into the Vaillant family and worked in their bookshop at the sign of the Ship in the Strand. He published catalogues of their stock in trade, 1728–1731, copies of which can be seen in the British Library.

Nicholas Prevost combined with other Huguenot booksellers in London, Jean Pierre Coderc and Samuel Jallason, to publish Voltaire's Essays and his Henriade.

PROVENANCE: *The French Hospital.*

LITERATURE: *Dr. Norma Perry, Voltaire in England, 'The Times', 22 April 1978.*

73 *Les Psaumes de David mis en vers*
PRINTED BY LA VEUVE LAURENT, BERLIN, 1740.

This book of psalms was published with the approval of the Consistory of the French Church in Berlin. It belonged to James Minet, who used the first four pages as a notebook. They contain epithets from classical authors and religious observations. The volume is adorned with a frontispiece, a rather crude woodcut of King David playing the harp. This miniature volume is bound in tortoiseshell.

James Minet (1698–1774), a relative of the Minet family who settled in England, was engaged in business in Berlin.

PROVENANCE: *James Minet; by family descent to Miss Susan Minet, deposited in the Huguenot Library.*

LITERATURE: *Irvine R. Gray, Huguenot Manuscripts: A Descriptive Catalogue, Huguenot Society Quarto Series, Vol.LVI (1983), p.153.*

74 *Marriage Chain of Pierre and Jeanne Du Quesne*
GOLD, 1636; INSCRIBED: NOUS PIERRE DU QUESNE ET IEANNE MAUROIS.

Pierre Du Quesne (1609–1671) and Jeanne Maurois (d.1672) were married in 1636 at Canterbury. The custom of wearing gold marriage chains was then popular in Europe.

The Du Quesne family came originally from Flanders late in the sixteenth century, settling first at Canterbury, but by 1600, they were recorded in London, when the son of the first arrival, Jean Du Quesne became a citizen. By September, 1630, Pierre was living in Needlers' Lane, a prosperous area according to Stow's Survey, 1598: 'There in Needlers' Lane have ye the Parish Church of St. Pancras, a proper small church, but divers rich parishioners therein'. Pierre was elected Alderman of Farringdon Without in 1666, and discharged, on payment of a fine of £500 and 20 marks towards the maintenance of ministers in the prisons.

Jeanne was the daughter of Elizabeth Desbouveries and Elias Maurois, both families having fled from Flanders to avoid persecution in the late sixteenth century.

By the end of the seventeenth century the family had become one of the most influential families in the City and their name was anglicised. Benjamin Ducane, younger brother of Pierre, was made Treasurer of Bridewell and Bedlam Hospitals, and received a silver tankard in 1677 as a reward for that office. (The tankard is displayed in the Late Stuart Gallery of the Museum of London.)

DIMENSIONS: *1230mm long.*

PROVENANCE: *Private Collection.*

LITERATURE: *E. F. Ducane, Some Account of the Family of Du Quesne 1876, p.16.*

72

73

74

74

74

Sacramental Plate

A small selection of plate used by the French Protestant congregations in London, Rye, Canterbury, Edinburgh, Southampton and Portarlington still survives. The earliest piece, the silver cup from Canterbury, 1632, closely resembles the form of the similar cups used by the Savoy and Threadneedle Street churches, and contemporary Anglican vessels. Communion was received seated at an altar table which was probably covered with a cloth such as the fine linen damask example from Canterbury. More than one cup was needed as the vessel was passed from hand to hand without the intervention of the minister; the same principle applied to the distribution of the bread. The giving of alms was an important feature of the service.

The vessels were often given by a prosperous member of the congregation and sometimes commissioned from one of the refugee goldsmiths. The Portarlington silver was made by the eminent goldsmith from Metz, David Willaume, and was presented to the congregation by Princess Caroline, wife of the Prince of Wales, later George II.

75 *Communion cup of the Walloon Church, Canterbury Cathedral*
SILVER, MAKER'S MARK IT, 1631.
INSCRIBED: IM/B A L'EGLISE VUALLONNE DE CANTORBERY 1632.

This bell-shaped cup, supported on a baluster stem and splayed foot, is one of eight similar vessels.

The initials stand for Jean Bulteel, Pastor of the Walloon or French Church, which met in the Crypt of Canterbury Cathedral, and his wife Mary.

Jean Bulteel opposed Archbishop Laud's attempts to force the Canterbury congregation to adopt the English liturgy, and in 1645, he published 'A Relation of the Troubles of the Three Foreign Churches in Kent'. Eight cups would have been needed for the congregation which consisted of five hundred communicants at this time.

DIMENSIONS: *175mm high.*

PROVENANCE: *The French Church, Canterbury, on loan to the French Hospital.*

LITERATURE: *E.A. Jones, The Old Silver Sacramental Vessels of Foreign Protestant Churches in England, 1908, pp.XV, 3, pl.II.*

76 *Flagon of the French Church, Rye*
PEWTER, *c*.1700; INSCRIBED: THIS FLAGON USED AT THE CELEBRATION OF THE LORDS SUPPER BY THE MINISTER OF THE PROTESTANT REFUGEES WHO FOUND AN ASYLUM IN RYE AFTER THE REVOCATION OF THE EDICT OF NANTES, 22ND OCTOBER 1685, WAS PRESENTED FOR THE USE OF THE CHURCH TO THE VICAR AND CHURCHWARDENS OF RYE, BY WILLIAM HOLLOWAY AND SARAH HIS WIFE, FORMERLY SARAH MERYON, A DESCENDANT OF ONE OF THE REFUGEES, 5 MAY 1860.

The flagon has a tall plain cylindrical body, with a flat cover, and a thumbpiece formed of two griffins' heads.

The Huguenot congregation is first recorded at Rye in the 1560s, although the refugees did not have their own church building. In 1682 permission to use the parish church was renewed.

'Wee, the inhabitants of the towne of Rye, here subscribed, doe declare our willing consent yt the french Protestants newly settled in this place, may continue their assemblys in our church, from eight of the clock in ye morning unto ten, and afterwards from twelve of the clock untill two in the afternoone; and that they may have the use of the pulpit and of the seats therein as heretofore; which we do hereby fully grant to them.'

Many of the refugees who settled in Rye in the 1680s were fishermen, and they helped to supply London with fish.

DIMENSIONS: *220mm high.*

PROVENANCE: *French congregation at Rye: Meryon family; presented to the St Mary's Church, Rye by William and Sarah Holloway, 1860.*

LITERATURE: *E.A. Jones, The Old Silver Sacramental Vessels of Foreign Protestant Churches in England, 1908, pp.8–9, pl.V.*

77 *Altar cloth*
FIGURATED LINEN DAMASK, GERMAN, EARLY EIGHTEENTH CENTURY.

The tablecloth represents the story of the Woman of Samaria. The woman is shown standing by a well beneath an oak tree, beside Christ, who is seated. Above, another figure crowned with a halo supports a basket of fruit on one arm and points to a larger basket of bread beside him. The legend reads IOH4, referring to the Gospel of St. John, Chapter 4. Above a townscape is the legend SICHAR. The border to the cloth is woven with conventional flowers and fruit. Each motive is repeated to the side in reverse, which was the weaver's method of cutting down labour in mounting the pattern.

The pattern is based on a seventeenth-century design, and was probably woven in Germany in the early eighteenth century.

This altar cloth was used at communion services in the French Church, Canterbury until 1958.

DIMENSIONS: *2660 × 1830mm.*

PROVENANCE: *The French Church, Canterbury.*

LITERATURE: *G.T. Ysselsteyn, White Figurated Linen Damask, 1962, pp. 42,99–100.*

75

76

76

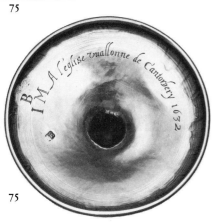

75

77

78 *Communion Plate of the Savoy Church*
CUP AND PATEN, ONE OF A PAIR, SILVER, LOUIS CUNY, LONDON, 1717.

The paten is of a plain circular form with narrow moulded edges and moulded foot which is detachable from the upper dish. The junction is decorated with cut-card work, incorporating the trefoil motif, a rare edition to a paten of this date, but also found on an earlier example by the same maker in Wishford Magna Church, Wiltshire. It is inscribed on the base with the original weight 24 = 12.

The cup has a plain bell-shaped bowl supported by a baluster stem on a moulded foot, and is inscribed with the original weight 26 = 18.

This communion plate was used by the conformist French Congregation at the Savoy until 1737, when the congregation merged with that of its annexe Les Grecs in Dudley Court, Hog Lane, Soho. In 1845 a new church was erected in Shaftesbury Avenue.

DIMENSIONS: *Paten 255mm diameter, 65mm high; cup 244mm high.*
PROVENANCE: *French Hospital.*

79 *Communion Plate of the French Church, Hoxton*
CUP AND PATEN, ONE OF A PAIR, SILVER, MAKER'S MARK HI, LONDON, 1717.

The paten is of plain circular form, with a moulded edge and is inscribed, 'The Gift of Lewis De Tudert Esq.ʳ to yᵉ: French Congregation at Hoxton yᵉ: 25th: March 1717'. Lewis de Tudert was one of the original directors of the French Hospital. He died in 1739 and was buried in the Dutch Church. He left bequests of £100 each to the French Hospital, and the Spitalfields 'Soupe' and also £25 to the Swiss Society; £250 to the hospital in Geneva and £100 for the fortifications of Geneva.

The cup has a plain bell-shaped bowl supported by a baluster stem on a moulded foot. One is inscribed 'The Gift of Mr. Stephen Romilly To the French Congregation at Hoxton The 25: March 1717'. Stephen Romilly was born at Montpellier in 1684. He went to Geneva in 1701, where he met Jacques Saurin, and then came to England. He established a bleaching business at Hoxton. He married Judith de Monsaillier, and had four sons. His third son Peter became a prosperous jeweller of Frith Street, Soho and the father of the eminent lawyer Sir Samuel Romilly (*Catalogue number 434*). Stephen Romilly died in 1733 in poverty.

The other cup (not exhibited) is inscribed 'The Gift of Mrs. Rachel Ribeaut To the French Congregation at Hoxton The 25: March 1717'.

The exact site of the non-conformist French Church, Hoxton is unrecorded. The surviving registers date from 1748 to 1783.

DIMENSIONS: *Paten 240mm diameter; cups 207mm high. The paten is inscribed with the original weight 16 = 5; and the cup is similarly inscribed 15 = 10.*
PROVENANCE: *French Hospital.*
LITERATURE: *E.A. Jones, The Old Silver Sacramental Vessels of the Foreign Protestant Churches in England, 1908, pp.12–14; G.B. Beeman, Notes on the sites and History of the French Churches in London, Proceedings of the Huguenot Society of London, Vol. 8 (1901–04), pp.55–6.*

79

The Gift of Mr. Stephen Romilly
the French Congregation at ...
The 25. March 1717.

79

78

78

78

80 *Communion plate of the French Protestant Church, Soho Square*

a. COMMUNION CUPS, TWO OF A SET OF FOUR, SILVER, JACOB MARGAS, LONDON, 1717–18.
INSCRIBED: DON DES DIACRES DE L'EGLIZE FRANCOISE DE LONDRES DANS
THREDNEDLE STREET 1717.

The cups are plain with inverted bell-shaped bowls, supported by baluster stems on splayed
feet.

b. ROUND PLATE, ONE OF A PAIR, SILVER, EDWARD JAY, LONDON, 1788–9.
INSCRIBED: PRODUIT DU DON DE MR. BOSANQUET EN 1697.

In that year, David Bosanquet (from Lunel in the South of France), who had recently served
as a deacon, had presented the church with eight silver communion cups.

c. RECTANGULAR DISH, SILVER, EDWARD JAY, LONDON, 1788–9.
INSCRIBED: PRODUIT DES COUPES DE L'EGLISE DE L'ARTILLERIE REUNIE EN 1786.

This plate belonged to the congregation of the original French Church in Threadneedle
Street, founded by John à Lasco in 1550. The church was rebuilt after the Fire of London,
and the new church was used for worship until 1841. The congregation then moved to the
church of St. Martin's Le Grand (*Catalogue number* 58).

DIMENSIONS: *a. 210mm high.*

DIMENSIONS: *b. 254mm diameter.*

DIMENSIONS: *c. 337 × 258mm.*
PROVENANCE: *French Church,
Soho Square.*
LITERATURE: *E.A. Jones, The Old
Silver Sacramental Vessels of Foreign
Protestant Churches in England, 1908,
pp.5–6, pl.III; Library of the French
Church, Soho Square, Ms.8, f.56r.*

81 *Alms dish of the French Church known as Le Carré, Soho*

SILVER, NO MAKER'S MARK, LONDON, 1720.
INSCRIBED: BIEN-HEUREUX SONT CEUX QUI SONT APPELLEZ AU BANQUET DES NOCES DE
L'AGNEAU.

A plain circular dish with a wide flat border, engraved in the centre with the Lamb. The
dish is traditionally attributed to the goldsmith Jonah Clifton. The plate was bought by
subscription of the congregation in 1720.

The conformist church of Le Carré was established in Soho Square in 1689, although in
1694 it moved to Berwick Street, where it continued to meet until 1769. It then moved to
Little Dean Street, and was dissolved in 1849.

The name derives from its original location in Soho Square.

DIMENSIONS: *285mm diameter.*
PROVENANCE: *Congregation of
Le Carré, until 1849; St. John The
Evangelist, Limehouse; Purchased,
1930, by the Directors of the French
Hospital.*
LITERATURE: *W. Minet, The
Communion Plate of the Church of
Le Carré, Proceedings of the Huguenot
Society of London, Vol.14 (1930), 101;
Huguenot Society Quarto Series,
Register of the Church of
Hungerford Market, later Castle Street,
Vol. XXXI, p.xxiii.*

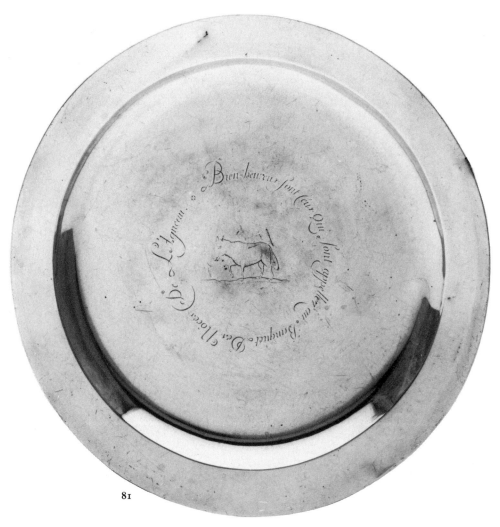

81

80*a*

80*b*

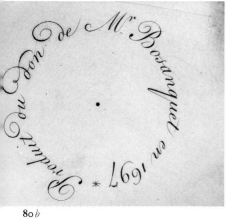

80*b*

80*c*

80*a*

80*c*

82 *Communion Plate of the French Church, Portarlington*

SILVER FLAGON, ONE OF A PAIR, A PATEN, COMMUNION CUP AND ALMS DISH,
DAVID WILLAUME, 1714.

INSCRIBED: DONNE PAR SON ALTESSE ROYALE MADAME WILHELMINA CAROLINA PRINCESSE
DE GALLES EN FAVEUR L'EGLISE FRANCOISE CONFORMISTE DE PORTARLINGTON LE 1 MARS
1714/5.

This fine set of sacramental plate was presented to the French Church, Portarlington by
Princess Caroline Wilhelmina of Wales, daughter-in-law of George I. This important
commission was executed by David Willaume, the son of Adam Willaume, goldsmith of
Metz, who is first recorded in London in 1687 when he became a denizen. By 1715, Willaume
was one of the leading Huguenot goldsmiths, and his patrons included the most eminent
members of the nobility (*Catalogue number 333*).

Princess Caroline also presented the church with a bell.

DIMENSIONS: *Flagon 330mm high;
paten 140mm diameter;
cup 229mm high;
alms dish 420mm diameter.*

PROVENANCE: *The French Church,
Portarlington.*

82

CHARITIES

From 1681, when Charles II issued a proclamation offering England as a place of refuge, the Huguenot refugees were assisted by house-to-house collections across the country. A broadsheet of 1688 records that a fund of £40,000 from collections in James II's reign met the needs of some 15,500 refugees of all classes, both in London and the ports where they landed.

Later, William and Mary gave generously from the Civil List; a Parliamentary grant was made throughout the eighteenth century, although it was steadily reduced as time went on. It supported conformist Huguenot churches, their ministers, the refugees and their descendants.

In the late seventeenth century, two soup-kitchens were opened for the Huguenot poor, one in Soho and the other in Spitalfields.

The Directors of the French Hospital administered four different charities, the Boislin, Coqueau, Dufour and Mounier Trusts, which were all founded in the eighteenth century by Huguenot refugees.

Other charitable groups included the Society of Saintonge and Angoumois and the Society of Poitou and the Loudonois. Their objectives were to assist aged and unemployed refugees from these provinces and to pay apprenticeship premiums for the children of Huguenot descent.

The Huguenots also founded Friendly Societies, clubs set up by workers for mutual support during times of hardship. They included the Friendly Benefit Society (originally the Society of Parisians), The Friendly Society, The Norman Society, The Society of Protestant Refugees from High and Low Normandy, and the Society of Lintot. They were the first Friendly Societies in England and served as models for later English Benefit Societies.

Two receipts from the papers of the Earl of Bedford

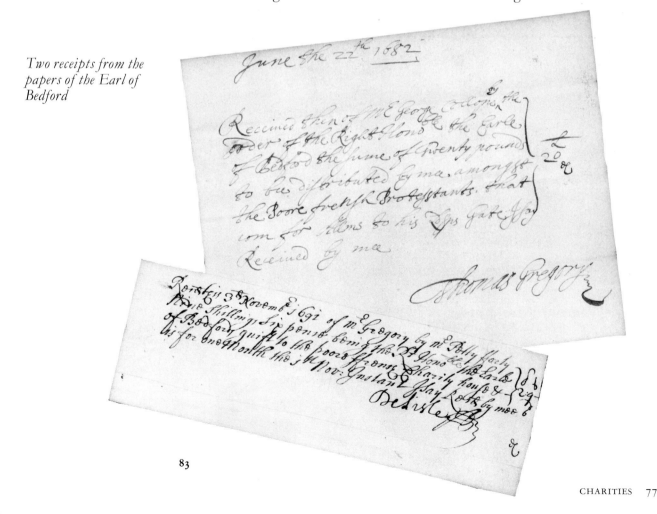

83

83 *Two receipts from the papers of the Earl of Bedford*

a. 'June the 22th (sic) 1682. Received then of Mr. George Collope by the order of the Right Honoble the Earle of Bedford the sume of Twenty pounds to bee distributed by mee amongst the Poore french Protestants that com for Alms to his Losps Gate . . . Thomas Gregory.'

b. 'Received 3rd November 1691 of Mr. Gregory by Mr. Petty forty nine shillings six pence being the Rt Honoble the Earle of Bedford's guift to the poore french Charity house & is for one Month the 1st Nov. Instant . . . Delisle.'

Thomas Gregory was Master of Horse to the 5th Earl of Bedford, and it was his task to distribute alms. The 'poore french Charity house' is probably the Soho 'Soupe', of which no records are known to survive.

ILLUSTRATED: *page 77.*
DIMENSIONS: *a. 144 × 85mm.*

DIMENSIONS: *b. 190 × 65mm.*
PROVENANCE: *The Marquess of Tavistock and the Trustees of the Bedford Estates.*
LITERATURE: *E.R. Briggs, Note upon the Benefactions to the Huguenots from William, the Fifth Earl of Bedford, Proceedings of the Huguenot Society of London, Vol. 23 (1977–82), p. 200; Gladys Scott-Thomson, Life in a Noble Household, 1641–1700, 1937, pp. 224–5, 363.*

84 *The Royal Bounty*
PRINTED ACCOUNTS, 1710.

This is the printed version of the accounts for the grant of £12,000 made in 1708 and 1709. The accounts were scrutinised by an English Committee, and administered by a French Committee. The beneficiaries are listed according to social class and the area in which they had settled. The accounts exhibited are for the distributions in Petticoat Lane and Brick Lane, Spitalfields.

PROVENANCE: *Huguenot Library.*
LITERATURE: *The Royal Bounty – Petition of the French Ministers to William III, Proceedings of the Huguenot Society of London, Vol. I (1885–6), pp.163–6, 324–9; ibid. Vol. 12 (1919–24), pp. 263–287; Huguenot Society Quarto Series, Vol. LI (1974), p. 3.*

85 *Spitalfields' Soupe*
RECEIVER'S ACCOUNTS, MANUSCRIPT VOL. 2, 16 MAY 1738 TO EASTER 1777.

This volume contains the record of all contributions to the Charity's funds. Some receipt lists are headed 'Brick Lane' and 'Artillery Lane'. Memoranda include a detailed inventory of furnishings at the 'Maison de Charité' which shows that the house then used contained a parlour and a kitchen, a room upstairs where the Directors held their meetings, and a bedroom for the steward, with a feather bed, sheets and striped bed-curtains, as well as an attic with an old chest and a flock bed. Equipment included a great cauldron, scales and large weights, one of 28 lbs, and two two-handled knives for cutting up the bread.

Applicants received a 'portion' consisting of 'a pan of good broth mixed with six ounces of bread and half a pound of meat; and the same weight of good bread'. Printed 'portion' tickets were allotted to applicants.

After 1741, the charity could no longer afford meat and only issued bread for the rest of the century on a gradually reduced scale.

PROVENANCE: *Huguenot Library Ms.M 2/6.*
LITERATURE: *Irvine R. Gray, Huguenot Manuscripts: A Descriptive Catalogue of the Remaining Manuscripts in the Huguenot Library, Huguenot Society Quarto Series, Vol. LVI (1983), pp.98–9.*

86 *Spitalfields' Soupe*
a. PRINTED ACCOUNT FOR AN APPEAL, 1776.

In 1776, the 'Soupe' still distributed bread to more than 127 families.

This appeal notes that since the foundation of the 'Soupe' in 'Flower the Luce' Street, previously in the early years of refuge, the charity had depended on outside contributions for its survival.

PROVENANCE: *Huguenot Library Ms. M2/13/1.*
LITERATURE: *Irvine R. Gray, Huguenot Manuscripts: A Descriptive Catalogue of the Remaining Manuscripts in the Huguenot Library, Huguenot Society Quarto Series, Vol. LVI (1983), p. 102.*

b. INVITATION TO THE ANNIVERSARY SERMON, 1817.

This document also appeals for funds for the Spitalfields' 'Soupe'.

It announces that the annual sermon would be presented at the French Church, Threadneedle Street by the minister Mr. Anspach on Sunday 16 March, 1817 at 11a.m.

PROVENANCE: *Huguenot Library Ms. M2/13/1.*
LITERATURE: *Irvine R. Gray, Huguenot Manuscripts: A Descriptive Catalogue of the Remaining Manuscripts in the Huguenot Library, Huguenot Society Quarto Series, Vol. LVI (1983), p. 102.*

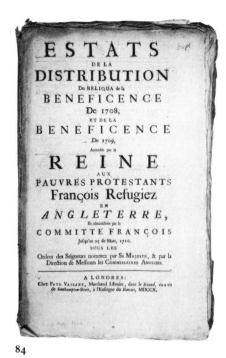

84

86*a*

86*a*

87 *Dufour Charity*

DISTRIBUTION OF £1200 IN WESTMINSTER, 1739/40.

Paul Dufour, one of the original Directors, was Treasurer of the French Hospital from 1719–1739.

In 1688, Paul Dufour and his wife Madeleine (née Mariette) received naturalisation. They became members of the French Church, Threadneedle Street on 23 April 1699. By her will, Madeleine Dufour bequeathed to the French Hospital the residue of her estate, £15,400 in New South Sea Annuities.

During the severe winter of 1739/40, when the Thames froze and coal was extremely expensive, £1,200 from the Charity was distributed to the needy of all classes in Westminster and a similar sum to those in the City and in Spitalfields. In some cases, in addition to the recipients' names, the document also gives their addresses, occupations, ages, the number of their children and their state of health.

The accounts are certified and signed by six commissioners, and dated 3 April, 1740.

PROVENANCE: *Huguenot Library Ms LI/6/1.*

LITERATURE: *Irvine R. Gray, Huguenot Manuscripts: A Descriptive Catalogue of the Remaining Manuscripts in the Huguenot Library, Huguenot Society Quarto Series, Vol. LVI, (1983), pp.81–4.*

88 *Norman Society*

CLAIMS REGISTER 1754–1851.

A heading in French on the first page introduces 'a list of members who have belonged to this Company, so far as I have been able to collect them, with the number of weeks they have drawn for sickness.'

The Norman Society was founded in 1703, in order to maintain mutual friendship among refugees from Normandy and to provide financial assistance in case of sickness and death. Until 1720, the Society only had six members, but had acquired a further fifty-five by 1730. They met every other Monday evening to discuss business and to share beer and tobacco. Although a new member had to join before the age of forty, the advantages included sick pay, of seven shillings a week after eight days consecutive illness, and in case of death, funeral expenses of up to fifty shillings. The Society survived into the 1960s.

PROVENANCE: *Huguenot Library Ms.C.3.*

LITERATURE: *Irvine R. Gray, Huguenot Manuscripts: A Descriptive Catalogue of the Remaining Manuscripts in the Huguenot Library, Huguenot Society Quarto Series, Vol. LVI, 1983, p.121; William Chapman Waller, Early Huguenot Friendly Societies, Proceedings of the Huguenot Society of London, Vol. 6 (1898–1901), pp. 201–236.*

DETAIL

101

90

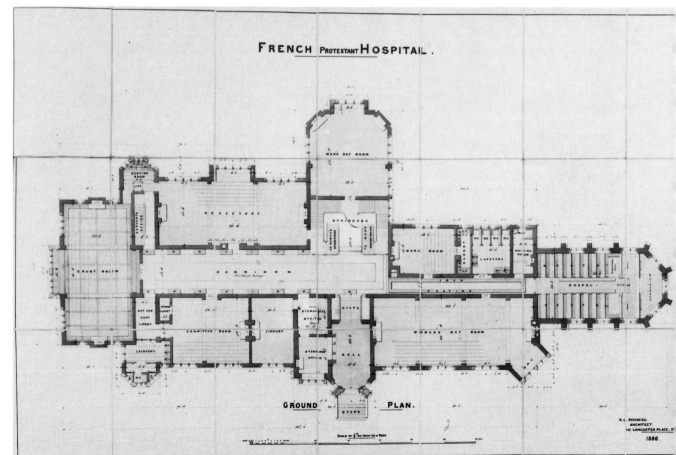

FRENCH PROTESTANT HOSPITAL.

GROUND PLAN.

SCALE OF ⅛ INCH TO A FOOT

R. L. ROUMIEU
ARCHITECT
10 LANCASTER PLACE, S.
1866.

103

THE FRENCH HOSPITAL

Jacques de Gastigny, founder of the French Hospital (left)

View and plan of the French Hospital, Victoria Park, Hackney (far left and bottom left)

In 1708, Jacques de Gastigny who had entered the service of the Prince of Orange at the Revocation of the Edict of Nantes, bequeathed £1000 towards extending and improving a hospice for distressed French Protestants and their descendants in England. In 1716, a piece of ground 'contiguous to the Pest Houses on the south side by St. Luke's parish' in a lane (later called Bath Street, City Road) leading from Old Street to Islington, was purchased from the Ironmongers' Company, and a building erected for the care of the poor, sick and elderly.

In 1718, a Charter was granted, and by 1760, the Hospital, La Providence, as it came to be known, sheltered 234 poor people. In 1862, the Directors of the Hospital bought three acres of land in Victoria Park, Hackney, for £3,600 and Robert Louis Roumieu, architect, of Huguenot descent, designed a new building in the fashionable Victorian Gothic style. The Hospital, with its own chapel and library, opened in June, 1865, with accommodation for 60 inmates and staff.

It was reported by the Hospital's Treasurer, Arthur Hervé Browning in 1934, that the London County Council had 'set envious eyes on our little Naboth's vineyard'. War damage, and the threat of a compulsory purchase order, encouraged the Directors to move the hospital elsewhere. After a period at Compton's Lea near Horsham, Sussex, the Hospital moved to Theobald Square, Rochester, Kent. This, its fourth home, comprising 39 flats, was opened on 21 June 1960. It still provides sheltered housing for elderly people of proven Huguenot descent.

Photograph of residents, French Protestant Hospital, August 1902

89 *Letters Patent granting the foundation of the French Hospital*
SIGNED BY KING GEORGE I, 24TH JULY 1718.

This Royal Charter of Incorporation was granted by George I to 'The Governor and Directors of the Hospital for Poor French Protestants and their descendants residing in Great Britain'.

The first Governor was Henri de Massue, Marquis de Ruvigny, 1st Earl of Galway, aide-de-camp to Marshal Turenne, and later a distinguished general in the British army.

NOT EXHIBITED.

DIMENSIONS: *680 × 880mm.*

PROVENANCE: *French Hospital.*

LITERATURE: *Huguenot Library, Ms. E 5/1; Printed Charter and By-Laws, 1876; Irvine R. Gray, Huguenot Manuscripts: A Descriptive Catalogue of the Remaining Manuscripts in the Huguenot Library, Huguenot Society Quarto Series, Vol.LVI (1983), J 52/5, p.76; Winifred Turner, Some letters of the Marquis de Ruvigny, Proceedings of the Huguenot Society of London, Vol. 27, (1942–6), pp.244–61.*

90 *Jacques de Gastigny (d.1708)*
OIL ON CANVAS, FRENCH SCHOOL, *c.*1700.

De Gastigny was appointed Master of the Royal Buckhounds to William III in 1688. He was a member of the French Committee for dispensing the Royal Bounty to the Huguenot Refugees. In his will (1708) Gastigny left £1,000 to benefit the sick and needy. This sum formed the nucleus of a fund devoted to the building of the hospital in St. Luke's parish, Finsbury in 1718.

COLOUR PLATE: *page 3.*

ILLUSTRATED: *page 80.*

DIMENSIONS: *600 × 760mm.*

PROVENANCE: *The French Hospital.*

LITERATURE: *Judge H.C.S. Dumas, Huguenot History written in the Portraits and Pictures at the French Hospital, Proceedings of the Huguenot Society of London, Vol.14 (1932), p.326; Irvine R.Gray, Huguenot Manuscripts: A Descriptive Catalogue of the Remaining Manuscripts in the Huguenot Library, Huguenot Society Quarto Series, Vol.LVI (1983), pp.2, 13.*

91 *Journal du Grand Livre*
ACCOUNTS OF THE FRENCH HOSPITAL, 1708–1806.

Following a memorandum 'drawn up in explanation of this first book and for the guidance of future Governors' the terms of Jacques de Gastigny's bequest are set out, including details of the property acquired for the Hospital, and an alphabetical list of contributors. The pre-hospital accounts date from 10 February 1708/9, when Gastigny's bequest of £1,000 was received by the French Committee. Regular accounts begin on 1st April 1719. From 1741 to 1759 there are entries for 'assistances externes' (out-gifts).

NOT EXHIBITED.

PROVENANCE: *Huguenot Library Ms. B2/3,4.*

LITERATURE: *Irvine R. Gray, Huguenot Manuscripts: A Descriptive Catalogue of the Remaining Manuscripts in the Huguenot Library, Huguenot Society Quarto Series, Vol. LVI (1983), p.13.*

92 *The French Hospital, Old Street*
OIL ON CANVAS, *c.*1860.

The site occupied by the hospital from 1718 to 1865 lay just north of Old Street, between Bath Street and Ironmonger Row. Built on semi-rural land called Golden Acre, the Hospital is described as abutting north on the Pest House Wall. The contractor was Peter Legrant, and the total cost of the building £2,750. The garden was surrounded by the orchards and market gardens which lined the lane to Islington. The present Radnor Street commemorates the title of the Earls of Radnor (descendants of the Huguenot Bouverie family) who have been almost continuously Governors of the Hospital. Galway Street is named after the 1st Governor, Henri de Massue, Marquis de Ruvigny, and first Earl of Galway.

NOT EXHIBITED.

DIMENSIONS: *720 × 1020mm.*

PROVENANCE: *French Hospital.*

93 *Contractor's receipt for building the French Hospital, Old Street*
MANUSCRIPT, 12 MARCH 1718/19.

The only surviving records of the original building work of the French Hospital, Old Street include 18 receipts for payments on account dated 11 July 1716 to 19 December 1718, and a detailed statement of account totalling £2,750 which was settled on 12 March 1718/19. This is the final receipt of the same date for a balance of £200. All the receipts are signed by the contractor, Peter Legrant.

DIMENSIONS: *285 × 185mm.*

PROVENANCE: *Huguenot Library Ms.F/2.*

LITERATURE: *Irvine R. Gray, Huguenot Manuscripts, Catalogue of the Remaining Manuscripts in the Huguenot Library, Huguenot Society Quarto Series, Vol. LVI (1983), pp. 59,60.*

89

92

94 *Reverend Philipe Ménard (d.1737)*
OIL ON CANVAS, FRENCH SCHOOL, *c.*1710.

Philipe Ménard was the executor of Jacques de Gastigny's will, and the driving force behind the establishment of the French Hospital. He was the first Chaplain and Secretary to the French Hospital, 1718–1737.

Previously Ménard had served as Chaplain to Queen Charlotte Amelia of Denmark and Pastor of the French Church, Copenhagen. He became Minister of the Chapel Royal, St. James's and in 1718, he preached the opening sermon at the inauguration of the Hospital.

DIMENSIONS: *730 × 570mm.*
PROVENANCE: *The French Hospital.*
LITERATURE: *Judge H.C.S. Dumas, Huguenot History written in the Portraits and Pictures at the French Hospital, Proceedings of the Huguenot Society of London, Vol. 14 (1932), pp. 326–332; Irvine R. Gray, Huguenot Manuscripts, Catalogue of the Remaining Manuscripts in the Huguenot Library, Huguenot Society Quarto Series, Vol. LVI (1983), pp. 2,7,47,49,67.*

95 *Orders and Rules for the Governor and Directors of the French Hospital, 1723*

This is the earliest printed edition of the Hospital Orders and Rules. The Court Minutes of 3 July 1723 record that 1,000 copies were ordered. Although the volume is printed in French, it also contains an English translation.

PROVENANCE: *Huguenot Library.*

96 *Letter from James Duplessis, 1740*

This letter from James Duplessis at Leyden is addressed to Philippe de Crespigny, Secretary of the French Hospital. Dated 21 November, 1740, it contains James Duplessis's acceptance of the post of Chaplain to the Hospital.

PROVENANCE: *Huguenot Library Ms.H1/5.*
LITERATURE: *Charles Marmoy, The Chelsea Pensioner and the Chaplain: the two Jacques Duplessis, Proceedings of the Huguenot Society of London, Vol. 23 (1977), pp. 36–48; Irvine R. Gray, Huguenot Manuscripts, Catalogue of the Remaining Manuscripts in the Huguenot Library, Huguenot Society Quarto Series, Vol. LVI (1983), pp.45–6,66.*

97 *Letter from Jacques Demedis, 1743*

This letter from Jacques Demedis in Spitalfields is addressed to Adam Roumieu, Steward of the French Hospital. Demedis was Surgeon-Apothecary to the French Hospital, 1718–1766, and this letter confirms the receipt of two quarters' salary.

DIMENSIONS: *280 × 160mm.*
PROVENANCE: *Huguenot Library, Ms.H1/14.*
LITERATURE: *Irvine R. Gray, Huguenot Manuscripts, Catalogue of the Remaining Manuscripts in the Huguenot Library, Huguenot Society Quarto Series, Vol. LVI (1983), p. 68.*

98 *Indemnity Bond for a Lunatic, 1734*

In addition to the old and poor, the Hospital cared for the mentally ill until 1783. One of these was James Ray, a goldsmith who had taken to 'running about the streets like a madman, forsaking his business and crying "oranges and lemons".'

Before admitting a 'distracted person', it was customary for guarantors to enter into a bond with the Hospital, for payment of any damages and costs caused by the inmate. Some of the early bonds also guaranteed the payment of a weekly pension. The signatures to Ray's bond and affidavit include that of the celebrated goldsmith, Paul de Lamerie.

DIMENSIONS: *330 × 420mm.*
PROVENANCE: *Huguenot Library, Ms.D8/5.*
LITERATURE: *Irvine R. Gray, Huguenot Manuscripts, Catalogue of the Remaining Manuscripts in the Huguenot Library, Huguenot Society Quarto Series, Vol. LVI (1983), p. 39.*

99 *Spoon and Fork*
SILVER, WILLIAM SCARLETT, LONDON, 1722

From a set of twenty-four rat-tailed spoons and three-pronged forks, each of which is engraved on the back of the handle 'French Hospital'.

DIMENSIONS: *spoon, 210mm long; fork, 195mm long.*
PROVENANCE: *French Hospital.*

100 *Pint mug*
PEWTER, NINETEENTH CENTURY;
INSCRIBED: FRENCH HOSPITAL

DIMENSIONS: *124mm high.*
PROVENANCE: *French Hospital.*

94

100

DETAIL

OFFICIERS
DE LA
CORPORATION.

Mr. *Gui de Viçouse*, Baron de la Court, Gouverneur.
Mr. *Pierre Cabibel*, Sen. Sous-Gouverneur.
Mr. *Philippe Ménard*, Min. Sécretaire.
Mr. *Paul Dufour*, Tresorier.

DIRECTEURS.

A.

Mr. *Claude Amyand.*

B.

Mr. *Jaques Baudouin.*
Mr. *René Baudouin.*
Mr. *Benjamin Baronneau.*
Mr. *Jean Louis Berchere.*
Mr. *Albert le Blanc*, Min.

Mr.

DIRECTEURS.

Mr. *Jacob de Blaquy.*
Mr. *René de Boisville.*
Mr. *Paul Buissiere.*

C

Mr. *Pierre Champion de Crespigni.*
Mr. *Jean Philippe Charles.*
Mr. *Jean le Clerc de Virly.*
Mr. *Anthoine Clevembaut.*
Mr. *René de la Combe de Clusel.*

D

Mr. *Albert Delande.*
Mr. *Pierre Jaques du Desert.*

F

Mr. *Philippe Fruschard.*

G

Mr. *Louis de Gaillardy.*
Mr. *Jaques Gautier.*
Mr. *Jaques Henri Guinand.*

L

Mr. *Charles Lebas.*
Mr. *Thomas Leheup.*

Mr.

95

98

101 *The French Hospital, Victoria Park, Hackney*

WATERCOLOUR, VIEW FROM THE SOUTH WEST, ATTRIBUTED TO R.L. ROUMIEU *c.* 1880; INSCRIBED (ON A LABEL ON THE REVERSE OF THE FRAME): SOUTH WEST VIEW OF THE HOSPITAL POUR LES PAUVRES FRANCOIS PROTESTANT (SIC) ET LEURS DESCENDANTS RESIDENTS DANS LA GRANDE BRETAGNE LATELY ERECTED IN VICTORIA PARK, LONDON, FROM DESIGNS OF R.L. ROUMIEU.

The building now houses a Catholic school.

COLOUR PLATE: *page 3.*
ILLUSTRATED: *page 80.*
DIMENSIONS: *980 × 620mm.*
PROVENANCE: *French Hospital.*

102 *Robert Lewis Roumieu (1814–1877)*

OIL ON CANVAS, ARTIST UNKNOWN

Robert Lewis Roumieu FRIBA was an architect of Huguenot descent. He became a Director of the French Hospital in 1856. Seven years later, as Honorary Architect to the Hospital he designed the new and imposing building in Victoria Park, Hackney. The Hospital opened in 1865 and was equipped with the most modern conveniences of mid-Victorian England. It provided accommodation for 58 inmates as well as staff. R.L. Roumieu became Treasurer of the Hospital in 1876.

NOT EXHIBITED.

DIMENSIONS: *915 × 915mm.*
PROVENANCE: *French Hospital.*
LITERATURE: *Charles Marmoy, More pages from the history of the French Hospital, Proceedings of the Huguenot Society of London, Vol. 22 (1973), pp. 235–247; Nikolaus Pevsner, The Buildings of England, London, I, pp. 102,238, pl. 149; ibid., London, Except the Cities of London and Westminster, 1952, p. 167.*

103 *Plan of the ground floor, French Hospital, Victoria Park, Hackney*

PHOTOGRAPH OF 1866 ORIGINAL, R.L. ROUMIEU.

This is one of three plans for the new French Hospital in Hackney, the others are of the basement and first floor. They were presented to the Hospital Library by R.S. Roumieu, a Director, and son of the architect.

The plan shows the Men and Women's Day Rooms, the Chapel, and the Court Room, where the Directors met.

NOT EXHIBITED.
ILLUSTRATED: *page 80.*
DIMENSIONS: *Scale; one sixth of an inch = one foot.*
PROVENANCE: *Huguenot Library.*

104 *Sketches of Inmates*

PENCIL, 1881, SUSANNAH AMES, WIDOW; JAMES ENGLEBURTT, WIDOWER AGED 80; SAMUEL MAY, WIDOWER, AGED 79.

Susannah Ames (née Chappell) was admitted to the French Hospital in 1876, as a result of age, increasing infirmity and want of means. She was the daughter of William Chappell of 37, Willmot Street, Bethnal Green. Her Huguenot descent was through her paternal grandmother, Catherine Piquet, whose ancestors came from Lyons. Mrs. Ames died in 1887.

James Engleburtt was admitted to the French Hospital in 1880 as a result of old age, and the failure of the silk trade. He was the son of William Engleburtt, of Crown Court, Curtain Road, Bethnal Green. His Huguenot connections were on his mother's side, his mother being a cousin of Peter Betambeau, who had entered the Hospital in 1860. James Engleburtt was a silk weaver by trade, but had left the weaving trade for the hat business.

Samuel May was admitted to the Hospital in 1878, with failing vision. He was the son of William May and Sarah Manchée, and his mother's great grandmother had come from France as a refugee. He was born in Bethnal Green, and had trained as a silk weaver; he had recently worked as a messenger to a printer.

DIMENSIONS: *140 × 110mm.*
PROVENANCE: *Huguenot Library.*
LITERATURE: *Charles Marmoy, The French Protestant Hospital: Extracts from the Archives of 'La Providence' relating to inmates and Applicants for Admission, 1718–1957 and to recipients of and applicants for the Coqueau Charity, 1745–1901, Huguenot Society Quarto Series, Vols. LII,LIII (1977), under Ames, Engleburtt and May.*

105 *Plan of the French Hospital Estate, St Luke's, Finsbury*

PHOTOGRAPH OF 1881 ORIGINAL.

The plan marks the site of the former Hospital, which was then occupied by the School Board of London. It also shows the house plans for Galway and Radnor Streets. Another copy of the plan is in the Guildhall Library.

NOT EXHIBITED.
DIMENSIONS: *Scale one inch = 20 feet.*
PROVENANCE: *Huguenot Library, Ms.J55.*
LITERATURE: *Irvine R. Gray, Huguenot Manuscripts, Catalogue of the Remaining Manuscripts in the Huguenot Library, Huguenot Society Quarto Series, Vol. LVI (1983), p. 76.*

106 *Property mark of the French Hospital*

IRON, NINETEENTH CENTURY.

This property mark came from one of the French Hospital properties in the City, and is one of two examples in the Museum of London. Several other property marks are still in the French Hospital collection.

DIMENSIONS: *255 × 285mm.*
PROVENANCE: *Presented to the Guildhall Museum by the French Hospital; Museum of London.*

102

104

104

107

106

107 *Loving cup and cover*

SILVER-GILT, GEORGE LAMBERT, 1892–3; INSCRIBED (ON THE RIM): THE FRENCH
PROTESTANT HOSPITAL LONDON DECEMBER 3RD 1892; (ON THE BASE) THE GIFT OF
LIEUTENANT COLONEL GEORGE LAMBERT, F.S.A. DIRECTOR 1881. PRIME WARDEN OF THE
GOLDSMITHS COMPANY, 1886; (ON THE COVER) THE COVER OF THIS CUP PRESENTED TO THE
FRENCH HOSPITAL ON THE OCCASION OF HIS TENTH ELECTION AS DEPUTY GOVERNOR,
5TH OCTOBER, 1907, BY ARTHUR GIRAUD BROWNING, F.S.A.

The surface of the cup is inset with four silvered bronze medallions commemorating the
coronation of William and Mary, 1689. They show the King and Queen in profile, enthroned,
in their full regalia, and the captain of the guard, B. Muikens and his companions.

This is one of four loving cups used at the French Hospital.

ILLUSTRATED: page 86.

*DIMENSIONS: 340mm high,
weight 35ozs.*

*PROVENANCE: Presented to the French
Hospital, 1892, by Lieutenant Colonel
George Lambert F.S.A., and Arthur
Giraud Browning, 1907.*

108 *Opening of the French Hospital*

ROCHESTER, 1960 (PHOTOGRAPH).

This shows from left to right the Rt. Hon The Earl of Radnor, Lord Cornwallis, the Lord
Lieutenant of Kent, and the Bishop of Rochester, C.M. Chavasse. The ceramic plaque of
the Ravens Feeding Elijah, with the motto of the Hospital, DOMINUS.PROVIDEBIT was veiled
with a French flag and a Union Jack.

109 *Meetings at the French Hospital*

a. MEETING OF THE COURT, THE FRENCH HOSPITAL, ROCHESTER 15TH DECEMBER 1984
(PHOTOGRAPH).

This shows seated from left to right C.G.H. Grellier (Surveyor); J.W. Letheren (Clerk),
S. Champion de Crespigny (Secretary), The Rt. Hon The Earl of Radnor (Governor),
P.J. Duval (Deputy Governor), J.R. Vigne (Treasurer), N.D. Ouvry, Cdr. A.A.C. Ouvry.

Standing from left to right are R.W. Place, O.J. Grace, Canon G.M. Young (Chaplain),
J.C.B. South, P.P.B. Minet, Col. P.A.E. Dumas, Canon H.C.E. Stapleton, E.L. Darwin,
Rev. J.P. Lefroy, J.G. Ouvry (Solicitor).

b. THE FRENCH HOSPITAL, CHRISTMAS LUNCH, THE CORN EXCHANGE, ROCHESTER,
15TH DECEMBER 1984 (PHOTOGRAPH).

109

108

EDUCATION

'The French have set up several great schools both at London and in the countries near it'. Maximilien Misson, 1698.

Refugees who settled in England from the 1680s onwards, continued and developed the educational traditions established by sixteenth-century Walloons and Huguenots. Many ministers, unable to find positions in French churches, became tutors in English households.

The Huguenots opened schools in and around London at Chelsea, Greenwich, Islington and Marylebone. In Chelsea, Jean Bion, the former Catholic chaplain of the galley 'Superbe' worked as a teacher and minister. In Marylebone, schools were established by Denis de la Place, Peter de la Touche and De la Mare, who opened a boarding school for young ladies. One of Marylebone's Coffee Houses was frequented by Abel Boyer, who wrote the 'Complete French Master' in 1694 and by Pierre Antoine Motteux and Pierre Coste, who in 1695 translated John Locke's treatise 'On Education' into French.

In the 1680s, Solomon Foubert established a riding school near Piccadilly, M. Metre opened an academy in Long Acre, and Abraham Meure another in Soho, near the French Church in Hog Lane. Further afield, the Sanxay family played an important part in the establishment of Cheam School.

In 1747 the Westminster French Protestant Charity School was founded to provide a primary education for some thirty boys and girls, limited to girls only after 1812. The school closed in the 1920s, but the Westminster French Protestant School Foundation still provides financial assistance for the education of children of Huguenot descent.

Sir John Chardin (1643–1712), merchant adventurer, orientalist and tutor to Lord Tavistock, oil on canvas, unknown artist, c.1690

110 *Subscription ticket to the Ecole de Charité Françoise de Westminster*

INSCRIBED: PAR SOUSCRIPTION COMMENCÉE 1747 . . . SCULP 1747 C. GRIGNION AND
SIGNED BY E. ARTAUD, TREASURER.

This card is decorated with two charity children and a rococo style cartouche. A similar card, in the Huguenot Library, was issued to Lady Ravensworth on 23 May, 1791 as a receipt for one guinea's subscription.

DIMENSIONS: *210 × 266mm.*

PROVENANCE: *Banks Collection, 1793; Department of Prints and Drawings, British Museum.*

EXHIBITED: *Rococo Art and Design in Hogarth's England, Victoria and Albert Museum, 1984, c.13, p. 45.*

LITERATURE: *The Westminster French Protestant School, Proceedings of the Huguenot Society of London, Vol. 2, (1887–8), pp. 464–8; Susan Minet, Ecole de Charité Française de Westminster, Proceedings of the Huguenot Society of London, Vol. 12 (1917–23) pp. 91–117.*

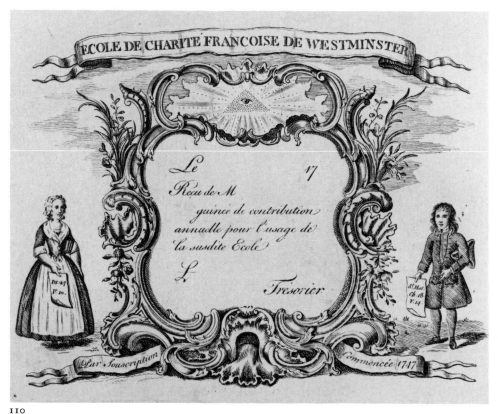

110

111 *Projet pour fonder, dans la Ville ou Libertés de Westminster une école pour l'entretien & pour l'Education des Enfants des Pauvres François Refugiés, c.1747*

PHOTOGRAPH.

This appeal expresses concern for the orphans and children of poor Huguenot refugees, who were being sent to the workhouse or being brought up illiterate, and wishes that such an establishment had been founded earlier. It states the intention to house, feed and clothe these children, and to educate them in the Reformed Religion. Subscribers are invited to contribute at least ten shillings a year.

Subscriptions were to be directed to the Huberts, father and son, in the Strand, opposite Durham Yard; to Messrs. Elin and Paillet in Thrift Street, Mr. Morelon in Compton Street, Mr. Roberts in Church Street, Soho, Mr. Mongeon in Porter Street, and Mr. Foullé in Union Court, Broad Street, in the City.

This is the only known record relating to the school's foundation, and although it was printed some sixty years after the Revocation, it was written entirely in French.

PROVENANCE: *Dr. Williams's Library, Vol.16.9.15(9).*

LITERATURE: *Irvine R. Gray, Huguenot Manuscripts, A Descriptive Catalogue of the Remaining Manuscripts in the Huguenot Library, Huguenot Society Quarto Series, Vol. LVI (1983), p.103; Susan Minet, Ecole de Charité Française de Westminster, Proceedings of the Huguenot Society of London, Vol.12 (1917–23) pp. 91–117 (Reprinted in full Appendix I, pp.106–7).*

112 *David Hubert (d.1754?)*

OIL ON CANVAS, ARTIST UNKNOWN, c.1740.

David Hubert was a Founder of the French Protestant Charity School at Westminster, 1747, and can be identified with one of the Huberts, father and son, who lived in the Strand (*Catalogue number* 111). The Hubert family were members of the Threadneedle Street Church.

DIMENSIONS: *430 × 240mm.*

PROVENANCE: *French Protestant Charity School Westminster; French Hospital.*

LITERATURE: *Susan Minet, Ecole de Charité Française de Westminster, Proceedings of the Huguenot Society of London, Vol.12 (1917–23), pp. 91–117; H. Wagner, Pedigree of the Hubert Family, ibid., Vol. 8 (1901–4), p. 385.*

PROJET

ur fonder, dans la *Ville* ou *Libertés* de *Weſtminſter*, une
Ecole pour l'entretien & pour l'Education des Enfans
des *Pauvres François Refugiés*.

OUT le Monde convient qu'une bonne Education eſt très avan-
tageuſe à la Société, & qu'elle eſt néceſſaire aux Enfants de
quelque Condition qu'ils ſoient: Les *Riches*, qui en ſentent ſi
bien le prix, & qui ſe donnent tant de ſoins & tant d'inquiétudes
pour la procurer à leurs Enfants, ne devroient-ils pas, lors qu'ils
nnent à refléchir, plaindre le ſort des *Indigens*, que la Providence a mis
s l'impuiſſance d'en donner une telle aux leurs.

Nous voions que, pour ſubvenir au manque de Moiens de ces derniers,
ntité de Perſonnes parmi cette Nation, ſi eſtimable par ſa Charité, s'uniſſent
r établir des *Ecoles Publiques* par voie de *Souſcription*, où les Enfants des
s Opulents reçoivent une auſſi bonne Education que s'ils fuſſent nés de
rents riches & acrédités: Qu'eſt-ce qui empêcheroit que l'on ne formât un
eil Etabliſſement parmi les *François de Weſtminſter?* Plût à Dieu que nos
décesſeurs y euſſent penſé de bonne heure: s'ils l'euſſent fait, il y a tout
de croire que beaucoup d'Enfans de *Pauvres du Refuge*, tant *Orphelins*
autres, que l'on a été obligé de mettre dans des *Maiſons de Paroiſſe*, & qui
ſont par là détachés de nous, ſeroient à préſent comptés parmi les meilleurs
mbres de nos Egliſes; pendant que par là auſſi nos *Conſiſtoires* auroient été
ucoup moins chargés, qu'ils ne le ſont, de *Pauvres*, parmi leſquels il s'en
ve un grand nombre, qui, faute d'un tel *Etabliſſement*, ſe ſont veus réduits à
riſte néceſſité de demander de l'aſſiſtance, tant pour ſubvenir à leurs propres
oins, que pour élever leurs Familles.

Une nouvelle Conſidération qui doit faire ſentir la néceſſité qu'il y a d'établir une
ole Publique pour l'éducation des Enfants des *Pauvres François Refugiés* de cette
te, c'eſt le peu de ſoin que ces derniers en général prennent de leur *Inſtruction*.
effet, combien ne s'en trouve t-il point qui, pouvant enſeigner ou faire apprendre
urs Enfants à lire & à écrire, négligent de le faire? Combien encore qui per-
t de vuë un Devoir qui eſt beaucoup plus eſſentiel encore, & qui conſiſte à les
ver dans la crainte de *Dieu*, & à les mettre en état de *rendre raiſon de leur Foi*:
ù il arrive trop ſouvent, ou que ces Enfants ignorent la *Religion* qu'ils profeſſent,
qu'ils la deshonnorent par une vie déréglée.

eſt dans la Vuë d'obvier à ces Inconveniens que l'on ſe propoſe, avec l'aide
Seigneur, de lever une Somme par *Souſcription* pour entretenir & pour élever
ſtiennement autant d'Enfants que le Produit des Contributions pourra le per-
ettre. Pour cet effet, I. On leur fera apprendre à *lire* & à *écrire*. II. On
fera inſtruire dans les Principes de notre *Sainte Religion Reformée*. III. On les
billera tous uniformement, & au cas que la Providence béniſſe cette Entrepriſe,
que nos Fonds le permettent, on les fera habiter tous dans un même lieu, où
l leur donnera avec la Nouriture un Maitre qui aura toûjours l'œil ſur leur Con-
te.

Au reſte, comme on ne peut pas ſe flater qu'une *Entrepriſe* de cette nature
ſſe être d'abord amenée à maturité; comme d'ailleurs ceux qui l'ont conçuë
t fort éloignés de croire qu'ils n'ont pas beſoin de nouvelles lumières pour
vancer & pour la perfectioner; ils invitent tous ceux à qui ce Projet pourra par-
nir, à leur en indiquer les défauts, ou à leur en propoſer un meilleur, eſpérant
'ils voudront bien leur communiquer leurs idées là deſſus, ſoit de bouche, ſoit
r écrit, en s'addreſſant aux Meſſieurs nommés ci-deſſous.

Après avoir prié *Dieu* de répandre ſa Bénédiction ſur ce Deſſein, qui a pour objet
vancement de ſa Gloire, il ne nous reſte qu'à avertir le Public,

I. Que chaque Souſcrivant ne pourra pas ſouſcrire moins de Dix Chelins par An.

II. Que l'on donnera l'argent en ſouſcrivant, & que l'on déclarera en même
ms ſi l'on eſt dans l'intention de continuer la même Somme annuellement.

III. Que tous les Six Mois on balancera les Comptes, & qu'ils ſeront remis
tre les mains d'une Perſonne que les Directeurs nommeront, afin que les Sou-
rivants puiſſent eux mêmes les examiner, & voir comment les choſes s'admi-
strent.

Ceux qui voudront ſouſcrire pourront s'addreſſer pour cet effet à Meſſ.
Hubert Père & Fils dans le *Strand*, vis à vis *Durham-Yard*, à Meſſ. *Elin &
Paillet* dans *Thrift-Street*, à Mr. *Morelon* dans *Compton Street*, à Mr. *Roberts*
dans *Church Street*, *Soho* ; à Mr. *Mongeon* dans *Porter Street* ; & à Mr. *Foulié*
dans *Union Court*, *Broad Street*, vis à vis *the Pay Office* dans la Cité.

111

112

113

113 *Chair*
MAHOGANY, *c.* 1750.

One of a set of eleven mahogany dining chairs used at the Ecole de Charité Française de Westminster. The chair has a waved toprail and pierced interlaced splats.

ILLUSTRATED: *page 91.*

DIMENSIONS: *910 × 510mm.*

PROVENANCE: *French Protestant Charity School, Westminster; Purchased by the French Hospital, 1924.*

114 *Dish*
PEWTER, EIGHTEENTH CENTURY; INSCRIBED: WESTMINSTER FRENCH CHARITY SCHOOL.

Used by the French Protestant Charity School, Westminster.

DIMENSIONS: *248mm diameter.*

PROVENANCE: *French Protestant Charity School, Westminster; French Hospital*

115 *Jug*
PEWTER, EIGHTEENTH CENTURY; INSCRIBED: WESTMINSTER FRENCH CHARITY SCHOOL.

Used by the French Protestant Charity School, Westminster.

DIMENSIONS: *207mm high.*

PROVENANCE: *French Protestant Charity School, Westminster; French Hospital.*

116 *Scroll recording Benefactors of the French Protestant School, Westminster*
OIL ON CANVAS, *c.*1766.

This scroll records the names of benefactors of the French Protestant School, Westminster between 1750–1765. They included that of Peter Delmé, a relative of the Lord Mayor of London, Sir Peter Delmé, who died in 1738.

DIMENSIONS: *1320 × 485mm.*

PROVENANCE: *French Protestant School, Westminster; Jonathan Ouvry.*

117 *Petition to the French Protestant School, Westminster*
MANUSCRIPT 8TH JULY 1780.

This petition is signed by Thomas Tijou and was presented to the French Protestant School, Westminster on behalf of his grand-daughters, Elizabeth and Henrietta Green. Thomas Tijou describes himself as a small-worker in gold, but nearing the age of eighty, is suffering from failing sight.

Thomas' father Jean Tijou was a refugee from St. Germain, and employed by William III on the ironwork at Hampton Court Palace (*Catalogue numbers 262–263*). Tijou did not complete this commission until the reign of Queen Anne, and only received part of the payment for the work.

PROVENANCE: *Huguenot Library, Ms. C2/1 669.670.*

LITERATURE: *Irvine R. Gray, Huguenot Manuscripts: A Descriptive Catalogue of the Remaining Manuscripts in the Huguenot Library, Huguenot Society Quarto Series, Vol. LVI (1983), p. 112.*

118 *Doll in the uniform of the French Protestant School, Westminster*
PORCELAIN FACE AND HANDS, STUFFED BODY, PAPER SHOES, *c.*1887.

The doll is dressed in the uniform worn by the girls at the Westminster Charity School. This consists of a blue woollen dress, and pink brushed cotton underskirt, white cotton pantaloons and a cotton bonnet with lace edging. The pinafore is made from one of the original pinafores worn by the girls. The doll appears in a group photograph of the girls at the school, *c.*1887–8.

DIMENSIONS: *370mm.*

PROVENANCE: *Jonathan Ouvry.*

LITERATURE: *Proceedings of the Huguenot Society of London, Vol. 2 (1887–8), p. 465; Susan Minet, Ecole de Charité Française de Westminster, Proceedings of the Huguenot Society of London, Vol. 13 (1923–1929), pp. 374–392, photograph facing p. 377.*

119 *Bible, with bookplate of the French Protestant School, Westminster*

The Bible is signed by the School Governor, A.H.G. Browning, and Secretary, E.C. Ouvry, and, as was customary, was given to Florence Hall when she left the school in 1924.

Mrs. Roper (Florence Gladys Kathleen Hall) was brought up in Old Ford Road, Bow. Her uncle was William Duval, and this Huguenot connection enabled her sister and herself, aged seven, to attend the French Protestant School, which was then at 233 Shaftesbury Avenue.

During the school year the girls visited the French Hospital, in Victoria Park, where they sang French psalms to the inmates, and Mrs. Roper particularly remembers visiting her uncle there. On Sundays, the girls attended two services, at the French Chapel adjoining the school and at the parish church.

Distinguishing features of the school year included an annual sermon on the Revocation, and a holiday on St. Bartholomew's Day, 24 August.

DIMENSIONS: *Octavo.*

PROVENANCE: *Presented to Florence Hall (Mrs. Roper) in 1924, by the French Protestant School, Westminster.*

114

115

118

117

120 *Crochet Tablecloth*
MADE BY MRS. ROPER, *c.*1929.

Florence Hall was one of sixteen girls under the care of the Headmistress Mme. Flecknoe, a part-time music teacher Mme. Stollery, and a French teacher. The pupils' ages ranged between seven and sixteen.

The curriculum consisted of Scripture, Geography, French, History, Drawing, Needlework and Singing lessons. Handmade crochet collars were part of the uniform. Mrs. Roper (née Florence Hall) still continues the crochet work she learnt at the school.

DIMENSIONS: *1040 × 1040mm.*
PROVENANCE: *Mrs. Roper.*

121 *Bell*

The bell came from the French Protestant Church School's premises which opened in Noel Street, in May 1895.

There does not appear to be any connections between this school, which was a day school for boys and girls, primary and secondary, and the French Protestant Charity School, which was in Bloomsbury Street.

DIMENSIONS: *400mm high.*
PROVENANCE: *French Protestant Charity School, Noel Street; French Church, Soho Square.*

122 *The Ten Commandments*
SAMPLER, WOOL ON LINEN, MARGUERITE IOANS, 1703.

This sampler, embroidered with the Ten Commandments in French, was worked by Marguerite Ioans in 1703.

Beneath the Commandments is a verse from Galatians 8 v.12 'l'homme qui fera ses choses vivra par elles'.

PROVENANCE: *French Hospital.*

123 *Arithmetic Book of Philip Ardouin*
EIGHTEENTH CENTURY.

Philip Ardouin was a school-master, in Bell Court, Wheeler's Street, Spitalfields. The book contains sums, weights and measures, rough workings and a printed multiplication table.

At the back of the book, on some blank pages, are recorded various births, marriages and deaths of members of the Busher and Jarman families of Bethnal Green and elsewhere in East London, 1796–1864. This book may have been produced by one Sarah Busher, a Hospital inmate from 1884–6, as evidence of descent.

PROVENANCE: *Huguenot Library, Ms.J. 29.*
LITERATURE: *Irvine R. Gray, Huguenot Manuscripts: A Descriptive Catalogue of the Remaining Manuscripts in the Huguenot Library; Huguenot Society Quarto Series, Vol. LVI (1983), p. 72.*

124 *The Compleat French Master*
ABEL BOYER, 1694.

Abel Boyer (1667–1729) was born at Castres, Upper Languedoc, and arrived in England in 1689. He became tutor to Allen, later 1st Earl Bathurst, and subsequently to William, Duke of Gloucester, for whom he wrote this manual. In 1702, he published his well-known Dictionnaire Royal Français et Anglais, which was greatly superior to any previous work of the kind, and the basis of many subsequent French-English Dictionaries; its forty-first edition was published in Paris in 1860.

Alexander Pope in his 'Dunciad' accused Boyer of being 'a voluminous compiler of annals, political collections etc'. Between 1702, and his death in 1729, Boyer's work included editing the 'Post Boy', a thrice weekly London news-sheet.

NOT EXHIBITED
PROVENANCE: *British Library.*
LITERATURE: *G.C. Gibbs, Abel Boyer, Proceedings of the Huguenot Society of London, Vol. 23 (1977–82), pp. 87–99.*

125 *Major Henry Foubert (d.1743)*
MEZZOTINT, J. FABER, AFTER THOMAS HUDSON, 1740.
INSCRIBED: SOLD BY FABER AT THE GOLDEN HEAD IN BLOOMSBURY SQUARE.

Major Foubert was the son of Solomon Foubert, who ran the Royal Riding Academy in the Faubourg St. Germain, Paris. On 20 January, 1679 an Edict of Council was passed against the Protestant Masters at the Academies. Solomon Foubert left Paris as a result, and settled in London where he established a similar institution in Sherwood Street, Piccadilly. Mathematics and its application to geography and navigation was an important part of the curriculum, as were riding, fencing and vaulting.

The Academy was regarded as of national importance in that it helped 'lessen the expence the nation is at yearly in sending children into France to be taught military exercises'. Charles II donated £100 towards the Academy in 1679, and John Evelyn took a keen interest in it. It was even proposed to make the Royal Society its 'trustees and supervisors'.

Major Foubert entered the army in 1685. At the Battle of the Boyne he was acting as A.D.C. to the Duke of Schomberg, and in dismounting to assist the great general when he had been fatally wounded, was himself wounded in the arm. He was promoted to the rank of Major in 1692.

On his father's death in 1696, Major Foubert took over the management of the Academy.

Other French Academies run by D'Agard *c.*1680 in the Savoy, Strand, and that run by Metre *c.*1686 in Long Acre, next to the White Hart Inn, followed continental practice and included mathematics, geography, and classics as well as dancing, fencing and painting. As the dearth of instruction in mathematics had caused contemporaries much concern, the French Academies helped to fill a major gap in English education.

DIMENSIONS: *320 × 225mm.*
PROVENANCE: *Cheylesmore Collection; Department of Prints and Drawings, British Museum.*
LITERATURE: *J. Chaloner-Smith, British Mezzotint portraits, 1878, Vol. I, p. 352, no.137; W.H. Manchée, The Fouberts and their Royal Academy, Proceedings of the Huguenot Society of London, Vol. 16 (1937–41), pp. 77–97; Freeman O'Donoghue, Catalogue of Engraved British Portraits, 1910, Vol. II, p. 242; E.G.R. Taylor, The Mathematical Practitioners of Tudor and Stuart England, 1954, p. 263.*

125

120

6 *Familiar Dialogues.*

Arrêtez Animal; & la laiſ-monter, puis que la fot-eſt faite.	Stay, beaſt, and let her come up, ſince the Folly is done al-ready.
Pour quoi, vous mettez s à rire ?	Why do you fall a laugh-ing ?
e me ris de la naïveté vôtre petit laquais.	I laugh at your little Lackeys Simplicity.
Ah Couſine ! que cette vi-m'embaraſſe à l'heure qu'il	Ah Couzen! how this Viſit troubles me now ?
'importe, il vous la faut re,	No matter, it muſt go down with you.

XXVIII. *Dialogue.*   XXXVIII. Dialogue.

Des Marionetes.   Of Puppet Shows.

OU Fûtes vous hier aprez midi ?	Were went you yeſterday in the Afternoon ?
allay faire ma cour au de Gloceſter.	I went to give my Attendance to the Duke of Gloceſter.
omment ſe porte t-il ?	How does he do ?
ſe porte fort bien.	He is very well.
fait toujours paroitre oup d'eſprit & de vi-é.	He always ſhews a great deal of wit and Liveliness.
iâtes vous avec lui ?	Did you play with him ?
ùy, Monſieur, nous j'o-es un peu en attendant, le Bateleur eût prépa-s Marionettes.	Yes, Sir, we play'd a little, whilſt the Puppet-player was getting his Puppets ready.
	Com-

124

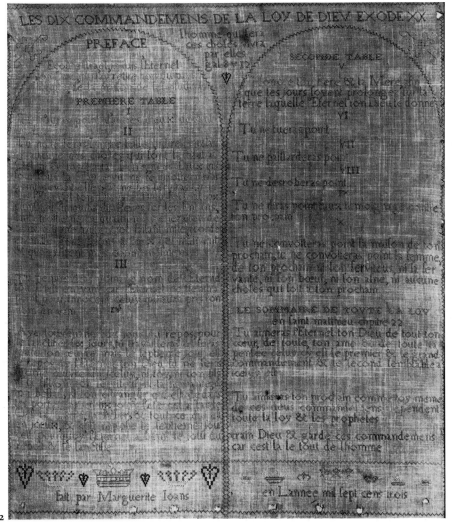

LES DIX COMMANDEMENS DE LA LOY DE DIEV EXODE XX

PREFACE

PREMIERE TABLE

SECONDE TABLE

Fait par Marguerite Ioans   en Lannee mil ſept cent trois

122

126 *Foubert's Academy*

WATERCOLOUR, TOMKINS; EARLY NINETEENTH CENTURY.
INSCRIBED: MAJOR FOUBERT'S RIDING SCHOOL IN SWALLOW STREET.

Major Foubert continued the riding academy established by his father Solomon Foubert, on the site of the present Foubert's Place, off Regent Street. After his death in 1743, the Academy continued under Solomon Durrell, a relative and executor of Major Foubert's will, until 1768.

The building remained until the second decade of the nineteenth century, when part of Swallow Street was pulled down to make way for improvements to Regent Street.

DIMENSIONS: 235 × 152mm.

PROVENANCE: *Crace Collection; Department of Prints and Drawings, British Museum.*

LITERATURE: *The Diaries of John Evelyn, ed. E.S. De Beer, Vol.II, pp.134, 201; Vol.IV, pp.257–8, 289, 290, 400–401; Hugh Phillips, Mid-Georgian London, 1964, pp.240–1, fig.326.*

DETAIL

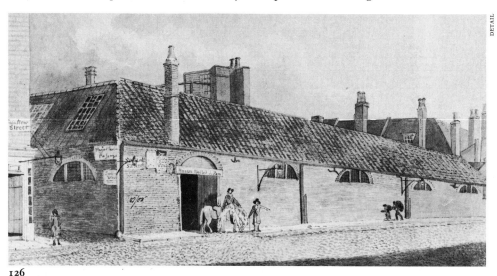

126

127 *Daniel Sanxay (d.1739)*

OIL ON CANVAS, UNKNOWN ARTIST, NINETEENTH CENTURY.

Daniel Sanxay was the son of a refugee Protestant minister from Tonnay Boutonne, who became minister to the French congregation which met at St. Olave's, Exeter. Daniel became an anglican priest after graduating from Oxford. He settled at Cheam near Epsom, where his wife, Jane Antrobus had property, and took over a school that had been established in 1646. By 1719, he was headmaster, and erected a new building on a site at the top of the High Street. Inside were two long schoolrooms, designed to hold classes at each end. The school, largely patronised by the nobility and gentry, flourished. In 1731, the annual fee was £25.

Daniel died in 1739, having handed over the school to his son James, who ran it for thirteen years. James became Rector of Cheam in 1746; however his wife Catherine Firmin objected to the school, which suffered as a result. In 1752, James Sanxay appointed William Gilpin to succeed him, although James' brother Robert, a druggist in the Strand, supported the venture financially when needed.

Instead of corporal punishment, William Gilpin substituted a system of trial by a jury consisting of the boys themselves. Fines were also introduced, and graduated according to the gravity of the offence.

Cheam was one of the first schools to introduce cricket as an organised game.

Cheam School continued to prosper, and is today best-known, as the preparatory school of the Duke of Edinburgh and the Prince of Wales. The oldest private school in the country and one of the oldest purely preparatory schools, Cheam demonstrates the growth of private education in England since the middle of the seventeenth century.

NOT EXHIBITED.

DIMENSIONS: 279 × 228mm.

PROVENANCE: *Private Collection.*

LITERATURE: *Edward Peel, Cheam School from 1645, 1974, pp. 26–33; Theodore F. Sanxay, The Sanxay Family, 1907; Foster Watson, Notes and Materials on Religious Refugees in their Relation to Education in England before the Revocation of the Edict of Nantes, 1685, Proceedings of the Huguenot Society of London, Vol. 9, (1909–1911), pp.463–7.*

NOTE: *Later evaluation of the portrait has revealed that it is unlikely to represent Daniel Sanxay.*

128 *Henry William Majendie (1754–1830)*

CUT PAPER SILHOUETTE, AUGUSTIN EDOUART, c.1830.

Dr. Majendie was Edouart's first full length portrait. It was considered an excellent likeness and he cut forty copies.

Henry William Majendie was from a Huguenot family in Bearn. His grandfather, Andrew Majendie, was minister to a Huguenot congregation at Exeter, and his father was minister at the French church of the Savoy. Henry William Majendie became tutor to Prince William, later William IV in 1781.

Later, as Vicar of Nether Stowey, from 1790, he established a Sunday School at a time when such institutions were considered by some clergy to be a dangerous novelty.

Majendie was a good preacher and an active administrator. He became successively Canon of Windsor, Canon Residentiary of St. Paul's, Bishop of Chester in 1800, and Bishop of Bangor in 1809.

The artist, Augustin Edouart (1789–1861) established himself in London about 1813. He travelled to Scotland, Ireland and America. He exhibited at the Royal Academy in 1815 and 1816. His subjects ranged from animals to the French Royal Family.

DIMENSIONS: 343 × 406mm.

PROVENANCE: *Anthony Vaughan.*

LITERATURE: *David C. Agnew, Protestant Exiles from France, Vol. II (1871), p. 273; Peggy Hickman, Two Centuries of Silhouettes, Celebrities in Profile, 1971, p. 126, fig. 68.1, H. Wagner, Pedigree of Majendie, Proceedings of the Huguenot Society of London, Vol. 9 (1909–1911), pp. 589–592.*

Huguenot contribution

The following Affociation of the Manufacturers and others inhabiting in or near Spital Fields, (who to their feveral fubfcribed Names have added the Numbers of Men each Manufacturer propofes to raife for his Majefty's Service,) has been prefented to his Majefty by Mr. Alderman Baker, accompanied by a numerous Body of Gentlemen, being introduced by the Right Honourable the Earl Waldegrave, one of the Lords of his Majefty's Bed-Chamber in Waiting: Which Affociation his Majefty was pleafed to receive very gracioufly.

Chrift Church, Middlefex, Sept. 26, 1745.

WE whofe Names are hereunto fubfcribed, Manufacturers and others inhabiting in or near Spital Fields, in the County of Middlefex, duly confidering the great and many Bleffings we enjoy under his moft facred and illuftrious Majefty King George, think it our Duty, (at this Time more efpecially) to manifeft our inviolable Attachment to his Perfon and Government. We do therefore declare our utter Deteftation and Abhorrence of the unnatural Rebellion now carried on in Favour of a Popifh Pretender, or fome of his Family: And we do, as much as in us lies, folemnly promife and engage ourfelves to ftand by each other to the utmoft of our Power and Ability, to defend his Majefty's Perfon and Government, by inducing our feveral Workmen, Servants and Dependants, to take up Arms with us whenever called thereto by his Majefty, againft all his Enemies, both Foreign and Domeftick.

A LIST of fuch Manufacturers and others inhabiting in or near Spital Fields, together with the Number of their Workmen, Servants and Dependants, who have been engaged by their Mafters to take up Arms when called thereto by his Majefty, in Defence of his Perfon and Government.

John Peck	
Reynolds and Bray	20
John and Robert Turner	107
Peter Campart	102
Captain James Dalbiac	74
John Baker	80
John Tall	75
Robert Lee	9
Thomas Jervis	41
Daniel Pilon	4
Daniel Gobbee	49
George Garrett	70
Peter Nouailles	20
Godin and Ogier	3
Elizabeth and Joseph Green	60
John Lamy	32
James Roberdeau	12
George Farmer	17
	11

John Maze	17
James Gautier	20
John Sabatier	34
Thomas Beck	10
Samuel Alavoine	39
John Rondeau	57
Jeremiah Mather	18
Rene Turquand	4
Abraham David, jun.	8
James Maze	25
James Beuzeville	5
John Payton	47
Riviete and Ogier	16
Abraham Dupree	3
Thomas Jones	6
Jacob Jamet	20
Peter Abraham Ogier and Sons	28
John Ogier	16
James Martell	9
Daniel Pineau	29
Henry Cline	3
James Auber	16
John Luke Landon	48
Ephraim Flammare	2
Chantrey and Co.	35
Peter Pontie	9
John Frederick Bernard	9
Peter Gallott	4
Lewis Chauvet	65
Lewis Deformeaux	19
Ann Barbutt	14
Lewis Chevelier	38
Simon Dalbiac, jun.	25
Abraham Newhoufe	18
Abraham Deheul	47
Henry Napton	10
John Campion	2
Thomas Triquet	7
Judith Sequeret and Bourdillion	14
James Maze	24
James Johnson	70
Francis Chanfat	6
Thomas Turner	13
John Ward	4
Samuel Savage	36
Bigot and De Lavau	30
Nicholas Hebert	25
Gabriel Pomier	8
James Ouvry	19
Peter Ougier	50
Peter Ferree	2
John Gibson	10
John Ouvry	35
Peter Farques	3
Benjamin Champion	50
Guy Bryan	4
John Powell	33
Peter Delamare and Co.	22
John Defoule	8
Daniel Giles	40
Samuel Worral	7
Paul Auder	14
John Shields	5
Gabriel Grillier	12
Mathurin Rivalin	4
Obadiah Agace and Sons	41
John Roy	10
John Batcheler	19
William Smith	8
Thomas Rogers	12

Thomas

LOYALTY

In France and in exile, French Protestants prayed for their king, and they hoped that eventually Louis XIV would relent and grant them liberty in their own country.

However, in Britain from 1681 patents of denization were made to the refugees in mass grants. Naturalisation by Act of Parliament brought additional rights of inheritance, but was expensive; a private bill could cost £50 or £60. Despite strong native opposition, an Act of General Naturalization was passed in 1709, but was soon repealed. On becoming English citizens, the Huguenots transferred their loyalty to the British monarch. The extent of their loyalty was shown in 1745 when 80 of the 133 silk manufacturers in Spitalfields who promised to raise men for service against the Catholic Young Pretender were of Huguenot origin.

William III's entry into London, 1688, oil on canvas, A. van Gaelen

PRIVATE COLLECTION, DETAIL.

129 The Arrival of Prince William of Orange in London
ETCHING; ROMEYN DE HOOGE, 1688.

At the invitation of Parliament, William of Orange entered London on 18th December 1688 after a march from the West Country at the head of an army in which many of the officers and men were Huguenots.

The Dutch artist Romeyn de Hooge was a great favourite of Prince William and although he never came to this country, he produced a fine series of prints celebrating the landmarks of William's reign.

The location of the events depicted is taken from prints of London available at the time. To make sense the engraving has to be reversed: the scene takes place outside St. James' Palace, looking towards Whitehall and Westminster. For a clearer view, de Hooge omits the Horse Guards. Old St. Paul's still looms in the background, although it had been completely demolished by the time of William's arrival. The print contradicts historical records of the event, as it was raining heavily, and William had insisted on approaching the Palace by a back route and was travelling in a closed carriage.

After the ambivalent attitude of the Catholic James II towards the Huguenots, the arrival of the Protestant William of Orange, was greeted with enthusiasm by the refugees. William had already made generous provisions for the Huguenots in Holland, and was engaged in a long struggle against the Catholic Louis XIV. The refugees hoped that William might be able to force a reversal of policy on Louis XIV by diplomatic and military means.

DIMENSIONS: *425 × 535mm.*

PROVENANCE: *Museum of London.*

LITERATURE: *Felix Barker and Peter Jackson, London, 2000 years of a City and its People, 1974, illustrated p.162.*

130 Panegyric on Queen Mary II
FRENCH TRANSLATION, JACQUES ABBADIE, 1695 (PHOTOGRAPH).

Queen Mary II, the wife of William III, was a woman of outstandingly charitable disposition, and a warm friend to the Huguenot refugees (*Catalogue number* 27). This 'Panegyric', written after her death in December, 1694, expresses their genuine regard and affection for her. Written by Jacques Abbadie in London, it was translated into French and published in Amsterdam, 1695.

Abbadie's life is a good illustration of the peregrinations of the refugees after they had left France. Born near Pau, Béarn, about 1654, Abbadie gained a DD at Sedan University and then went to Berlin, where he was minister for most of the 1680s. Accompanying Marshal Schomberg to Holland, England and Ireland, he returned to London and became minister at the Savoy church, the post he held when he wrote the Panegyric. This work, together with his 'Defence of the British Nation', won him the regard of William III, and in 1699 he became Dean of Killaloe in Ireland. He died at Marylebone in 1727.

PROVENANCE: *British Library.*

LITERATURE: *Dictionary of National Biography, under Abbadie.*

131 Mausoleum for Queen Mary II
ENGRAVING BY SIMON GRIBELIN, 1695 (PHOTOGRAPH).

This mausoleum was designed by Sir Christopher Wren and erected in Westminster Abbey in 1695. The design reflects Wren's interest in Lars Porsenna's tomb.

John Evelyn noted that the pomp of Queen Mary's funeral cost 'above £50,000, very unseasonably and against her desire'.

PROVENANCE: *British Museum, Department of Prints and Drawings.*

LITERATURE: *The Wren Society, Vol.V, p.12 reproduces another engraving of the Mausoleum by J. Mynde; Ibid., Vol.XIX, p.145; Diary of John Evelyn, edited E.S.de Beer, Vol.V, 1955, p.204.*

132 Copy of Act for the Naturalisation of Stephen Benovad, John Girard, Francis Beteilhe and others
LONDON, 1702.

To encourage Huguenot refugees to come to England, Charles II offered them free denization when the dragonnades started in 1681. Grants of denization were an act of royal prerogative, but the rights they conferred were not as full as those gained through Acts of Naturalisation passed by Parliament. The intention of both processes was to make the recipient an Englishman, but naturalisation grants made the purchase and transfer of land legally secure. Consequently, wealthier refugees normally sought to be naturalised. Except for a short period after 1709, when an Act of General Naturalisation was passed (though soon repealed), this involved the expensive and painstaking task of preparing individual bills. Often these were amalgamated, and the individuals named here were amongst a list of 150 people, the vast majority Huguenot, naturalised by Act 1 Anne number 112, in 1702.

PROVENANCE: *Huguenot Library, Ms. F Ha 2/1.*

LITERATURE: *Irvine R. Gray, Huguenot Manuscripts: A Descriptive Catalogue of the Remaining Manuscripts in the Huguenot Library, Huguenot Society Quarto Series, Vol.LVI (1983), p.145; William A. Shaw (ed.) Letters of Denization and Acts of Naturalisation, Huguenot Society Quarto Series, Vols.XVIII (1911) and XXVII (1923); C. Parry, Nationality and Citizenship Laws of the Commonwealth, 1957.*

131

132

133 *Communion Certificate of James Eude*
LONDON, 1709.

This certificate was presented by James Eude's great grandson, also James, with his petition for admission to the French Protestant Hospital on 30th March, 1858, as evidence of his Huguenot origins. The original James Eude is described as of the parish of Stepney, and the document, signed by Samuel Besombes, minister of the French Church, Threadneedle Street, certifies that James Eude received communion on 1st May, 1709 at the French church called 'The Hospital', an annexe of the Threadneedle Street Church (*Catalogue number* 66). The document also bears a testimony from Francis Martel, weaver, and James Martel, cooper, both of the parish of Stepney.

DIMENSIONS: *188 × 246mm.*

PROVENANCE: *Huguenot Library.*

LITERATURE: *James W. Hood, Eude to Hood, Suggested evolution of a name, Proceedings of the Huguenot Society of London, Vol.23 (1977–82) pp.187–192.*

134 *Canary birds naturaliz'd in Utopia: a Canto*
LONDON, 1709

These verses, published by the Booksellers of London and Westminster at the price of 2d, were intended to turn public opinion against the Act for Naturalisation of Foreign Protestants, which was then going through Parliament. The choice of the title was probably suggested by the fact that the weavers of Spitalfields installed canaries in their garrets, to entertain them while they worked.

The author of this canto asks how, 'anyone of Sense and Reason' is prepared to undermine 'his natural fellow free born subjects for any interloping Canary-Birds, or naturaliz'd Foreigners'. The Huguenot settlers in London were already prospering,

'Here they grew fat, and liv'd at Ease,
And bigger look'd than Refugees'.

They were not prepared to till the ground, and as a result, 'fruitful Fields lie fallow', while they, 'In good Mechanicks their Trades follow'.

'With Caution then let's give our votes
'Gainst cutting our own Subjects throats'.

PROVENANCE: *Guildhall Library.*

135 *Considerations upon the mischiefs that may arise from granting too much indulgence to foreigners*
LONDON, 1735.

The anonymous compiler of this pamphlet refers to the imprudent conduct of King Charles I in assisting the French Protestants at La Rochelle, and that of Charles II in giving 'no small encouragement and Protection to the Refugees of that Kingdom, upon the Revocation of the Edict of Nantes'.

'Hither for God's sake and their own they fled
Some for Religion came and some for Bread'.

The author's main argument against the encouragement given to the refugees bears witness to their extraordinary qualities.

'As the French are, of all People, the most enterprizing, the most industrious; and frugal, so we have the more Reason to be jealous of their Designs, and to provide against their Admission into any places of Power, Profit, or Trust. For considering their Frugality, Oeconomy, and Industry, they will in time engross all the profitable Branches of Trade as they have already that of the Silk Manufacture, for I believe it can be demonstrated, that nine Parts in ten of that Traffick is in their hands, with a great share of that of Wines.

Nor are they less considerable with regard to their Numbers ... and considering their Sobriety and Diet, and the Fruitfulness of their Women, the City, in time, will probably be called a French Colony'.

PROVENANCE: *Guildhall Library.*

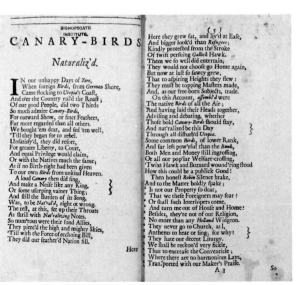

133   134   135

HUGUENOTS IN THE BRITISH ARMY

Huguenots figured prominently in the French Army in the seventeenth century and included the great leaders Marshal Turenne and the Duke of Condé. By the 1690s, Vauban, the famous French military engineer, estimated that as a result of Huguenot emigration, France had lost between 18,000 and 21,000 fighting men and 500–600 officers.

Many of these officers fled to Holland, where they enrolled in the regiments of the Dutch Army, and were maintained by the revenues of William of Orange. In 1688, they accompanied William to England, and they formed four regiments for service in Ireland. The refugee soldiers fostered a professional approach, a superior attention to duty, and an increased sense of motivation. In 1706, a brigade of foot consisting of six regiments was formed from the refugees on the Irish pension list for service in the Iberian peninsula.

In the 1690s, a fresh wave of immigrants to this country included Jean Louis de Ligonier (1680–1770) from Castres, who served initially in Marlborough's campaigns, and eventually became Commander-in-Chief of the British Army in 1757.

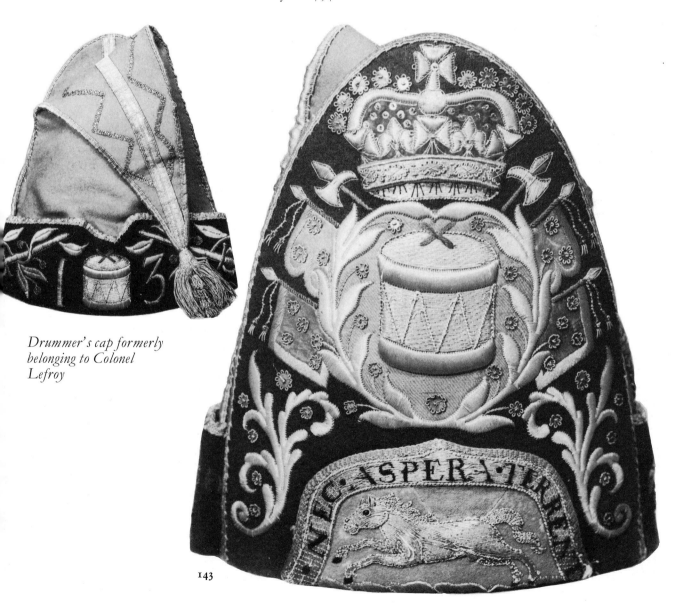

Drummer's cap formerly belonging to Colonel Lefroy

143

136 *Frederick, 1st Duke of Schomberg (1615–1690)*

MEZZOTINT BY I. SMITH AFTER SIR GODFREY KNELLER, *c.*1690.

INSCRIBED: FREDERICK DUKE OF SCHONBERG, MARQUIS OF HARWICK, EARLE OF
BRANTFORD, BARON OF TAYS, GEN.LL OF ALL HIS MA.TIES FORCES, MASTER GEN.LL OF HIS
MA.TIES ORDNANCE, ONE OF HIS MA.TIES MOST HONOBLE PRIVY COUNCIL, KNIGHT OF YE
MOST NOBLE ORDER OF THE GARTER, COUNT OF YE HOLY EMPIRE, & MERTOLA, GRANDEE OF
PORTUGAL, GEN.LL OF YE ELECTOR BRANDENBURGS FORCES, STADTHOLDER OF PRUSSIA ETC.

The Duke is shown on horseback, in armour, with an attendant to his right. Beyond, a battle
scene is in progress.

Although Schomberg was by birth a German Count, from 1651 he served in the French
army, and embraced French Protestantism. On the Revocation, Schomberg retired to
Portugal. He then settled initially in Brandenburg.

Frederick, Duke of Schomberg landed with William III in England in 1688 as his second-
in-command. In Ireland he led the refugee cavalry regiment, known as Schomberg's French
Horse, and commanded the Royal Forces until his death at the Battle of the Boyne, 1690.

DIMENSIONS: *383 × 258mm.*

PROVENANCE: *National Portrait
Gallery.*

LITERATURE: *D.C. Agnew, Protestant
Exiles from France, Vol.II, 1871,
pp.82–108; T.M. Maguire, Huguenot
Commanders, Proceedings of the Huguenot
Society of London, Vol. 4 (1892–3),
pp.309–329.*

137 *Battle of the Boyne, medal*

SILVER, JAN LUDER, 1690.

INSCRIBED: OBVERSE: GVILIELMUS.III.D.G.MAG.BRIT.FRAN.ET.HIB.REX.

REVERSE: APPARUIT ET DISSIPAVIT (HE APPEARED AND DISPERSED THEM) LIBERATA
HIBERNIA MDCLXXXX.

The medal shows on the obverse a bust of William III, to the right, crowned with laurels, in
scale armour with a lion's head on the shoulder and a mantle with a fringed edge. The reverse
shows William on horseback to the left, commanding and about to cross a river. In the
background, a battle is in progress, James II is shown in flight, and the Duke of Schomberg
is lying dead.

Lüder engraved a large number of medals for William III. His work is not of great merit,
and he is said frequently to have copied designs of other medallists. Some of his medals may
have been cut when visiting England.

Struck after the Battle of the Boyne, this medal illustrates various incidents on that
occasion. William attacked the army of James II so soon after coming within view of it that
his appearance and his victory were deemed almost simultaneous. The success of William's
campaign was ascribed to this victory.

DIMENSIONS: *57mm diameter.*

PROVENANCE: *British Museum,
Department of Coins and Medals.*

LITERATURE: *E. Hawkins, Medallic
Illustrations of British History, 1969,
Vol.I, p.716, no.135; L. Forrer,
Biographical Dictionary of Medallists,
1907, Vol.III, under Lüder.*

138 *Commission from Frederick, 1st Duke of Schomberg, 1689/90*

This commission from Frederick, 1st Duke of Schomberg was granted to Louis Chevalleau
de Boisragon, Chevalier de la Chenaye (1666–1736) at Lisburn on 18th March 1689/90.
Boisragon served as a Cornet in Schomberg's Horse, as a Lieutenant and according to family
tradition as Schomberg's Aide-de-Camp at the Battle of the Boyne. He later served under
Henry, Viscount Galway, in Portugal as Lieutenant-Colonel of a Regiment of Horse.

PROVENANCE: *By family descent to
Major C.J.C. Beckett.*

LITERATURE: *I.H. Layard, Chronicles
of the Boisragon Family, Proceedings of
the Huguenot Society of London,
Vol. 6 (1898–1901), pp.81–111.*

139 *Frederick, 1st Duke of Schomberg*

MEDAL, SILVER, PHILLIPP HENRICH MULLER AND FRIEDRICH KLEINERT.

INSCRIBED: OBVERSE: FRIDERICUS MARESCHALCUS SCHOMBERG AND SIGNED P.H.M.

REVERSE: PLANTAVIT UNIQUE FERACEM (HE HAS EVERYWHERE PLANTED A FRUITFUL
CLUB) CONTINUATIS TRIUMPHIS OBDURATA IN DEUM FIDE IN HIBER.MILITANTI, 1690.
(TO HIM WHO SERVED IN IRELAND WITH CONTINUED SUCCESS, AND WITH ENDURING
TRUST IN GOD). EDGE: PRO RELIGIONE ET LIBERTATE MORI VIVERE EST (TO DIE FOR
RELIGION AND LIBERTY IS TO LIVE). SIGNED; F.K.

The obverse shows a bust of Marshal Schomberg, three quarters to the right, in a cravat and
armour, with a riband across the breast. The reverse shows Schomberg, full-length in Roman
dress, resting on his shield, which is ornamented with the Christian monogram. Like another
Hercules, his club takes root and flourishes as an olive tree. A coronet and cornucopia lie
neglected on the ground, and a snake bites in vain at his shield. Behind him rise a pyramid
and a laurel branch which bears the shields of France, Germany, Scotland, Spain and Ireland,
the locations of his military achievements.

This medal was executed at Nuremberg; it was also struck in wood for use as a
draughtsman.

At a moment when William's troops were very hard pressed and almost overpowered,
Schomberg, who had kept a strong body around him to act in any emergency, dashed into the
midst of the fight and turned the fortune of the day. He was himself hurried away amidst a
party of James' horse in their flight, and killed by a discharge from his own men, who were
not aware of his entanglement with the fugitives.

DIMENSIONS: *47mm.*

PROVENANCE: *British Museum,
Department of Coins and Medals.*

LITERATURE: *E. Hawkins, Medallic
Illustrations of British History, 1969,
Vol.I, pp.717–8, no.139.*

137

137

FREDERICK Duke of SCHONBERG, Marquis of Harwich, Earle of Brentford, Baron of Teys, Gen.ᵗ of all his Maᵗⁱᵉˢ Forces, Master Genᵗˡ of his Maᵗⁱᵉˢ Ordnance, One of his Maᵗᵘˢ most honᵇˡᵉ Privy Councell, Knight of ŷ most noble Order of the Garter, Count of ŷ Holy Empire &c. Mestre de Grandee of Portugal, Genˡˡ of ŷ Elector of Brandenburgs Forces, Stadtholder of Prusia &c.

G. Kneller pinx   I. Smith fecit ex.

136

139

139

140 *List of Pensions to Huguenot Officers, 1692*

This manuscript contains 'An Establishment of Pensions' to former officers who served in William III's Regiment of Horse, commanded by Henry de Massue de Ruvigny, Lord Galway, who succeeded Schomberg as Commander-in-Chief of William III's forces in Ireland. It also includes Huguenot officers who had served in the three Regiments of Foot under Colonel de La Melonnière, Colonel du Cambon, and Colonel de Belcastel. The names of the Captains of Horse include that of Captain Isaac Dumont de Bostaquet (1632–1709), the author of 'Mémoires inédites de Dumont de Bostaquet Gentilhomme Normand sur les temps qui ont précédé et suivi la Révocation de l'Edit de Nantes, sur le Refuge et les expéditions de Guillaume III en Angleterre et en Irlande' (printed in Paris, 1864) who settled at Portarlington, where he eventually died.

This manuscript volume in a fine contemporary binding, elaborately tooled in gold, contains the bookplate of Thomas Pelham, Ist Earl of Chichester, who married in 1754, the granddaughter of René Baudouin, a refugee from Tours.

PROVENANCE: *Thomas Pelham, 1st Earl of Chichester; Library of the French Hospital; Huguenot Library.*

LITERATURE: *David C.A. Agnew, Protestant Exiles from France, 1871, Vol.II, pp.4–10; Charles E. Dumas, The Huguenot Refugees from Normandy and the escape from France of Isaac Dumont, 1954; Henry Wagner, A List of Pensions to Huguenot Officers in 1692, Proceedings of the Huguenot Society of London, Vol. 9 (1909–11), pp.581–588.*

141 *Lieutenant-General de Jean (d.1764)*
OIL ON CANVAS, ATTRIBUTED TO PHILIP MERCIER, *c.*1740.
INSCRIBED: LT. GENERAL DE JEAN.

De Jean is shown half length in a scarlet coat and white cravat. The painting was described as by Mercier when it was at Upton House in the early nineteenth century. Another portrait of De Jean, signed by Mercier and dated 1737, is in a private collection.

In 1727, Major De Jean subscribed for five copies of Laval's 'History of the French Protestant Church'. On his appointment as a Director of the French Hospital in July, 1740 he was a Lieutenant-Colonel in the Grenadier Guards. De Jean apparently proposed that Sir John Ligonier should be made a Director of the French Hospital. In 1744, a number of Swiss in London and Westminster offered to form a regiment to serve his Majesty in case of invasion. They were mustered in April that year under the command of Colonel De Jean.

De Jean was appointed Colonel of 37th Foot in 1746, of the 3rd Horse in 1750, of the 14th Light Dragoons in 1752 and was promoted to the rank of Major-General in 1756 and Lieutenant-General in 1759.

He married Louisa, daughter of James Roussy, a burgess of Geneva, and eventually settled in Dublin, where he died.

He was a client of the Huguenot gunsmith whose account book is also exhibited (*Catalogue number* 327).

COLOUR PLATE: *page 4.*

DIMENSIONS: *1000 × 870mm.*

PROVENANCE: *Upton House, Northamptonshire; William Butlin; Christie's 28 March 1898 (95); Sir Henry Peek; Presented to the French Hospital, 1898.*

LITERATURE: *David C.A. Agnew, Protestant Exiles from France, Vol.I, 1871, p.281; Judge H.C.S. Dumas, Huguenot History written in the Portraits and Pictures at the French Hospital, Proceedings of the Huguenot Society of London, Vol.14 (1932), illustrated, facing p.328; John Ingamells and Robert Raines, A Catalogue of the Paintings, Drawings and Etchings of Philip Mercier, The Walpole Society, Vol.XLVI, 1976–8, pp.1–70, under no.26.*

142 *Monument to Isaac Garnier, Chelsea*
PHOTOGRAPH OF MARBLE ORIGINAL.

This handsome monument supports the Garnier coat of arms.

Isaac Garnier (1631–1712) was born at Vitry, Champagne in 1631. In France, he studied medicine and chemistry as a pastime, for on account of his religion, he was denied his apothecary's diploma. He took refuge in England in 1685, when he also obtained naturalisation. He became Apothecary General to Chelsea Hospital. On his death in 1712, he was buried in ground adjacent to the Hospital, where his monument can still be seen.

He was succeeded by his eldest son, also Isaac (1671–1736), who became Apothecary General to Chelsea Hospital in 1692.

PROVENANCE: *Derek Garnier.*

LITERATURE: *A.E. Garnier, The Garniers of Hampshire, 1900, pp.13–14.*

143 *Drummer's cap 13th dragoons*
WOOL AND SILVER GILT EMBROIDERY 1751–68; INSCRIBED: 13 NEC ASPERA TERRENT.

One of a pair; the other is still in the possession of the Lefroy family.

This mitre cap is made of scarlet and green woollen cloth with gold, silver and silk thread. The front is decorated with a laurel wreath, and a drum, and four banners, two blue and two crimson surmounted by a monarchial crown. The frontal flap is embroidered in silver thread with a running horse against a green and yellow silk field. The back is embroidered with another drum flanked by the numerals 1 and 3 and two swords.

Colonel Anthony Peter Lefroy, to whom this cap belonged, served in the 13th Light Dragoons in Ireland, 1755–1783.

The Lefroy family came originally from Cambray. Their ancestor, Antoine L'Offroy settled at Canterbury in about 1586. The Lefroys later worked in the silk dyeing industry in Canterbury.

Anthony Peter was the son of Anthony Lefroy (1703–1779) a merchant banker of Leghorn. He entered the army and became an ensign in the 33rd Regiment, 1763; a Lieutenant in the 49th Regiment, 1765 and later captain, 1769; In 1775 he was a captain in the 13th Light Dragoons, a Major in 1779, he rose to command the 9th Light Dragoons in 1785. Almost all his service was spent in Ireland and on his retirement he settled in Limerick, where he died in 1819. His eldest son Thomas, was called to the Irish Bar and became Lord Chief Justice of Ireland. He bought Carriglas estate in Longford, which is still in the possession of the family.

ILLUSTRATED: *page 103.*

PROVENANCE: *Lieutenant Colonel A.P. Lefroy; presented to the National Army Museum by Miss P. Lefroy.*

LITERATURE: *Loffroy of Cambray, A Supplement by A. Cadet (J.A.P. Lefroy) privately printed, 1961, p.14. E.A. Campbell, Journal of Army Historical Research, Vol. XXI, p. 56.*

L.^t:General
De Jean

141

144 *The Elements of Fortification*

STEPHEN RIOU, 1746.

This volume is dedicated to William, Duke of Cumberland. The frontispiece shows Minerva, Fame and Mars supporting a medallion of the Duke of Cumberland, and was engraved by the Huguenot Paul Fourdrinier. The volume was inspired by 'the Scarcity of books in the English language which treat methodically of this art', and many of the plates are derived from Vauban and Belidor. As the first authoritative treatment of this subject in English, Riou's book made a major contribution to military education. Stephen Riou (1720–1780) was a Captain in the 1st Regiment of the Grenadier Guards. His father was the son of Jean Le Brun de Rieux, and served at 17 in Piedmont as a cadet in Lord Galway's Regiment. He settled in London, and was naturalised in 1702. He worked as a merchant, and was for twenty years in partnership with Henry Guinand.

Stephen Riou eventually practised as an architect, but it was through his earlier training in the army that he developed an interest in architecture and engineering. He later published 'Short Principles for the Architecture of Stone Bridges with practical observations and a new geometrical diagram to determine the thickness of the Piers to the Height and Base of any given arch'. His second son, Captain Edward Riou (1762–1801) was killed in the attack on Copenhagen, 2 April, 1801. A monument to him, the 'gallant good Riou' of Campbell's ballad, is in St. Paul's Cathedral.

NOT EXHIBITED.

PROVENANCE: *British Library.*

LITERATURE: *P.H. Ditchfield, The Family of Riou, Proceedings of the Huguenot Society of London, Vol.10 (1912–1914), pp.236–238; Wagner, Pedigree of the Riou Family, Miscellanea Genealogica et Heraldica, June, 1901.*

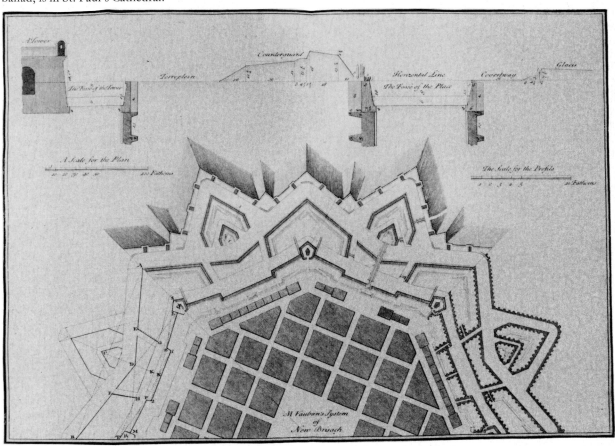

144

145 *Field Marshal Jean Louis Ligonier (1680–1770)*

BUST, MARBLE, LOUIS FRANCOIS ROUBILIAC, c.1760.

INSCRIBED: L.F. ROUBILIAC SC. AD VIVUM.

The son of Louis de Ligonier, of Castres, Jean Louis left France under an assumed name and reached Dublin in 1697. He served under Marlborough in 1702, and grew to be universally respected for his professional abilities and his personal integrity. He became Commander-in-Chief of the British Army and Master General of the Ordnance during the Seven Years War.

It is probable that Ligonier commissioned this bust and its companion, also at Windsor, of George II. Ligonier had served as the King's personal Staff Officer and it is possible that this commission was executed after Ligonier's retirement and the monarch's death in 1760. The bust of Ligonier by Roubiliac was exhibited at the Society of Artists in 1761 (153) and on 3rd February 1763, an entry in the Regimental Account kept by Ligonier's agent Richard Cox reads 'To paid Roubiliac's bill for £153 11s.' Furthermore, the marble of George II is signed 'L.F. Roubiliac Invt.' which indicates that this bust was not done from life.

The great soldier is portrayed dressed in a fur-lined cloak, draped over a cuirass, and wearing the star and ribbon of the Order of the Bath. A smaller preparatory terracotta model for the bust is in the National Portrait Gallery. This is the most dignified and distinguished portrait bust of Roubiliac's maturity.

DIMENSIONS: *610mm high.*

PROVENANCE: *Presented to the Prince Regent by Mrs. Lloyd, June 1817; Her Majesty the Queen.*

EXHIBITED: *The Grenadier Guards, A Tercentenary Exhibition, 1656–1956, St. James' Palace, 30 May–23 June, 1956(69).*

LITERATURE: *K.A. Esdaile, The Life and Work of Louis François Roubiliac, 1928, pp.56, 80, 91–2, 184; pl.XXIV; John Kerslake, Early Georgian Portraits, 1977, Vol.I, pp.168–170, Vol.II, plates 478 & 479; Rex Whitworth, Field Marshal Ligonier, A Story of the British Army, 1702–1770, 1958, frontispiece.*

145

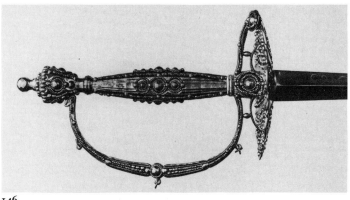

146

148

146 *Dress Sword of Lord Ligonier*

STEEL HILT AND BLADE WITH ORIGINAL SCABBARD, ENGLISH *c.*1770.
INSCRIBED ON THE TOP MOUNT OF THE SCABBARD; BLAND & FOSTER, CUTLERS TO HIS
MAJESTY PRINCE OF WALES & DUKE OF YORK. ST. JAMES'S.

The cut steel grip, pommel and knuckle guard are decorated with attachments of faceted steel beads strung on wires. The oval guard is elaborately decorated with eight pierced cut steel sections with floral design of riveted steel beads surrounded by beads of differing sizes strung on wire. The steel blade of hollow triangular section bears traces of etched and engraved decoration including a clothed female figure with upraised sword. The scabbard is of darkened fishskin with polished steel mounts.

John Bland, Sword Cutler, St. James's Street, appears in the Kent Directory for 1774.

By the 1760s, the small sword was an indispensable part of a gentleman's dress, and as a result, the hilt fittings and scabbard mounts become highly decorative; the cut steel hilt was particularly popular from about the 1770s, both in a highly decorated style such as this, and in a number of simpler designs without the faceted steel additions. Many of the best of these were produced in and around Birmingham, which was famous for the production of 'steel toys', where mass production of high quality hilts was initiated by the well-known Matthew Boulton in partnership (1762–1781) with John Fothergill.

DIMENSIONS: *1045mm.*

PROVENANCE: *Presented to the Grenadier Guards by David Balfour Esq., 1963.*

147 *Death of John André*

ENGRAVING, GOLDAR AFTER HAMILTON *c.*1780.
INSCRIBED: 'THE UNFORTUNATE DEATH OF MAJOR ANDRE (ADJUTANT GENERAL TO THE
ENGLISH ARMY) AT HEAD QUARTERS IN NEW YORK, OCTR. 2 1780 WHO WAS FOUND WITHIN
THE AMERICAN LINES IN THE CHARACTER OF A SPY'.

This engraving was used to illustrate Bernard's 'New complete & Authentic History of England', *c.*1780.

John André (1751–1780) was the son of a Genevese merchant who settled in London. In 1771, he received a commission in the British Army and joined the forces in America. He became Adjutant-General to Sir Henry Clinton and conducted the correspondence with Benedict Arnold, the American General who was plotting the betrayal of West Point to the British. These communications were disguised as a mercantile transaction; Arnold was known as Gustav and André adopted the name of John Anderson.

On 20 September 1780, André proceeded up the Hudson River in the British sloop, 'Vulture', to hold an interview with General Arnold. A secret meeting took place, at which Arnold delivered full particulars of the defences of West Point. Although André wore his military uniform for the meeting, the Americans opened fire on the 'Vulture' and André was forced to take cover at a farmhouse and to disguise himself as a civilian. He returned the next day, and was captured by three American militia men, when in sight of the British lines.

Compromising papers were found in his boots and were sent to General Washington. Meanwhile, General Arnold escaped to the British lines. A military board convoked by General Washington found that André had acted in the character of a spy. He was sentenced to execution by hanging.

The British Army went into mourning for André, and a monument, designed by Robert Adam, was erected to his memory in Westminster Abbey.

DIMENSIONS: *380 × 235mm.*

PROVENANCE: *National Army Museum.*

LITERATURE: *A.G. Nathan, The Gentleman Spy, 1970; Frances Vivian, The capture and death of Major André, History Today, December, 1957, Vol. VII, no.12, pp.813–817; Dictionary of National Biography under André.*

148 *Snuff box*

PEACHWOOD; INSCRIBED: TO THE MEMORY OF MAJOR JOHN ANDRE, TAPPAN 10TH AUGT. 1821.

According to tradition, this snuff box was carved from the peach tree which grew on John André's grave.

John André's remains were originally buried in America, where he met his death.
In 1821 they were transferred to Westminster Abbey.

DIMENSIONS: *80 × 50 × 30mm.*

PROVENANCE: *Dorset Military Museum; on loan to the National Army Museum.*

LITERATURE: *David C.A. Agnew, Protestant Exiles from France, Vol.II, 1871, pp.281–2.*

HUGUENOTS IN LONDON

London had a magnetic attraction for the Huguenot refugees of the 1680s and 1690s. It was the centre for relief, and the home of the two most important French churches in the country at Threadneedle Street in the City and the Savoy at Westminster; and it offered unparalleled employment opportunities. Consequently, by 1700, there were some 20,000 to 25,000 Huguenots in the area of modern Greater London, and two of the capital's suburbs, Spitalfields and Soho, resounded to the hum of French conversation.

The French communities in the capital differed markedly from one another. The largest, in Spitalfields, depended heavily on the weaving trade. The most remote, at Wandsworth, was notable for its hatmakers. The most varied was in the Western suburbs based on Soho, where a wide range of trades were followed; the common factor bringing them together was their market, for the English gentry coming to Parliament or the royal court welcomed the opportunity to acquire the latest in French fashions. There were Huguenot gardeners at Chelsea, glassmakers at Greenwich, and schoolmasters in many London suburbs. The richest coterie was composed of merchants who frequented the City, many of whom contributed to the capital of the Bank of England, and the new world of stocks and shares. The Huguenots met, not only at work and in church, but in London's coffee houses and at the Masonic Lodges.

As Englishmen noted, the larger communities remained distinctively French in the 1730s, half a century after the Revocation; but they fragmented during the next thirty or forty years. The Spitalfields refugees did not assimilate quite as quickly as their Soho fellows, who had more direct contact with English customers and stronger links with the Anglican Church. But virtually all the descendants of the Huguenots who settled in London had abandoned familiar use of the French language by the third quarter of the eighteenth century, and had become irreversibly assimilated into English society.

Detail from John Rocque's 'Map of London', 1746, showing the location of the French Church at the Savoy

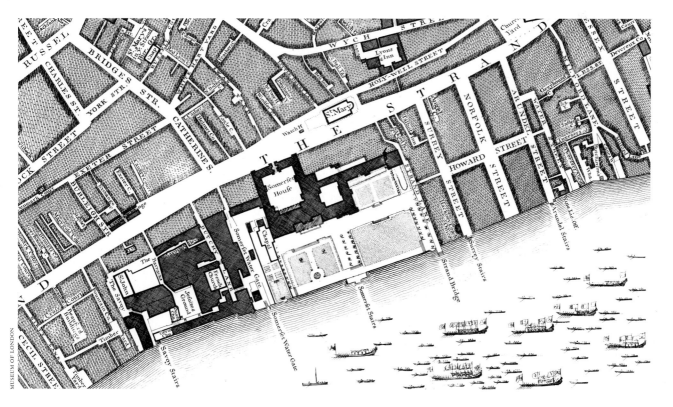

149 *The Four Times of Day, Noon*

ENGRAVING (1ST STATE), WILLIAM HOGARTH, PUBLISHED 4TH MAY, 1738.

The engraving (in reverse) is based on the original painting at Grimsthorpe Castle, one of a set depicting 'The Four Times of Day'.

This engraving shows the French congregation emerging from L'Eglise des Grecs, the daughter church of the Savoy Chapel, which was situated in Hog Lane, Soho. It was the first congregation to be formed out of the refugees who arrived in the 1680s, and was in use by 1682. The Church was originally built for the use of a Greek Orthodox congregation, hence its name. Hogarth contrasts the soberly dressed members of the French community, with the disorderliness of the natives on the other side of the gutter. The foppish couple in the foreground are probably English mimics of French taste.

COLOUR PLATE: *page 5.*

DIMENSIONS: *450 × 380mm.*

PROVENANCE: *British Museum, Department of Prints and Drawings.*

LITERATURE: *Ronald Paulson, Hogarth's Graphic Works, 1970, Vol. I, pp. 179–180; Vol. II, pl. 165; Robin D. Gwynn, The Distribution of Huguenot Refugees in England, II; London and its Environs, Proceedings of the Huguenot Society of London, Vol. 22 (1971–76), p. 524.*

150 *Slaughter's Coffee House*

PEN, INK, AND WATERCOLOUR, THOMAS H. SHEPHERD, EARLY NINETEENTH-CENTURY.
INSCRIBED: OLD SLAUGHTER'S COFFEE HOUSE ST MARTIN LANE TAKEN DOWN 1843, AND SIGNED T.H. SHEPHERD.

Slaughter's Coffee House was one of the meeting places for the French community in London. Here many of the latest inventions and ideas in art were discussed. It was frequented by the Huguenot quack, Dr. Misaubin, who lived at 96, St. Martin's Lane (*Catalogue number* 172), the mathematician Abraham de Moivre, and the sculptor Louis François Roubiliac, who also lived in St. Martin's Lane. In 1738, the engraving of James Vauloué's engine for driving the piles of the new bridge at Westminster could be purchased at the Coffee House.

DIMENSIONS: *175 × 216mm.*

PROVENANCE: *Crace Collection, Department of Prints and Drawings, British Museum.*

EXHIBITED: *Rococo Art and Design in Hogarth's England, Victoria and Albert Museum, 1984, E.10. p. 69.*

LITERATURE: *Bryant Lillywhite, London Coffee Houses, 1963, no. 937, p. 421; Mark Girouard, Coffee at Slaughters; The Two Worlds of St. Martin's Lane, English Art and the Rococo, Country Life, January–February 1966. I, pp. 58–61; II, pp. 188–190; III, pp. 224–227.*

151 *List of members of the French Lodge, 1725*

PHOTOGRAPH

There were two lodges in London with predominantly Huguenot membership. The French Lodge or Solomon's Temple Tavern in Hemmings Row (off St. Martin's Lane) would appear to have been constituted late in 1724. It probably ceased meeting between 1725 and 1729 when the next list of extant lodges was printed.

The Master of the French Lodge was Dr. J.T. Desaguliers (*Catalogue number* 152), and the members included the watchmaker Daniel Grignion, the gunsmith Israel Segalas, and the engineer Charles Labelye.

The other French Lodge was constituted on 12 June 1723 and met at the Dolphin's Inn, Tower Street. It moved in 1730 to the Swan Inn, Long Acre, and again in 1744, to the Vine Tavern in the same street. It ceased to operate after March, 1745. (Information kindly communicated by Mr. J. Hammill.)

PROVENANCE: *Library of the United Grand Lodge of England.*

152 *Jean Theophilus Desaguliers (1683–1744)*

PORTRAIT ENGRAVING, J. TOOKEY AFTER H. HYSING, EARLY NINETEENTH-CENTURY.

Dr. J.T. Desaguliers D.D. was born in La Rochelle, 1683, the son of Jean Desaguliers, a minister in the Protestant temple there. The family took refuge in England and Jean Desaguliers opened an academy in Islington. J.T. Desaguliers was educated at his father's school, and then at Christ Church, Oxford. In 1714, he was elected a fellow of the Royal Society.

Desaguliers' association with the Freemasons is first recorded in 1719, when he was elected Grand master of the Grand Lodge of England. Dr. Desaguliers was largely responsible for the initiation of members of the English nobility into Freemasonry in the 1720s, and he also founded Masonic charities. He served as Master at the inauguration of Masonic lodges in Holland and Paris.

DIMENSIONS: *122 × 92mm.*

PROVENANCE: *National Portrait Gallery.*

LITERATURE: *Margaret E. Rowbottom, John Theophilus Desaguliers (1683–1744), Proceedings of the Huguenot Society of London, Vol. 21 (1965–70), pp. 196–218.*

153 *Invitation to the Grande Loge Anglaise de France*

ENGRAVING, GERARD SCOTIN, 1737; LETTERED WITH AN INVITATION IN FRENCH.
INSCRIBED: STUDIOMI F. DOCRIS, BEAUMONT MAGTRI.CURA FRERE G.SCOTIN SCULP.

A Freemasons' lodge was founded in Paris between 1716 and 1736, by which date it was no. 90 on the Register of the Grand Lodge of England, having been formally constituted on 3 April, 1732. It met every Wednesday at the Louis d'Argent Restaurant in the Rue des Boucheries. Its members were largely Protestants and foreigners. By 1743, a French Masonic Headship was authorised under the title 'La Grande Loge Anglaise de France'.

Although Freemasons' lodges were founded as early as 1687 at Arras and at Bayonne, in the second half of the eighteenth century lodges were founded in many French towns that had strong Protestant associations. For the 'nouveaux convertis', Freemasonry, with its theme of harmony and brotherly love, became a substitute for Protestant worship.

DIMENSIONS: *320 × 275mm.*

PROVENANCE: *Banks Collection; Department of Prints and Drawings, British Museum.*

EXHIBITED: *Rococo Art and Design in Hogarth's England, Victoria and Albert Museum, 1984, C.8., p. 44.*

LITERATURE: *Histoire des Protestants en France, 1977, pp. 236–240; Freemasonry in France, in A.E. Waite, New Encyclopaedia of Freemasonry, Vol. I, n.d., pp. 290–299.*

J.T. DESAGULIERS.

152

153

149

150

154 *Bill heading of Edward de Santé, Cheesemonger*
THE SIGN OF THE DOLPHIN, 83, LEADENHALL STREET, 1770.

This bill for two double Gloucester cheeses came to 17s 9½d. Other bills in the same collection from de Santé are dated 1756 and 1771.

The names Dusantoy and Dusantoit occur in the registers of the Threadneedle Street Church in 1743 and 1748.

DIMENSIONS: *76 × 19mm.*

PROVENANCE: *Heal Collection; Department of Prints and Drawings, British Museum.*

155 *Trade card of James Bouchet, wine merchant*
PETTY FRANCE, WESTMINSTER, *c.*1750–1760.

James Bouchet, specialised in the sale of foreign wines. He supplied Brandy, Jamaica Rum, Orange Shrub, Cinnamon and Fine Barbadoes Citron Water, French Ratafias, Green and Yellow Irish Usquebaugh.

The name Bouchet occurs in the registers of the Savoy Church from the early eighteenth century until the 1730s.

DIMENSIONS: *64 × 96mm.*

PROVENANCE: *Heal Collection: Department of Prints and Drawings, British Museum.*

156 *Témoignage of François Richard, 1743*

This témoignage 'pour servir d'attestation de vie & de moeurs & non de Passeport' was given to François Richard by the Pastors and Elders of the French Church in Berlin, on 17 July, 1743. It is signed by Lorent, the Moderator and S. Gaillard, an elder and Secretary of the church.

François Richard worked as a wigmaker and settled in London after 1743.

DIMENSIONS: *185 × 228mm.*

PROVENANCE: *Records of the French Protestant School, Westminster: Huguenot Library.*

LITERATURE: *Irvine R. Gray, Huguenot Manuscripts: A Descriptive Catalogue, Huguenot Society Quarto Publications, Vol. LVI (1983), p.115.*

157 *Trade card of Benjamin Orpin, peruke (wig) maker*
IN PRINCESS STREET, OPPOSITE ST. ANN'S CHURCH, SOHO, *c.*1750.

The name Orpin or Arpin occurs in the registers of the churches of Le Carré and Berwick Street, both in Soho, in the late seventeenth century.

DIMENSIONS: *80 × 84mm.*

PROVENANCE: *Heal Collection: Department of Prints and Drawings, British Museum.*

158 *Bill of Stephen Gaudry, hat maker*
AT THE SIGN OF THE HAT AND BEAVER, LITTLE NEWPORT STREET, LEICESTER FIELDS, 1757.

The bill, addressed to Lady Caroline Russell, daughter of the Duke of Bedford, was for a white beaver hat, a blue feather, and a silver button, band and loop, and came to a total of £2 8s.

DIMENSIONS: *125 × 128mm.*

PROVENANCE: *The Marquess of Tavistock and the Trustees of the Bedford Estates.*

LITERATURE: *Gladys Scott Thomson, The Russells in Bloomsbury, 1669–1771, 1940, p. 276.*

159 *Trade card of Peter Debaufre, hat maker*
AT THE ENGLISH MANUFACTORY, LITTLE GRAVEL LANE, NEAR BLACKFRIARS BRIDGE, 1769.

The card announces that Peter Debaufre has been granted a patent 'for the sole shaving, cutting and preparing of Wood for making of Chip Hats and Bonnets'. In fact, on 21 March, 1769, Debaufre was granted patent no. 922 for 'Tools for shaving, cutting and preparing wood for making Leghorn hats and bonnets'.

A similar card in the Heal Collection makes the same announcement, but Debaufre's address is given as 'over against the Turnpike, Westminster Bridge'.

It was probably his son, David Debaufre, born in 1772, who was educated at the French Protestant School in Westminster.

DIMENSIONS: *105 × 177mm.*

PROVENANCE: *Heal Collection, Department of Prints and Drawings, British Museum.*

Mr. Wm. Innes   London 11th October 1770

Bought of Edwd. De Santè

Cheesemonger, at the Dolphin, No.83, in Leadenhall Street,

2 Amb Gloucherses at 4½ @ 5/   17 .. 3½

    0 .. 6

    17 .. 9½

Pr. The Aberdeen Merchant
Alexr. Murray

154

James Bouchet

In Petty France, WESTMINSTER.

SELLS

Foreign Brandy, Jamaica Rum,
Orange Shrub, Cinnamon & Fine
Barbadoes Citron Water, French Ratafia,
Green & Yellow Irish Usquebaugh.

N.B. Foreign Wines

155

Benj. Orpin
Peruke Maker,
in Princess Street,
Opposite St. Ann's Church,
Soho
LONDON.

157

Pour servir d'attestation de vie & de
mœurs, & non de Passeport à François Richard
Perruquier

NOus les Pasteurs & les Anciens de l'Eglise Françoise de Berlin, certifions que le ... sus nomme
a demeuré parmi nous pendant longtems
qu'il a frequenté nos saintes Assemblées, participé dans
les occasions au Sacrement de la Sainte Cene, & vé-
cu chrétiennement sans donner aucun scandale qui
soit venu à nôtre connoissance.   Fait en Consistoire à Berlin le 17 Juillet
1743
Lorent   J. Gaillard
Moderateur.   Ancien & Secre-
taire.

156

HIS MAJESTY'S ROYAL LETTERS PATENT having
been granted to PETER DEBAUFRE, and his Assigns, for
the sole shaving, cutting and preparing of Wood for making
of Chip Hats, and Bonnets: PETE DEBAUFRE and Co. at their
English Manufactory, in Little Gravel Lane, facing the Peacock
Brewhouse, near Black Friars Bridge; makes and sells all Sorts of
Chip Hats for covering, fine and superfine platted Hats, and
openwork Hats of the newest Fashion, at reasonable Rates;
Wholesale only.

159

160 *Bill of Henry Jaffray, glover*

AT THE SIGN OF THE GLOVE AND FAN NEAR DURHAM YARD, IN THE NEW BUILDINGS,
STRAND, 1745.

Henry Jaffray worked as a glover in the Strand from at least 1745, the date of this bill. The
London Directory for 1777 gives his address as No. 65, Strand, and describes his trade as
undertaker and glover.

DIMENSIONS: *217 × 170mm.*

PROVENANCE: *Heal Collection,
Department of Prints and Drawings,
British Museum.*

161 *Trade card of William Barbaroux, leatherman*

AT THE SIGN OF THE GOLDEN LION FRONTING THE SOUTH DOOR IN ST. PAUL'S CHURCH
YARD, *c.*1750.

William Barbaroux succeeded to the business of his uncle, John Hutton. He specialised in gilt
leather which was used for room hangings, for covering tables, harpsichords, chairs and
screens.

This card was engraved by Morrison of Moorfields, who worked in the 1760s and also
produced a trade card for the cabinetmaker William Henshaw. James? Morrison was
apprenticed in 1726 to Charles Beard. The latter was also the master of Copland and Clark,
engravers who specialised in producing trade cards. (Information kindly supplied by Michael
Snodin.)

The name Barbarot occurs in the Registers of the Threadneedle Street Church in the 1640s.

DIMENSIONS: *204 × 158mm.*

PROVENANCE: *Heal Collection,
Department of Prints and Drawings,
British Museum.*

162 *Trade card of Derussat, last and patten maker*

16, NEWPORT COURT, NEWPORT MARKET, *c.*1740.

The card indicates that Mr. Derussat succeeded to the trade of a Mr. Richier. Newport Court
was the fashionable centre for tailors, wigmakers and shoemakers. Last making was a
separate business, and the last maker produced wooden heels as well as shoe-trees and
boot-trees.

DIMENSIONS: *80 × 125mm.*

PROVENANCE: *Heal Collection;
Department of Prints and Drawings,
British Museum.*

LITERATURE: *Robin D. Gwynn,
Huguenot Heritage, 1985, p. 71.*

163 *Wandsworth Cemetery*

ETCHING, C.R.B. BARRETT. *c.*1888.

INSCRIBED: PUBLISHED BY C.R.B. BARRETT, GRASMERE, ALL FARTHING LANE, WANDSWORTH,
FEB 16TH 1888 AND SIGNED IN PENCIL WITH THE ADDITIONAL INSCRIPTION, MOUNT NOD,
THE HUGUENOT BURIAL GROUND, AT WANDSWORTH SURREY, 1887.

Wandsworth was the home of a considerable Huguenot colony. Stowe's 'Survey of London'
(1720 edition) notes that 'In Wandsworth live a great many French people employed in
making Hats . . . and have a French church'. The river Wandle appears to have had special
properties for fixing dyes, and this, combined with the development of a felt and hat making
industry in the area, is said to have led to the manufacture of Roman Catholic Cardinals' hats
by Huguenot refugees.

The burial ground at Wandsworth was known as the 'French Churchyard' from early in
the eighteenth century, although it was by no means exclusive to Huguenot refugees.

The Wandsworth coat-of-arms includes tears, representing the suffering of the Huguenot
refugees.

DIMENSIONS: *280 × 380mm.*

PROVENANCE: *Huguenot Library.*

LITERATURE: *J.T. Squire, The
Huguenots at Wandworth in the County
of Surrey and their Burial Ground at
Mount Nod, Proceedings of the
Huguenot Society of London, Vol. I
(1885–6), pp. 229–242; 261–312;
Robin D. Gwynn, Huguenot Heritage,
1985, p. 68.*

164 *Funeral card of Peter Motteux*

INSCRIBED: SIR YOUR COMPANY IS DESIRED TO ATTEND THE FUNERAL OF PETER MOTTEUX
ESQR FROM HIS LATE DWELLING HOUSE IN CHARTER-HOUSE SQUARE TO THE BURIAL
GROUND AT BUNHILL ON MONDAY NOVR 20TH 1769 AT 2 O'CLOCK.

The card shows the three Fates, spinning, measuring and cutting the thread of life. The figure
of Time with his scythe on the right, is held back by the figure of Life, but Death, in the form
of a skeleton, intervenes.

Bunhill Fields was the burial ground for dissenters in the City Road, and still survives
today.

An earlier impression of this card, for the funeral of Mrs. Elizabeth Baldero, is in the same
collection. Another version of the card in a private collection is dated 1737.

DIMENSIONS: *224 × 258mm.*

PROVENANCE: *Noble Collection;
Department of Prints and Drawings,
Guildhall Library.*

LITERATURE: *Victoria Moger, The
Favour of Your Company, Tickets and
Invitations to London Events and Places
of Interest, 1750–c.1850, 1981, no. 8b,
p.11.*

160

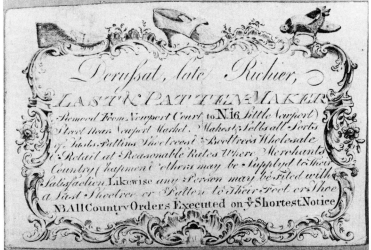

162

161

164

163

165 *Trade card of Sabourin and Marchant, cabinetmakers*

47, CHURCH STREET, BETHNAL GREEN, EARLY NINETEENTH CENTURY.

The London Directories for 1805–7 give the name of George Sabourin, a cabinetmaker, working at 51, Shoreditch. Another trade card in the Heal Collection records a Mr. Marchant, cabinetmaker, upholder and undertaker at 48, Church Street, Bethnal Green.

The trades of cabinetmaker, upholder and undertaker were frequently combined in the eighteenth century.

The card was engraved by W. Newman who gave his address as 27 Widegate Street, Bishopsgate.

DIMENSIONS: *101 × 70mm.*

PROVENANCE: *Heal Collection; Department of Prints and Drawings, British Museum.*

166 *Breast plate*

PEWTER, CAST, PUNCHED, AND CHASED WITH TRACES OF GILDING, RECTANGULAR.
INSCRIBED: MRS SUSAN.H: LEMAISTER DIED 8TH DECEMR. 1761. AGED 78.

This plate is engraved with a lozenge containing the above inscription, which is set within a rectangle surmounted by an irregular cartouche, with spandrels filled with stylised flowers and fruit.

The plate, which was fixed to the lid of the outer coffin, is grander in quality and design than the majority of plates of a similar date. It was probably supplied by an undertaking firm.

Funerary heraldry followed noble heraldry and a lozenge generally denotes either a spinster or a peeress.

DIMENSIONS: *420 × 320mm.*

PROVENANCE: *Private Collection.*

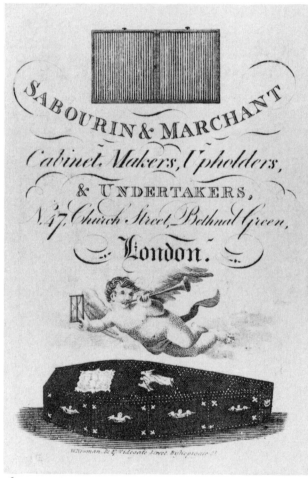

165

166

MEDICINE

From the late sixteenth century, several notable Huguenot doctors are recorded in England. Gideon de Laune (1565–1659) and Sir Theodore Turquet de Mayerne (1573–1655) were instrumental in founding the Society of Apothecaries. Mayerne is important for the exactness and detail of his case reports. The Chamberlens are famous for their invention of the obstetric forceps, a trade secret which they kept for generations. Hugh Chamberlen wrote the first satisfactory English textbook on midwifery, 'The Accomplisht Midwife', 1673 and translated in 1683, 'The Diseases of Women with Child and in Childbed', from the French of François Mauriceau.

Marriage-a-le-Mode, III: visit to the quack doctor, oil on canvas, William Hogarth, 1743

167 Obstetric instruments

a. THE CHAMBERLEN OBSTETRIC FORCEPS.

b. CHAMBERLEN FORCEPS, IN TWO PORTIONS UNITED BY A CORD; ENABLING EITHER OR BOTH TO BE USED AT ONE TIME.

c. MODERN FORCEPS.

d. FILLET; WHALEBONE AND SATIN RIBBON, FOR DRAWING DOWN THE FETAL HEAD.

'I will now take leave to offer an Apology for not publishing the Secret I mention we have to extract Children without Hooks, where other Artists use them. ...'

Hugh Chamberlen's translation of François Mauriceau, 'The Diseases of Women with Child and in Child-bed', 1672(*e*).

At this date, no instrument was generally available for effecting the delivery of a living child; the hooks and levers normally used were often lethal to both mother and baby.

In the first satisfactory English textbook on midwifery, Hugh Chamberlen advertises the obstetric forceps, invented by a senior member of his family who had arrived as a Huguenot refugee from Paris in 1569, Protestant physicians not being allowed then to practise in France.

The family settled first in Southampton and attended the French church. Their fame as doctors spread. One grandson, Peter, was appointed physician to James I, Charles I and Charles II. Although by the early eighteenth century, the Chamberlen's secret was beginning to be known, and forceps were developed by other doctors, it was not until 1813, when the wooden box containing the instruments was discovered at the family home, Woodham Mortimer Hall, Essex, that the first experimental forceps were fully revealed. Modern forceps follow the same basic design.

PROVENANCE: *Royal College of Obstetricians and Gynaecologists.*

LITERATURE: *J.H. Aveling, The Chamberlens, 1882; Walter Radcliffe, The Secret Instrument, 1947; A. Eccles, Obstetrics and Gynaecology in Tudor and Stuart England, 1982.*

168 Gideon Delaune (?1564–1659)

OIL ON CANVAS, CORNELIUS JANSEN, 1635.

INSCRIBED: AETATIS SUA'.71 ANNO DOMINE. 1635.

The sitter is shown half-length facing three-quarters to the right.

Gideon was the son of William Delaune, a French protestant pastor, and was born in Rheims. He accompanied his father to England and was appointed apothecary to Anne of Denmark, wife of James I. Delaune became a member of the Court of Assistants of the newly incorporated Society of Apothecaries. He served the office of Junior Warden in 1624, Senior Warden in 1627 and Master in 1637.

Delaune was a great benefactor to the Society of Apothecaries, having been a principal means for procuring the monopoly needed for the incorporation, and for the purchase of Apothecaries Hall. It is said that he died worth £93,000, much of which was derived from the sale of a proprietary pill containing colocynth. In addition to London and country properties, he had extensive estates in Virginia and the Bermudas.

Delaune is said to have presented another portrait by Jansen to the Company in 1641; a massive marble bust of him can also be seen at the Hall.

DIMENSIONS: *940 × 680mm.*

PROVENANCE: *Delaune family; acquired by the Society of Apothecaries in 1939.*

LITERATURE: *British Library, Sloane Ms.2149, f.60; Leslie G. Matthews, London's Immigrant Apothecaries, 1600–1800, Medical History, 1974, XVIII; Proceedings of the Huguenot Society of London, Vol. 20 (1958–64), p. 680 (note on the extant portraits of Delaune).*

169 Sir Theodore de Mayerne (1573–1655)

OILS AND BLACK CHALK ON PAPER, SIR PETER PAUL RUBENS, *c.* 1635.

The sitter is shown more than half length, his head turned slightly to the right.

After the Massacre of St. Bartholomew, 1572, Mayerne's father fled from Lyons to Mayerne near Geneva, where his son Theodore was born. Educated in Heidelberg and Montpellier, Mayerne was appointed physician in ordinary to Henry IV. His fame grew quickly despite opposition from Paris doctors.

Between 1613 and 1643 Mayerne is recorded as living in St. Martin's Lane, and after 1648, in Chelsea. Mayerne was appointed Chief Physician to James I (whom he treated for melancholy) and subsequently Charles I. He was admitted to the Royal College of Physicians in 1616 and was closely connected with the production of the first London 'Pharmacopoeia', 1618. In 1624, he was knighted by James I.

Mayerne is chiefly remembered for his case reports. He was among the first to record all the physical signs of an illness, including the patients temperament and the prescribed remedies. He played a part in creating the Society of Apothecaries, and the Distillers' Company. He is reputed to have discovered a means of making enamel that became carnation coloured after firing and is said to have passed this information on to the miniaturist Jean Petitot. Mayerne also wrote one of the earliest travel guides to France in 1592. One of Mayerne's formulae is still the basis for the preparation of the oil used in the monarch's coronation.

After his death in 1655, Mayerne left £100 to the poor of the French Church in London. He was buried in St. Martin's in the Fields.

COLOUR PLATE: *page 6.*

DIMENSIONS: *308 × 219mm.*

PROVENANCE: *Sir Thomas Lawrence; Woodburn; purchased by the British Museum, Department of Prints and Drawings.*

LITERATURE: *Irene Scouloudi, Sir Theodore Turquet de Mayerne, Proceedings of the Huguenot Society of London, Vol.16, (1940), pp. 301–337 (includes a discussion of the extant portraits); A.M. Hind, Catalogue of Drawings by Dutch and Flemish Artists in the British Museum, 1923, Vol. II, p. 29, no. 94.*

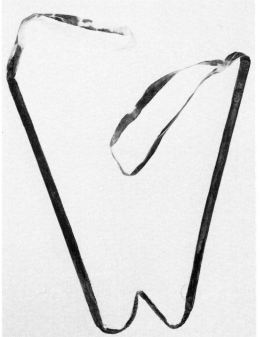

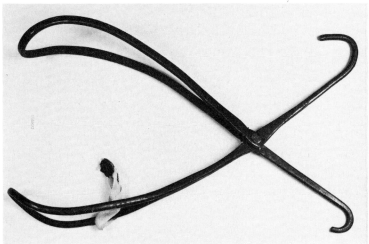

167a

167d

xvi   The Tranſlator to the Reader.

*the conveying ſharp Inſtruments into the Womb, to extract
a Head, which is a dangerous Operation and may be much better done by our foremention'd Art, as alſo the Inconvenience
and Hazard of a Child dying thereby prevented, which
he ſuppoſes in the twenty ſeventh Chapter of this ſecond Book.
    I will now take leave to offer an Apology for not publiſhing
the Secret I mention we have to extract Children without Hooks,
where other Artiſts uſe them, viz. there being my Father and
two Brothers living, that practiſe this Art, I cannot eſteem
it my own to diſpoſe of, nor publiſh it without Injury to them;
and think I have not been unſerviceable to my own Country,
altho' I do but inform them that the foremention'd three Perſons of our Family, and my Self, can ſerve them in theſe
Extremities, with greater Safety than others.
    I deſign not this Work to encourage any to practiſe by it,*

167e

168

169

170 Pill Tile

POLYCHROME LAMBETH DELFTWARE, 1670.

INSCRIBED: THOMAS FAUTRART.

This, the earliest known dated pill tile, bears the arms of the London Society of Apothecaries. Although no records exist of an apothecary of this name ever being apprenticed in London or gaining its freedom, it is believed that Thomas Fautrart was a Huguenot refugee who arrived in England before the Revocation. A Sara and Rebecca Fautra(r)t are recorded in the registers of the Threadneedle Street Church for 1601 and 1603.

Thomas was probably born in 1633 at St. Helier, Jersey, the son of Thomas Fautrart. (The family of Faultrart, Fautras or Fautrart are recorded in both Jersey and Guernsey from the mid-sixteenth century.) The diary of M. Brevint of Sark contains the following entry, in 1644, 'On dit que Jean le Hardy a perdu un oeil qui lui tomba (avec douleur violente) par application des médicaments corrosifs par le fils de Th. Fautrart'.

On 14 April, 1675, Thomas was married to Marthe Chevallier, the granddaughter of Jean Chevallier, the famous Jersey diarist.

DIMENSIONS: *280mm high.*

PROVENANCE: *Pharmaceutical Society of Great Britain.*

LITERATURE: *J. Burnby, Pharmaceutical Historian, Vol. 7, no. 3, December, 1977, pp. 3–4.*

171 Mortar

BELL METAL.

INSCRIBED: CHARLE ANGIBAVD ME APPRE (MAITRE APOTHICAIRE) ET ORDINAIRE DV ROY A PARIS 1678.

This mortar bears the Royal Coat of Arms of France and the armorial bearings of Angibaud. It was presented by Louis XIV to his apothecary.

Charles Angibaud came from a family of apothecaries in Saintes. It is recorded that a pass from France was issued to Mr. Angibaud, Apothecary to the French King, on 13 September, 1681. In December of that year, he and his family were granted denization, and they were naturalised in 1685. Two years earlier his shop is recorded in St. Martin's Lane, where he sold 'Troches, or Juyce of Liquorice of Blois' (London Gazette, October, 1683).

In 1685, Angibaud (described as 'a French protestant') became a freeman of the Society of Apothecaries. He is included in a 1708 list of 'Subscribers or Benefactors toward the reviving, and Improving the Physick Garden at Chelsea'. Angibaud became Master of the Society of Apothecaries in 1728. His lozenges of Blois were included in schedules of dutiable medicines until 1904.

Angibaud's daughter, Marthe, married Dr. John Misaubin (*Catalogue number* 172).

DIMENSIONS: *360mm high, 480mm diameter; weight 129 kilos.*

PROVENANCE: *Presented to the Pharmaceutical Society of Great Britain in 1902 by Percy Robbins.*

LITERATURE: *J. Burnby, The Mortar of Charles Angibaud, Pharmaceutical Historian, Vol. 9, no. 1, April, 1979; Leslie G. Matthews, De Quelques Apothicaires Français en Angleterre durant le XVIIe Siecle, Bulletin de L'Ordre des Pharmaciers, no. 123, Août–Septembre, 1967, pp. 523–7; Ibid., London's Immigrant Apothecaries, 1600–1800, Medical History, 1974, Vol. LVIII, pp. 262–274; Agnes Lothian Short, Charles Angibaud and his mortar, The Pharmaceutical Journal, March, 1966, pp. 287–8; Pierre Tulien, Angibaud and the pastilles of Blois, op.cit., pp. 289–290.*

172 John Misaubin (1673–1734)

ETCHING BY ARTHUR POND AFTER WATTEAU.

INSCRIBED: AD.FECIT 1739(?).

Dr. Misaubin MD is shown standing whole length to the left, holding a hat and a syringe.

Jean Misaubin, a prominent Huguenot physician, was born in the Dordogne. He graduated in medicine from Cahors University in 1687. He is first recorded in London in June, 1701, when he and his father reaffirmed their Protestant faith at the Threadneedle Street Church. Jean was naturalised in 1707. He was practising in Berwick Street when he married Marthe Angibaud in the French Church of Hungerford Market on 6 January 1709. Marthe's father Charles, the apothecary (*Catalogue number* 171) was a witness to the marriage and gave a £400 marriage portion. Jean was licensed by the College of Physicians in 1719. He later practised at 96, St. Martin's Lane, and both Misaubin and his house appear in plate 3 of Hogarth's Marriage à la Mode, although this was only published in 1745, 11 years after Misaubin's death.

The Misaubin and Angibaud families were not on very good terms. In his will (6 April 1734) Jean Misaubin left his wife only one shilling and his best French bible. His considerable estate, including diamonds, jewels, watches, plate, pictures, household furniture, coaches, chariots, horses, goods and chattels, he bequeathed to his son Edmund. If the latter died, the bequest was 'to go to the sole use of a French hospital near Hoxton, commonly called the Providence (sic), and that the same or any part thereof shall never come to my wife or any of her relations of the family of Angibaud'. All his medicines and their recipes should be published for the general public good. The Dukes of Richmond and Montagu, and Lord Baltimore, were to be his executors.

Misaubin's widow, Marthe Angibaud, continued to sell her father's famous lozenges of Blois.

DIMENSIONS: *255 × 195mm.*

PROVENANCE: *British Museum, Department of Prints and Drawings.*

LITERATURE: *Misaubin's Will, PRO Prob. 11, 1734, f. 222; J. Burnby, The Mortar of Charles Angibaud, Pharmaceutical Historian, Vol. 9, no. 1, April 1979; Freeman O'Donoghue, Engraved British Portraits in the British Museum, 1912, Vol. III, p. 246.*

170

171

172

173

173 *Trade card of Paul Savigny*

AT THE HALBERT AND CROWN IN ST. MARTIN'S CHURCH YARD, *c*. 1730.

In 1726, John Tessier Savigny is recorded as a razormaker working at the Acorn and Crown in Gerrard Street, Soho. The Savigny family persisted in the trade throughout the eighteenth century and into the nineteenth century. They had premises in Pall Mall, St. James's Street and New Bond Street. In 1798, J.H. Savigny, who worked in King Street, Covent Garden, published an illustrated catalogue of the most modern and approved instruments used in the practice of surgery.

ILLUSTRATED: *page 123.*

DIMENSIONS: *170 × 139mm.*

PROVENANCE: *Banks Collection, 1791; British Museum, Department of Prints and Drawings.*

LITERATURE: *Elizabeth Bennion, Antique Medical Instruments, 1979, pp. 331–2.*

174 *Cupping set in contemporary wooden box*

MADE BY SAVIGNY & CO., *c*.1800.

The set consists of a retractable cutting instrument, a small silver pot, a small glass medicine jar with a glass stopper, and four cupping glasses of varying size.

DIMENSIONS: *170 × 155 × 100mm.*

PROVENANCE: *On loan to the Museum of London.*

LITERATURE: *Elizabeth Bennion, Antique Medical Instruments, 1979, pp. 44–50.*

174

SCIENCE

In late seventeenth-century England, 'Science' covered mathematics, mechanics, astronomy, botany, chemistry and natural philosophy.

The mathematician Abraham de Moivre (1667–1754) discovered the equation for the normal curve of error and deduced a method for computing the rate of interest of life annuities and life assurances. In the field of pneumatic chemistry, Denis Papin (1647–1712) invented the first pressure cooker with a safety valve in 1675, and later tried to realise the potential of steam power. In metallurgy, James Taudin introduced a superior pewter alloy containing antimony.

John Theophilus Desaguliers (1683–1744) played an important part in the dissemination of the ideas of experimental science, the Newtonian philosophy, and mechanics. He invented the planetarium, and designed the first air conditioning system for the House of Commons. His disciples included Stephen Demainbray, later King's Observer at the Royal Observatory, Kew, and Charles Labelye, who designed the first Westminster Bridge; the engine used to drive the piles was invented by the watchmaker James Vauloué.

In 1757, John Dollond (1706–1761), a Spitalfields weaver, re-invented the achromatic lens, and his first achromatic telescope was shown to the Royal Society in 1758. His son Peter transformed the optical instrument industry, and the business is still active as the Dollond and Aitchison Group Ltd. Jan Six (1731–93) devised the first effective self-registering thermometer recording both maximum and minimum temperatures on the same instrument.

Astrolabe by John Prujean, Oxford, c.1680

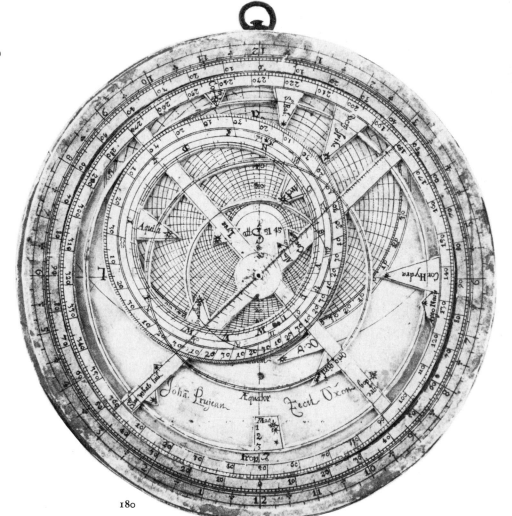

180

175 Les Raisons des Forces Mouvantes avec diverses Machines tant utilles que plaisantes Aus quelles sont adjoints plusieurs desseings de grotes et fontaines
SALOMON DE CAUS, 1615.

Salomon de Caus (1576–1626), engineer and architect, was a native of Normandy, probably of Caux. He was mathematical tutor to Henry, Prince of Wales and also worked for Frederick V, the Elector Palatine, husband of Princess Elizabeth. While in England in 1611–13, De Caus built a gallery at Richmond Palace, subsequently completed as a picture gallery by Charles I, and erected the south front of Wilton House, which was burnt in 1647. He was also employed on the gardens at Greenwich Palace and Somerset House.

This work contains many designs formerly made at Richmond for the adornment of the Palace or the entertainment of Prince Henry. The earlier part of the book contains De Caus's calculations on the expansion and condensation of steam, and of the elevation of water by the application of heat. De Caus claims no originality for the invention of the steam engine, which he used only for fountains and other waterworks. A more elaborate form of this machine was described by Edward Somerset, Marquis of Worcester, in 1663, when an engine along these lines was erected at Vauxhall and raised water to a height of 40ft. according to eyewitness accounts.

PROVENANCE: British Library.

LITERATURE: British Library, Lansdowne Ms.164; Archaeologia, XV, p.17; D.K. Clark, Steam and the Steam Engine, 1890.

176 A continuation of the New Digester of Bones: together with new uses of the air pump
DENIS PAPIN, 1687.

Denis Papin (1647–1712) was born in Blois and came to England in 1675, where he worked with Robert Boyle. Papin was associated with the French Church, Threadneedle Street, where his presence is recorded at a baptism in 1677, and his cousin Renée Gousset was married there in 1681 (Huguenot Society Quarto Series, XIII, 1899).

In 1680, he was elected to the Royal Society. In 1681, he published an account of a 'Digester' (pressure cooker) which included a new invention, the safety valve. The 'Digester' softened bones by boiling them with water in a closed vessel; the water, boiling under pressure, boiled at a higher temperature, and this increased its power of solution.

'I took beef bones', wrote Papin, 'that had never been boiled but kept dry a long time, and of the hardest part of the leg; these being put into a little glass pot, with water, I included in the engine together with another little glass pot full of bones and water too, but in this case the bones were ribs and had been boiled already. Having pressed the fire until the drop of water would dry away in 3 seconds and 10 pressures, I took off the fire, and the vessels being cooled I found very good jelly in both my pots, but that which was made out of ribs had a kind of reddish colour, which I believe, might proceed from the medullar part; the other jelly was without taste or colour like hartshorne jelly; . . . and . . . having seasoned it with sugar and juice of lemon, I did eat it with as much pleasure, and found it as stomachical, as if it had been jelly of hartshorne'.

In order to avoid an explosion in a vessel subject to considerable steam pressure, Papin inserted a valve in the top.

Evelyn records in his Diary on 12 April 1682, how he took part in a 'philosophical supper' at the Royal Society cooked in Papin's digester. His portrait at Marburg University, Germany, where he became a Professor in 1688, shows him holding a copy of his account of the digester.

Papin's edition of 1687 includes a description of improvements to his digester, and stated that demonstrations could be seen at 'Mr Boissonet's in Black-Fryers, in Water Lane, over against the Blew Boot' (perhaps Jacques Boissenet from Paris, naturalized in 1685, and a deacon of the Threadneedle Street Church from 1683–86). Papin produced the first steam engine with a piston, published in 1690, and experimented with the air pump.

PROVENANCE: Guildhall Library.

LITERATURE: T. Birch, History of the Royal Society, 1757, Vol. IV; Ernest Gerland, Leibnizens und Huygens' Briefwechsel mit Papin, Berlin, 1881; Margaret E. Rowbottom, Some Huguenot Friends and Acquaintances of Robert Boyle, Proceedings of the Huguenot Society of London, Vol. 20 (1958–64), pp. 177–195; E.G.R. Taylor, The Mathematical Practitioners of Tudor and Stuart England, 1954, p. 278 (mentions also Papin's nephew who worked in Boyle's laboratory and later set up as an instrument maker); A. Wolf, A History of Science, Technology and Philosophy in the sixteenth and seventeenth centuries, 1935, pp. 548–550.

177 Presentation set of navigational instruments
IVORY WITH SILVER MOUNTS, THOMAS TUTTELL, c.1700.
INSCRIBED ON EACH INSTRUMENT: THOMAS TUTTELL, CHARING CROSS, LONDINI FECIT.

The set consists of a back staff, cross staff, 24-inch Gunter's scale and 12-inch Gunter's scale.

The back staff, or Davis quadrant, was derived from that invented by the seaman, John Davis, which he described in his book 'The Seaman's Secrets,' 1595. It was used to calculate the altitude of the sun without direct sighting.

The cross staff was adopted as an important surveying and navigational instrument during the sixteenth century. It was used to measure inaccessible heights. Both the cross and back staff were obsolete by the mid-eighteenth century.

The Gunter's scales (calculating rules) were invented by Edmund Gunter in c. 1620. They were used, with the aid of a pair of compasses, in the solution of mathematical problems in navigation, dialling and astronomy. The more convenient slide rule developed from this first logarithm scale.

Members of the Tuttell family were granted denization in 1567, and their names occur in the registers of the French Church, Threadneedle Street. Thomas Tuttell (c.1674–1702) became a member of the Clockmakers' Company in 1695. He had two shops, one in the City

PROVENANCE: National Maritime Museum.

LITERATURE: E.G.R. Taylor, The Mathematical Practitioners of Tudor and Stuart England, 1954, p.292; Nicholas Goodison, English Barometers and their Makers, 1680–1860, 1968, p. 244.

175

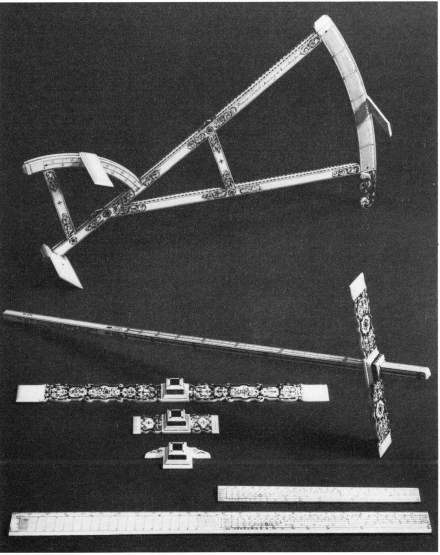

177

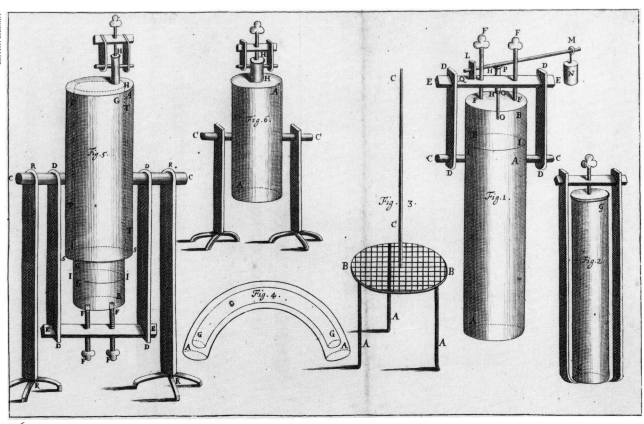

176

'over against the Royal Exchange in Cornhill', and one in Westminster, at the Sign of the King's Arms and Globe in Charing Cross, where 'all parts of the Mathematics', including the use of instruments, were taught. Tuttell worked in association with Joseph Moxon of Cornhill who supplied Samuel Pepys with globes. Tuttell's trade card (*c.* 1700) claimed that he worked 'to very great perfection in silver, brass, ivory and wood' and advertised a wide selection of astronomical, navigational, and surveying instruments, besides stock mathematical instruments and globes. He became Mathematical Instrument Maker to William III in 1700.

Other instruments by Tuttell can be seen in the London and Oxford Science Museums, the British Museum and the Whipple Museum, Cambridge. Tuttell was drowned in 1702.

178 *Mathematical playing cards*

FOUR FROM A SET OF THIRTY-ONE, THOMAS TUTTELL, LONDON, 1701.

a. THE KING OF CLUBS; INSCRIBED: THESE CARDS, GLOBES, SPHERES, MATHEMATICAL BOOKES, AND INSTRUMENTS FOR SEA AND LAND, WITH MANY OTHER CURIOSITYS IN GOLD, SILVER, STEEL, BRASS, IVORY AND WOOD, AND THE BEST CHARTS, MAPS AND PRINTS AT YE KING'S ARMES AND GLOBES AT CHARING CROSS, AND AGAINST THE ROYALE EXCHANGE IN CORNHILL BY THO. TUTTELL MATHEMATICAL INSTRUMENT MAKER TO YE KING'S MOST EXCELLENT MAJESTY WHERE ARE TAUGHT ALL PARTS OF THE MATHEMATICKS.

b. THE TWO OF HEARTS; INSCRIBED: CROSS-STAFFE AN INSTRUMENT MUCH USED AT SEA FOR TAKEING YE ALTITUDE OF YE SUN, OR STARRS, IN ORDER TO FIND YE LATITUDE.

c. THE FOUR OF HEARTS; INSCRIBED: SEA QUADRANT AN INSTRUMENT CONTAINING YE. 4TH. PART OF A CIRCLE, OR 90 DEG: WELL CONTRIVED FOR YE MARINERS USE, YE GREAT ARCH PLAC'T AT A CONVENIENT DISTANCE FOR YE EYE, YE LESSER FOR YE SHADOWS.

d. TEN OF CLUBS; INSCRIBED: SECTOR & SCALES EXCELLENTLY COMPOSED FOR DYALING, SURVEYING, NAVIGATION, AND ALL YE PRACTICAL PARTS OF MATHEMATICKES CONTRIVED TO BE VERY PORTABLE.

These cards were apparently designed by Boitard and engraved by J. Savage; they represent various kinds of mathematical instruments, together with the trades and professions in which they were used.

DIMENSIONS: *90 × 57mm.*

PROVENANCE: *British Museum, Department of Prints and Drawings.*

LITERATURE: *William Hughes Willshire, A Descriptive catalogue of playing and other cards in the British Museum, 1876, p. 236.*

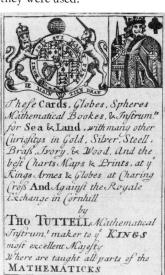

178

179

179 *Mathematics made Easie or a Mathematical Dictionary Explaining the Terms of Art and difficult Phrases used in Arithmetick, Geometry, Astronomy, Astrology, and other Mathematical Sciences, wherein the true meaning of the Word is rendered, the Nature of the thing discussed, and (where need requires) illustrated with apt figures and diagrams.*

THOMAS TUTTELL AND JOSEPH MOXON, FOURTH EDITION 1705.

This volume was sold by the authors at Tuttel's shops at the sign of the King's Arms and Globe at Charing Cross and against the Royal Exchange, Cornhill, and at Moxon's at the Atlas in Warwick Lane. Joseph Moxon had published a similar volume in 1679. This, the third edition, contains at the back, an engraved plate containing 'The Description and Explanation of Mathematical Instruments. Alphabetically disposed as now made with all their Improvements, wherein the Nature and Meaning of every Instrument is made Plain and Intelligible to every capacity'. Tuttel worked in association with Moxon at Cornhill.

PROVENANCE: *British Library.*

LITERATURE: *E.G.R. Taylor, The Mathematical Practitioners of Tudor and Stuart England, 1954, in no. 416.*

180 *Astrolabe*

WOOD AND PASTEBOARD, JOHN PRUJEAN, OXFORD, *c.* 1680.
INSCRIBED INSIDE THE 'MATER': JOHA PRUJEAN FECIT OXON.

This astrolabe has no loose plates and the 'mater' bears a projection for latitude $51^° 45'$. The ecliptical circle is marked with both the zodiac and the calendar of months. The scales and projections were printed from engraved copper plates.

John Prujean (fl. 1667–1701) was a mathematical instrument maker of Oxford. He matriculated on 11 March 1664 as a tradesman 'privilegiatus' (this enabled him to enjoy the privileges of members of the University). He was established in New College Lane, on the west side of Short's Coffee House to the west of Hell Passage, opposite where Hertford College now stands. He can probably be identified with the John Prigeon listed in the Clockmakers' apprenticeship lists in 1646. In 1701, Prujean published a list of his instruments, which is of particular importance in that he usually gives the name of the designer, and explanatory notes or books accompanied each instrument.

Prujean died in poverty. Hearne records angrily on 3 May 1712, that he 'died very poor, wanting bread' and that he 'was an ingenious Man, & had done a great deal of service for the University for several Years'.

Other collections with examples of his work include the Victory Museum, Portsmouth, the Bodleian Library, and the Municipal Museum of Kingston-upon-Hull.

ILLUSTRATED: *page 125.*

DIMENSIONS: *203mm diameter.*

PROVENANCE: *Lewis Evans; Museum of Science, Oxford.*

LITERATURE: *R.T. Gunther, The Astrolabes of the World, 1932; R.T. Gunther, Early Science in Oxford, 1923; E.G.R. Taylor, The Mathematical Practitioners of Tudor and Stuart England, 1954, p. 256.*

181 *Quadrant*

OAK WITH BRASS SIGHTS AND BOB, JOHN PRUJEAN, OXFORD.
INSCRIBED: JOHN PRUJEAN OXON: FECIT, LATE SEVENTEENTH CENTURY.

This quadrant is made for latitude 51° 45′. The scales are printed from engraved copper plates. The front bears a Gunter's quadrant and a quadrant similar to the Allen type, and there is a Collins' quadrant on the back.

DIMENSIONS: *303mm wide.*

PROVENANCE: *Sir Francis Newdegate; presented to the Museum of Science, Oxford.*

LITERATURE: *R.T. Gunther, Early Science in Oxford, 1923; E.G.R. Taylor, The Mathematical Practitioners of Tudor and Stuart England, 1954, p. 256.*

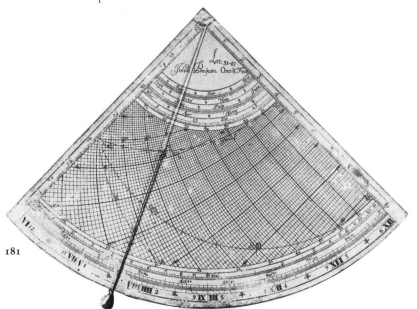

181

182 *Abraham de Moivre (1667–1754)*

PORTRAIT, OIL ON CANVAS, JOSEPH HIGHMORE, 1736

Abraham de Moivre left his home in Vitry, Champagne aged eighteen and settled in London, in the vicinity of Slaughter's Coffee House in St. Martin's Lane. In 1687, he is mentioned with his brother Daniel, in the lists of 'reconnaissances' of the French Church of the Savoy, and he received denization in the same year. De Moivre was a contemporary of Dr. Desaguliers, and a friend of Newton and Halley. In 1697, he was elected a fellow of the Royal Society.

In his 'Doctrine of Chances', 1718, De Moivre indicated the nature of 'recurring series', and also introduced the principle that the probability of a compound event is the product of the probabilities of the simple events composing it.

It has been said of De Moivre, that in the long list of men ennobled by genius, virtue and misfortune who have found asylum in England, it would be difficult to name one who has conferred more honour on his country. He was buried in St. Martin's in the Fields.

DIMENSIONS: *890 × 760mm.*

PROVENANCE: *Royal Society.*

LITERATURE: *C.R. Weld, Descriptive Catalogue of Portraits in the possession of the Royal Society, 1860, p. 49; Isaac Todhunter, History of the Theory of Probability, 1865, p. 134.*

183 *Annuities upon Lives*

ABRAHAM DE MOIVRE, 1725

De Moivre and Halley were the founders of the science of life-contingencies. In this work, de Moivre demonstrated that 'the decrements of life are in arithmetical progression'. The book was republished in 1743, 1750, 1752, and 1756, and was translated into Italian in 1776. De Moivre's techniques for calculating the rate of interest of life annuities and life assurance have been taken over by the actuarial profession. The normal curve of error which he constituted would now be regarded as part of statistics.

PROVENANCE: *British Library.*

LITERATURE: *P.L. Griffiths, Mathematical Discoveries 1600–1750, 1977.*

184 *John Dollond (1706–1761)*

PORTRAIT BUST, PLASTER, REPRODUCTION, TWENTIETH CENTURY.

The bust is a plaster cast of a bronze in the National Maritime Museum.

John Dollond, whose family fled from Normandy at the Revocation, was originally a Spitalfields silk weaver, but studied optics, mathematics and astronomy in his spare time. He instructed his son Peter in these sciences, and probably financed the small optical workshop that Peter opened in Vine Street, Spitalfields in 1750.

Two years later, John Dollond gave up weaving, and joined his son in new premises at the sign of the Golden Spectacles and Sea Quadrant in the Strand.

Newton's assumption that the chromatic aberration of refracting telescopes was irremediable was shown by Chester More Hall in 1733 to be incorrect. He succeeded in constructing achromatic lenses which produced images devoid of colour. The same discovery was made independently in 1758 by John Dollond. His experiments on achromatic lenses were to revolutionise the construction of optical instruments. Dollond's achromatic lenses consisted of a convex lens of crown glass combined with a concave lens of flint glass, which corrects the colour dispersion caused by the crown lens.

PROVENANCE: *Dollond and Aitchison Museum.*

ANNUITIES
UPON
LIVES:
OR,

The VALUATION of
ANNUITIES upon any
Number of LIVES; as
alfo, of REVERSIONS.

To which is added,

An APPENDIX concerning the
EXPECTATIONS of LIFE, and
Probabilities of SURVIVORSHIP.

By A. DE MOIVRE. F. R. S.

LONDON,
Printed by *W. P.* and fold by *Francis Fayram,*
at the *South-Entrance* of the *Royal Exchange*; and
Benj. Motte, at the *Middle Temple Gate, Fleetftreet*;
and *W. Pearfon,* Printer, over-againft *Wright's-*
Coffee-Houfe, Alderfgate-Street. MDCCXXV.

183

182

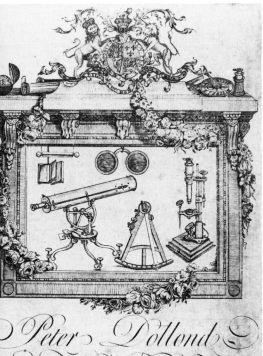

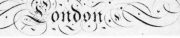

Peter Dollond
Optician to his MAJESTY, and to his
Royal Highnefs the Duke of York
At the Golden Spectacles & Sea Quadrant
Near Exeter Exchange in the Strand
London

185 b

185 a

185 Peter Dollond

a. PETER DOLLOND (1731–1820).
OIL ON CANVAS, JOHN HOPPNER.

Peter, son of John Dollond, was born in Spitalfields in 1731. He made many improvements to optical instruments, his improvement of Hadley's quadrant being laid before the Royal Society by the Astronomer Royal.

b. TRADE CARD AT THE SPECTACLES AND SEA QUADRANT IN THE STRAND, *c.*1752.

Peter Dollond opened an optician's shop in the Strand in the early 1750s, where he was joined by his father. Peter improved on his father's telescope, which only had a binary objective, by inventing a telescope with a triple objective. These achromatic telescopes were immensely popular with astronomers. Peter became known as 'the father of practical optics'. He obtained a patent for his new telescope, but in 1764, some 35 London opticians signed a petition against the patent, and the Spectacle Makers' Company, of which both Dollonds were members, contributed £20 towards the cost of the petition. The patent remained valid.

In 1766, Peter moved to 59, St. Paul's Churchyard, larger premises, necessary for his expanding business. The firm began to sell telescopes with brass draw-tubes and the portable instruments which were needed in the Napoleonic wars.

Peter Dollond retired, aged 85, in 1819. He served as a Director of the French Hospital, and was three times Master of the Spectacle Makers' Company.

NOT EXHIBITED.
ILLUSTRATED: *page 131.*
DIMENSIONS: *635 × 760mm.*
PROVENANCE: *Yale Centre for British Art, Paul Mellan Collection.*

ILLUSTRATED: *page 131.*
PROVENANCE: *Dollond and Aitchison Museum.*

186 Culpeper microscope

BRASS WITH GLASS ON WOODEN BASE, PETER DOLLOND, *c.* 1780.

A common brass three pillar or Culpeper microscope, on a rectangular wooden base with a drawer and accessories. This type of microscope continued to be made until the nineteenth century.

DIMENSIONS: *450mm high.*
PROVENANCE: *Dollond and Aitchison Museum.*

187 Telescope

BRASS, PETER DOLLOND, *c.* 1800.

DIMENSIONS: *965mm long.*
PROVENANCE: *Dollond and Aitchison Museum.*

188 Copley medal of the Royal Society

GOLD, 1758.
INSCRIBED: G. COPLEY BART. DIGNISSIMO; JOHN DOLLOND. ESQ MXDCC.LVIII.

The medal shows Minerva seated holding a laurel. The Copley medal was awarded to John Dollond in 1758 for his production of achromatic lenses. This is one of the highest awards to be conferred on an optician, and an honour that Dollond shared with Desaguliers. Dollond was made a Fellow of the Royal Society in 1761.

PROVENANCE: *Dollond and Aitchison Museum.*

189 Catalogue of optical, mathematical and philosophical instruments made by Peter and John Dollond, opticians to His Majesty, c.1785

The title of the catalogue presumably refers to Peter Dollond's brother, John (*d.* 1804), as their father died in 1761.

The catalogue is classified under the headings of telescopes to be used at sea and on land; other optical instruments including spectacles, opera glasses, microscopes and magic lanterns and mathematical instruments, including thermometers, barometers and hygrometers. Nose spectacles in tortoise-shell or silver cost 4 shillings; if made of horn or steel, as little as 1 shilling and 6 pence, whilst the best double-joint silver spectacles with glasses cost 1 guinea; if 'Brazil pebbles' were used, the price went up to 36 shillings.

DIMENSIONS: *355 × 560mm.*
PROVENANCE: *Dollond and Aitchison Museum.*

190 Great Exhibition medal

SILVER, 1851.
INSCRIBED: EXPOSITION UNIVERSELLE INTERNATIONALE DE 1878, PARIS.

This medal was presented to Dollonds in 1851 in recognition of the excellence of their production.

PROVENANCE: *Dollond and Aitchison Museum.*

LITERATURE: *E.G.R. Taylor, The Mathematical Practitioners of Hanoverian England, 1966, nos. 164, 469,955; Margaret Mitchell, The Dollond and Aitchison Museum, The Optician, 9.1.1976.*

186

188

190

CATALOGUE

OF

OPTICAL, MATHEMATICAL, and PHILOSOPHICAL INSTRUMENTS,
made by P. and J. DOLLOND, Opticians to His MAJESTY, in St. PAUL'S
CHURCH-YARD, LONDON.

TELESCOPES TO BE USED AT SEA OR LAND.

	£	s.	d.
ACHROMATIC Telescopes, with Mahogany Tubes, from one Foot to eight Feet long, at per Foot	1	1	0
Ditto with Object-Glasses of larger Apertures, one Foot long	1	18	0
Ditto ditto, two Feet	3	13	6
Ditto ditto, three Feet	6	6	0
Ditto ditto, four Feet	10	10	0
Ditto ditto, made with Brass Sliding Tubes, which make them very portable, and consequently the most convenient for the Army, called MILITARY TELESCOPES, one Foot long when drawn out, and five Inches when shut up	2	2	0
Ditto ditto, one and half Foot when drawn out, and seven Inches when shut up	3	3	0
Ditto ditto, two Feet when drawn out, and nine Inches when shut up	4	4	0
Ditto ditto, three Feet when drawn out, and ten Inches when shut up	7	7	0
Ditto ditto, four Feet when drawn out, and fourteen Inches when shut up	12	12	0
Night Telescopes to be used at Sea.			

	£	s.	d.
Ditto two Feet	12	12	0
Ditto with four different Powers and Rackwork Stand, supporting the Telescope in the Center of Gravity	21	0	0
Ditto, three Feet, with ditto	36	15	0
Micrometer with Achromatic Object-Glass for a two Foot reflecting Telescope	14	14	0
Ditto for a three Foot ditto	18	18	0

Other OPTICAL INSTRUMENTS.

	£	s.	d.
Best double joint Silver Spectacles with Glasses	1	1	0
Ditto with Brazil Pebbles	1	16	0
Best single joint Silver ditto with Glasses	0	13	0
Ditto with Brazil Pebbles	1	8	0
Double joint Steel ditto with Glasses	0	7	6
Single joint ditto	0	5	0
Ditto	0	2	6
Nose Spectacles Tortoiseshell and Silver	0	4	0
Ditto Horn and Steel	0	1	6
Spectacle Cases from 1s. to	0	10	0
Concave Glasses for short-sighted Persons, in Horn	0	1	6

	£	s.	d.
Concave and Convex Mirrors, from 10s. 6d. to	17	17	0

MATHEMATICAL INSTRUMENTS.

	£	s.	d.
Hadley's Octant in Mahogany, 16 Inches Radius with diagonal Divisions	1	11	6
Ditto with Ivory Arch and Nonius Divisions	2	8	0
Ditto in Ebony with ditto	3	3	0
Hadley's Sextants in Mahogany, with Ivory Arch, adjusting Screw to the Index, and a Telescope	6	6	0
Ditto with a Brass Arch and dark Glasses behind the Horizon Glass	8	8	0
Ditto in Brass, 3 Inches Radius	8	8	0
Ditto ditto, 6 Inches ditto	9	9	0
Ditto ditto, 9 Inches	10	10	0
Ditto ditto, 12 Inches	12	12	0
Ditto ditto, 15 Inches	13	13	0
By his Majesty's Letters Patent, the improved HADLEY's OCTANT for observing the Altitude of the Sun at Sea, in which the back Observation is rendered useful; with several other Advantages above those of the common Construction	5	5	0
Hadley's Sextants, with the same Im-			

189

191 *Trade card of Vandome & Co.*

FACSIMILE OF ORIGINAL, *c*.1820.

INSCRIBED: RICHARD VANDOME SCALEMAKERS TO HIS MAJESTY'S PUBLIC BOARDS, MINT, EXCHEQUER, BANK OF ENGLAND, AND THE HON'BLE UNITED EAST INDIA COMPANY.

DIMENSIONS: *143 × 100mm.*

PROVENANCE: *Vandome and Hart Ltd.*

LITERATURE: *The Vandome and Hart Tercentenary, The Monthly Review, Journal of the Institute of Weights and Measures Administration, 1960.*

The origin of the firm Vandome is believed to date from 1660, when Richard Vandome, a Huguenot refugee, designed and sold a weighing machine to his fellow coal merchants, and set up shop in Leadenhall Street.

There are references to Vandome, Titford and Co., the successors to Richard Vandome, in the Bank of England archives, with whom there has been a long association since the Bank's founding in 1694.

In 1930, Vandome's amalgamated with Hart's, makers of heavier machines, thus claiming a comprehensive manufacturing range of quality weighing equipment.

192 *Troy pound*

GUN METAL; INSCRIBED: LB T 1758.

DIMENSIONS: *90mm high.*

PROVENANCE: *Vandome and Hart Ltd.*

LITERATURE: *Tom Graham, The Troy Pound Mystery, in Equilibrium, Autumn 1981, pp. 390–3.*

This is believed to be the original standard used to adjust the set of Troy Standard weights which were supplied to the Jamaican Government in 1758.

In that year, there were a large number of Exchequer standards, both Troy and Avoir dupois, none of which was delineated as the Imperial Standard. On the instructions of the Carysfort Committee three examples of a Troy Pound were ordered, as the true weight of such a standard. Of the three, one 'The Parliamentary Pound' or Standard Troy Pound 13 oz. (legalised in 1824) was lost in the House of Commons fire in 1834; the second example, that on display, was kept by the scale and weight maker to the Mint, Samuel Freeman, and his successor, Richard Vandome. The Troy pound displayed is therefore probably the only remaining link with the missing standard, and is the most important weight, next to the present Imperial Standard Pound.

193 *Dissertation on electricity*

J.T. DESAGULIERS, 1742.

PROVENANCE: *French Church, Soho Square.*

LITERATURE: *Margaret E. Rowbottom, John Theophilus Desaguliers (1683–1744), Proceedings of the Huguenot Society of London, Vol. 21, (1965–70), pp. 196–218.*

John Theophilus Desaguliers was a Freemason and Chaplain to Frederick, Prince of Wales.

Desaguliers was also a lecturer in Experimental Philosophy, specialising in optics, hydrostatics and mechanics. In 1714, he became demonstrator and curator to the Royal Society, and was said to have been the first to deliver learned lectures, often with experiments, to general audiences. He delivered his lectures at the Marine Coffee House in 1707 (advertised in the Daily Courant, 23 October, 1707) at Mr. Brown's, bookseller, at the Black Swan and Bible without Temple Bar, at Channel Row, Westminster and at Bedford Coffee House, in the Piazza, Covent Garden. He considered Demainbray and Labelye among his disciples.

Desaguliers also wrote prolifically on a wide variety of scientific topics. He invented the planetarium, a machine to determine the exact distances of the heavenly bodies according to the Newtonian and Copernican systems. He installed the first ventilation system in the House of Commons in 1723, for which he was paid £105. He was awarded the Royal Society's Copley gold medal in 1741/2 in recognition of his successful experiments.

Towards the end of his life, Desaguliers demonstrated a long series of electrical experiments before the Royal Society. Although he was helped in the early stages of his work by Stephen Gray, who was famous for his experiments on electrical conduction, Desaguliers did not make any important discoveries in electricity, although he improved the terminology. In 1742, Desaguliers was awarded the first prize of the Academy of Bordeaux, for the best essay on electricity. Desaguliers was buried at the Savoy Church.

194 *The geometrical elevation of the north front of Westminster Bridge*

ENGRAVING, P. FOURDRINIER, AFTER CHARLES LABELYE, 1739.

ILLUSTRATED: *page 137.*

DIMENSIONS: *327 × 1263mm.*

PROVENANCE: *Guildhall Library.*

LITERATURE: *R.J.B. Walker, Old Westminster Bridge, The Bridge of Fools, 1979, pp. 81,154,160, pl. 6.*

The possibility of a bridge at Westminster had been investigated seriously in 1644, and again in 1721. The House of Commons appointed a Committee of 189 members to report on the proposed bridge, and in 1736, passed the first Bridge Act. Designs for the bridge were supplied by Nicholas Hawksmoor, Batty Langley, Thomas Ripley, and Charles Labelye. The latter was chosen for his contacts with skilled French bridge builders, and appointed by the Commissioners in May, 1738.

As well as the opposition from the other architects, in particular, Batty Langley, who was affronted because his design had not been taken seriously (*Catalogue number* 196), Labelye faced considerable opposition from the Thames Watermen, who feared that they would lose their livelihoods as a result of the new bridge.

Labelye's original design of thirteen semi-circular arches, which was published in 1736, was altered to include fifteen arches and fourteen piers.

Charles Labelye arrived in England in 1720, although he is known to have visited Madrid in 1727–8. In 'A Course of Experimental Philosophy', 1745, Dr. Desaguliers described Labelye as 'formerly my disciple and my Assistant'. Dr. Desaguliers also sponsored Labelye's membership of the French Masonic Lodge in Hemmings Row in 1725 (*Catalogue number* 152).

191

192

195 *A perspective view of the engine now made use of for driving the piles of the new bridge at Westminster*
ENGRAVING, W.H. TOMS AFTER H. GRAVELOT, 1738.
INSCRIBED: WITH TITLE . . . TO THE HONBLE COMMISSIONERS FOR BUILDING THE SAID BRIDGE, BY THE INVENTOR JAMES VAULOUÉ WATCH-MAKER.

On 12 December 1738, Read's Weekly Journal announced, 'Curiously engraved on a Copper Plate by Mr. Toms after the drawing of Mr. Gravelot, A Perspective View of the Engine made use of for driving the Piles of the New Bridge at Westminster . . . to be had at Slaughter's Coffee House, and Mr. Hardings, both on the Pavement in St. Martins Lane.'

In 'A Description of Westminster Bridge', 1751, Charles Labelye described James Vauloué as 'a very ingenious watchmaker of my Acquaintance, who has published a print of the Engine, with an Explanation; for which reason it will be sufficient for me to mention, that having viewed the Model of that contrivance and calculated the Effect of such an Engine, I found that supposing the Ram or Weight to be 1700 lb and the Height of the Strokes at a Mean 20 Feet perpendicular the Engine would give about 48 strokes per Hour, by the help of three Horses. This effect being much Superior to that of any of the Engines commonly used for that Purpose though it took a great deal of time in making.'

A model of Vauloué's engine, from the collection of George III, is in the Science Museum (*a*).

DIMENSIONS: *436 × 348mm.*
PROVENANCE: *Guildhall Library.*
EXHIBITED: *Royal Westminster, 1981, no. 186, illustrated p. 93.*
LITERATURE: *R.J.B. Walker, Old Westminster Bridge, The Bridge of Fools, 1979, pp. 89,199–200,214, pl. 10.*

196 *A Survey of Westminster Bridge as 'tis now sinking into ruin*
BATTY LANGLEY, 1748.

In the summer of 1746, one of the piers on the western side of Westminster Bridge shifted thirteen inches. This event provided a popular topic for ballads and pamphlets.

Batty Langley's shilling pamplet lampooned Charles Labelye for his 'unparall'd gross Ignorance, Madness and Knavery' in omitting to pile the foundations. The pamphlet has an engraved frontispiece in which Labelye, 'Mr. Self Sufficient' is shown hanging from a gibbet beneath one of his own arches, and is labelled, 'The Swiss Imposter Rewarded as his Ignorance justly deserves'.

In order to remedy the problem, Labelye piled the foundations, and two arches were rebuilt. As a result, in 1750, the bridge withstood the two earthquakes that were felt at Westminster.

PROVENANCE: *Museum of London.*
LITERATURE: *R.J.B. Walker, Old Westminster Bridge, The Bridge of Fools, 1979, pp. 182–3, pl. 37.*

197 *Plans of London Bridge*
ENGRAVING, B. COLE AFTER CHARLES LABELYE, 1746; INSCRIBED: THESE PLANS OF LONDON BRIDGE . . . ARE MOST HUMBLY PRESENTED UNTO THE RT.HONBLE SIR RICHD HOARE LORD MAYOR OF THE SAID CITY AT WHOSE REQUEST THEY WERE DRAWN BY HIS LORDSHIPS MOST OBLIG'D AND MOST OBEDIENT SERVANT CHARLES LABELYE ESQ.

NO. I. AS IT MAY BE AMENDED BY REDUCING THE STERLINGS. THE PLAN AND WESTERN FRONT OF LONDON BRIDGE EXCLUSIVE OF THE HOUSES WITH THE STERLINGS REDUCED TO SUCH A SIZE AS TO AFFORD TWICE AS MUCH WATER-WAY AS THEY DO AT PRESENT. N.B. BY THIS SKETCH IT APPEARS THAT THE CLEAR WATER-WAY AT HIGH-WATER IS 430 FEET AND AT LOW WATER 400 FEET AND THE PERPENDICULAR FALL ONLY 15 INCHES.

NO. 2. AS IT MAY BE AMENDED BY REDUCING THE ARCHES. THE PLAN AND WESTERN FRONT OF LONDON BRIDGE TO WHICH IT MIGHT BE ALTERED IS ACCORDING TO THE OPINION OF THE CELEBRATED ARCHITECT SIR CHRISTOPHER WREN BY TAKING AWAY EVERY OTHER ARCH & REDUCING TWO INTO ONE. N.B. BY THIS SKETCH IT APPEARS THAT THERE WOULD BE AT ALL TIMES A CLEAR WATER-WAY OF UPWARDS 540 FEET & THE FALL WOULD NOT BE ABOVE 9 INCHES AT THE MOST.

In 1736, Nicholas Hawksmoor had produced a scheme for the alteration of London Bridge, in order to improve navigation. His death in the same year forestalled the project, and it was not until 1746, that Charles Labelye proposed new Gothic arches for the bridge, 'London Bridge so mended would be the finest and most commodius Gothick Bridge in the World'.

The original drawings for the plan and elevation of Labelye's scheme for London Bridge, inscribed to Sir Richard Hoare, are at Wilton House, Salisbury, the seat of the Earls of Pembroke. They were presumably acquired by the 9th Earl of Pembroke who laid the first and last stone of Labelye's Westminster Bridge.

In 1751, Labelye, 'greatly afflicted with Asthma and unfit for Business', left England for Béziers in the South of France. He is believed to have died in Paris some thirty years later.

DIMENSIONS: *260 × 410mm.*
PROVENANCE: *Hoare's Bank.*
LITERATURE: *R.J.B. Walker, Old Westminster Bridge, The Bridge of Fools, 1979, pp. 27–8.*

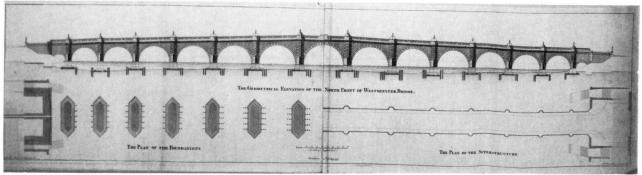

194

195 *a*

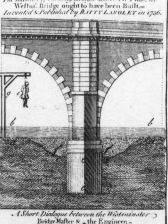

196

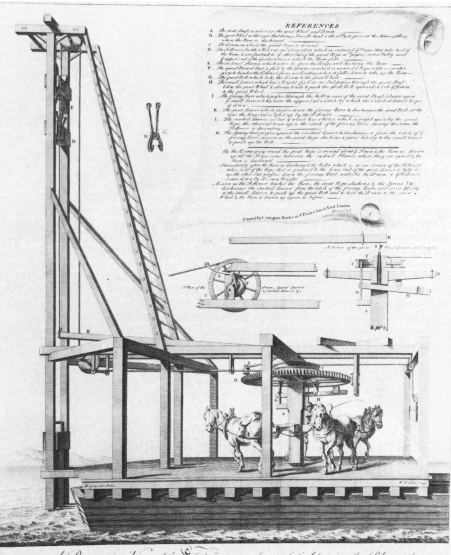

195

198 *James Six's thermometer*

a. THERMOMETER WITH MERCURY AND ALCOHOL TO SHOW MAXIMUM AND MINIMUM TEMPERATURES, JAMES SIX, FRS, *c.* 1782.

James Six produced an effective self registering thermometer recording the maximum and minimum temperatures on the same instrument.

Six was descended from a Walloon silk weaving family that had settled in Canterbury during the late sixteenth century. With the decline in the textile trade, Six devoted himself to natural philosophy and invented his thermometer in 1780. From a series of readings, Six discovered that although air temperatures usually decreased with height, the reverse was true at night, the coldest place being nearest the ground. This was due to the radiational cooling at the earth's surface.

Six was made a Fellow of the Royal Society for his invention in 1792. His thermometer has played an important part in meteorology and oceanography; its basic design changed little in two hundred years. Today, it remains a popular and reliable domestic instrument. Six also adapted his thermometer for marine use; fourteen such experimental thermometers are in the Science Museum's collection.

b. THE CONSTRUCTION AND USE OF A THERMOMETER, JAMES SIX, 1794.

In this book, Six discusses both the practicalities of making an air thermometer, its tubes and indexes, and his new interest, marine thermometry.

Six's thermometers were used to record maximum and minimum temperatures by the Royal Society from 1794 and the Royal Observatory at Kew from 1798.

The marine thermometer is first recorded in use by the Russian ships Neva and Nadezhda during their circumnavigation of the world in 1803–6.

DIMENSIONS: *470mm long.*

PROVENANCE: *Science Museum.*

LITERATURE: *Jill Austin and Anita McConnell ed. The Construction and Use of a Thermometer, 1794 by James Six, 1982; Anita McConnell, James Six – His Scientific Life and Works, Proceedings of the Huguenot Society of London, Vol. 23 (1982), pp. 396–404.*

PROVENANCE: *British Library.*

199 *Plate*

PEWTER, ONE OF A SET OF FIVE, JAMES TAUDIN, *c.* 1675–80.

The broad rim has a narrow cast multiple reeding at the edge, and is engraved at the front with an armorial crest, a lion rampant with an anchor, in contemporary mantling.

James Taudin, a Huguenot refugee pewterer of repute, was granted the Freedom and Livery of the Pewterers' Company in 1658. He was responsible for the introduction of a superior alloy, containing antimony, at a period when pewter contained mainly tin, lead and copper. This inevitably lead to disputes with the Pewterers' Company.

Taudin lived in the parish of St. Martin in the Fields, Westminster, on the west side of St. Martin's Lane, and virtually opposite the church. The site of his house is now covered by the south east corner of the National Gallery. Taudin's burial is recorded in the Registers of St. Martin's in the Fields for 25 July 1680.

A recent analysis of the set of five Taudin plates in the collection of the Pewterers' Company reveals that they contain 2.3% antimony, 0.6% copper and 0.2% bismuth.

DIMENSIONS: *250mm diameter.*

PROVENANCE: *Worshipful Company of Pewterers.*

LITERAUTRE: *H.H. Cotterell, Old Pewter, its Makers and Marks, 1929, no. 4651; J. Hatcher and T.C. Barker, A History of British Pewter, 1974, pp. 225–7; Ibid., A short history of The Worshipful Company of Pewterers of London and a Catalogue of Pewterware in its Possession, 1968, p. 22; Ron F. Homer, The Story of James Taudin, The Journal of the Pewter Society, Vol. 4, no. 4, 1984, pp. 118–122.*

199

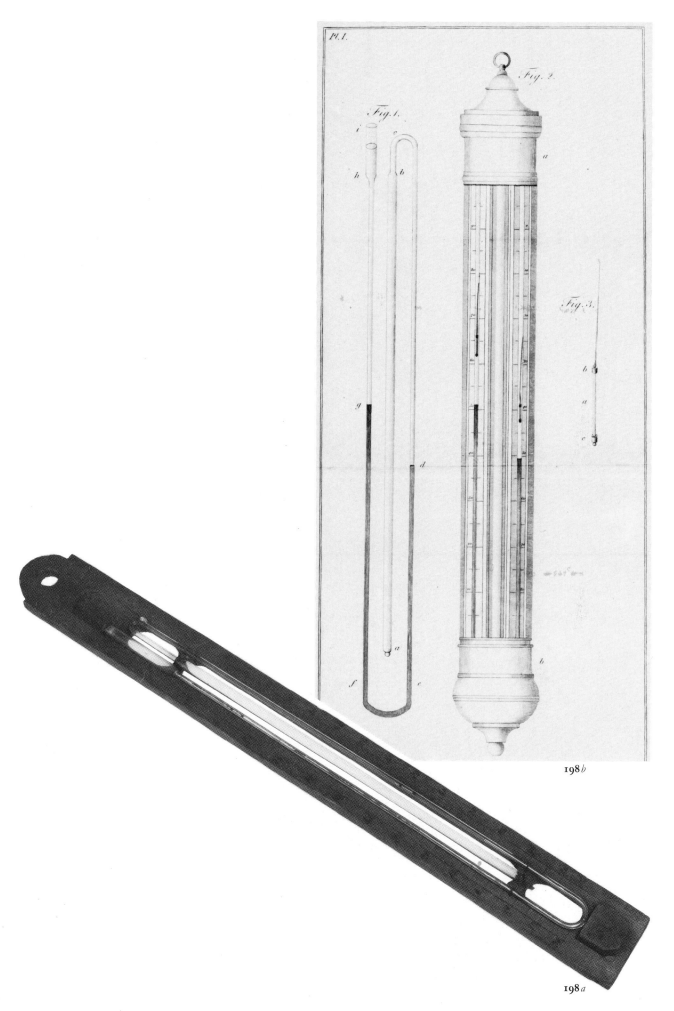

198*b*

198*a*

200 *Daniel Augustus Beaufort (1739–1821)*

PORTRAIT DRAWING, PENCIL, NO DATE.

D.A. Beaufort was the son of a French refugee who became Minister of a Huguenot church in Spitalfields in 1728. He was vicar of Collon, Co. Louth and a founder of the Royal Irish Academy. His most valuable contribution to geography was his 'New Map of Ireland, civil and ecclesiastical', 1792.

Ignoring all recently published general maps of Ireland, he combined his own travel notes with a wide range of local and regimental surveys by reputable cartographers and dove-tailed the whole assemblage into a framework of accurate astronomical data. Printing and publication were a source of much anxiety to the author, on one occasion he ran in headlong flight through the streets of London from a colourist angrily demanding payment! However, the new map was still being described in 1824 as the most accurate version of Ireland obtainable.

DIMENSIONS: *110 × 807mm.*

PROVENANCE: *National Portrait Gallery.*

LITERATURE: *J.H. Andrews, Irish Maps, The Irish Heritage Series, 18, 1978; K.K. Yung, National Portrait Gallery, The Complete Illustrated Catalogue, 1981, no. 5255; Alfred Webb, Compendium of Irish Biography, 1878, pp. 13–14.*

DANIEL AUGUSTUS BEAUFORT, L.L.D.

200

HUGUENOTS AND THE THEATRE

The profane theatre was forbidden in Calvin's Geneva. Ironically descendants of Huguenot refugees wrote plays and became great theatrical stars.

Alexander Pope considered the Huguenot playwright Thomas D'Urfey as the 'only poet of tolerable reputation in this country' and he said of David Garrick, 'That young man never had his equal and he never will have a rival'.

Garrick (1717–1779), the grandson of a Huguenot refugee from Bordeaux, made his first appearance on stage, at a little known theatre in London's East End, but he rose to become Actor-Manager of the Theatre in Drury Lane. He brought a new naturalness and vivacity to audiences who were used to solemn declamation and traditional gesture. He also did much to promote the reputation of William Shakespeare.

Peter Prelleur, organist at Christ Church, Spitalfields, composed music for the same theatre in Goodman's Fields, where Garrick had first performed.

David Garrick as Richard III, oil on canvas, William Hogarth, 1745

201 *David Garrick (1717–1779)*
MEDALLION PORTRAIT, GILT BRONZE, LOUIS FRANCOIS ROUBILIAC, 1758.
INSCRIBED ON THE REVERSE: DAVID GARRICK ARMR. L.F. ROUBILIAC SCT.AD VIVUM 1758.

This portrait cast in gilt-bronze in high relief shows the actor in a three-quarters profile. The medallion has been attached to a separate gilt-bronze backplate.

1758 marks the date of the completion of Roubiliac's marble statue of Shakespeare which was housed in a temple in Garrick's garden at Hampton (*Catalogue numbers* 204, 205). Roubiliac also modelled a portrait bust of Garrick which is shown in terracotta in the portrait of Roubiliac by Andrea Soldi in the Garrick Club, also dated the year 1758. It is probable that the terracotta bust pre-dated the bronze medallion portrait, although the former is only known today from the plaster cast in the National Portrait Gallery. The medallion portrait is enlivened by the addition of buttons and button-holes, not present in the bust.

The sale catalogue of the sculptor's effects after his death lists a set of plaster medals, including Garrick, Pope, Conyers Middleton, Handel, Inigo Jones, Oliver Cromwell and Isaac Newton. With the exception of Inigo Jones, medallions of all these sitters are known today in either bronze or terracotta.

DIMENSIONS: *265mm high.*

PROVENANCE: *Peter Norton, presented to the Garrick Club, 1833.*

LITERATURE: *J.V.G. Mallet, Some Portrait Medallions by Roubiliac, Burlington Magazine, Vol.104, 1962, pp.153–158, figs. 27, 31.*

202 *Suit worn by David Garrick*
BROWN VELVET, *c.*1763/64.

The suit consists of a coat, vest and breeches in a chestnut-coloured velvet. It was worn by David Garrick for a portrait painted by Pompeo Batoni in Rome, 1764, which is now in the Ashmolean Museum.

COLOUR PLATE: *page 7.*

PROVENANCE: *Sotheby's 19 June 1928 (395); Given to the London Museum by Mr. and Mrs. Ernest Makower; Museum of London.*

EXHIBITED: *David Garrick Jubilee Celebrations, Stratford-upon-Avon, 1969; David Garrick, A Bicentenary Exhibition, The British Library, 1979–1980, (1); Buxton Festival Exhibition, 1981.*

LITERATURE: *Helen R. Smith, David Garrick, 1717–1779, A brief account, 1979, p.8.*

203

203 *Ring belonging to David Garrick*
INTAGLIO CORNELIAN IN A GOLD MOUNT.

This ring is traditionally said to have been given to Dr. Robert Emmet, physician to the Viceroy in Ireland, in 1742, when David Garrick visited Dublin.

PROVENANCE: *Dr. Robert Emmet; Sarah Carrau; Henry Cullen; Grace V. Rea; presented to the London Museum, 1945; Museum of London.*

204 *Mr and Mrs Garrick in front of the temple of Shakespeare*
OIL ON CANVAS, JOHANN ZOFFANY, 1762.

The painting shows the temple built to house Roubiliac's statue of Shakespeare (*Catalogue number* 205) in David Garrick's garden at Hampton. The temple was begun by August, 1755, when Horace Walpole wrote from Strawberry Hill, 'I have contracted a sort of intimacy with Garrick, who is my neighbour. He is building a grateful temple to Shakespeare'.

Although the design of the temple has been variously attributed to Robert Adam, and Capability Brown, it is probable that the temple was built with the co-operation of the sculptor, and with the position of the statue in mind. The windows are placed so as to give the statue the best possible natural lighting.

The painting originally hung in the dining room of David Garrick's house in the Adelphi.

COLOUR PLATE: *page 7.*

DIMENSIONS: *997 × 1250mm.*

PROVENANCE: *Christie's 23 June 1823 (54); bought by Seguier for the Earl of Durham, Trustees of the Fifth Earl of Durham's Picture Settlement.*

EXHIBITED: *Conversation Pieces, 1930 (107); The Georgian Playhouse, Arts Council, 1975 (83); Johann Zoffany (1733–1810); National Portrait Gallery, 14 January – 17 March, 1977 (12).*

201

202

204

205 *William Shakespeare*

TERRACOTTA; LOUIS FRANCOIS ROUBILIAC, 1757.
INSCRIBED ON THE LEFT OF THE BASE: F. ROUBILIAC 1757.

The poet is shown standing at a moment of inspiration, his left hand, with a forefinger extended, is raised to his face; his right arm rests on a lectern.

This appears to be the first sketch for the marble statue of Shakespeare, 1758, which was made for David Garrick, and bequeathed by him to the British Museum. The model is identical with that represented in the portrait of Roubiliac by Adrien Carpentiers (two versions, Yale Center for British Art and National Portrait Gallery at Beningbrough) although the portrait is dated 1762. It is likely that Garrick himself posed for the statue, although Roubiliac also took considerable pains to achieve a likeness of Shakespeare, using his own painted copy of the Chandos portrait, the earliest authentic contemporary portrait of Shakespeare. (Roubiliac's copy is now in the British Museum.)

Several other models for this commission are recorded. One was bought by Warren Hastings, and is now at Stratford-upon-Avon. Another passed through the Paris salerooms (J.P.F. Le Brun sale 11.4.1791 (354); E. Chappey sale 1907, Vol.I (391) (information kindly communicated by Alistair Laing). Another, perhaps the exhibited version, was in the sale of Edward Stevens, architect, 7.2.1776 (38). A gouache drawing for this commission is also recorded.

PROVENANCE: *Mr. Myers, purchased by the Victoria and Albert Museum, 1867.*

EXHIBITED: *David Garrick, A Bicentenary Exhibition, The British Library, 1979–1980 (23); O. Sweet Mr. Shakespeare! I'll have his Picture, National Portrait Gallery, 18 April–30 June 1964, p. 28, pl. 12.*

LITERATURE: *H.C. Andrews, Garrick's Statue of Shakespeare, Architectural Review, Vol.39, 1916, pp.93–4; Martin Anglesea, David Garrick and the Visual Arts, unpublished M.Litt Thesis, University of Edinburgh, 1971, pp.39–42; K.A. Esdaile, The Life and Works of Louis François Roubiliac, 1928, p.124; David Piper, Roubiliac's Statue of Shakespeare, text of a lecture delivered to the British Museum Society.*

206 *Alexander Pope (1688–1744)*

BUST, MARBLE; LOUIS FRANCOIS ROUBILIAC, 1741.
INSCRIBED: L.F. ROUBILIAC SC. AD VIVUM MDCCXLI A. POPE, AET.LIII.

This is one of four signed marble busts of Pope, which were apparently made for his close friends. This version originally belonged to David Garrick; two of the others were probably made for Lord Bolingbroke, and William Murray, Lord Mansfield.

In 1741, when George Vertue visited Roubiliac's studio he noted, 'besides several works in Marble-moddels in Clay – had modelled from the life several Busts portraits extreamly like – Mr. Pope more like than any other Sculptor'.

Sir Joshua Reynolds noted in 1742, that Roubiliac observed that the poet's countenance 'was that of a person who had been much afflicted with headache, and he should have known the fact from the contracted appearance of the skin above the eyebrows, though he had not been otherwise apprised of it'.

DIMENSIONS: *415mm.*

PROVENANCE: *David Garrick; Christie's 23 June 1823 (72); bt. Seguier for the Earl of Durham; G.L. Collins, 1932; Samuel Smith, presented to Shipley Art Gallery, Gateshead.*

EXHIBITED: *British Portraits, Royal Academy, 1956–7 (663); A Candidate for Praise, York City Art Gallery, 1973 (17).*

LITERATURE: *W.K. Wimsatt, The Portraits of Alexander Pope, 1965, pp.241–4; K.A. Esdaile, The Life and Works of Louis François Roubiliac, 1928, pp.47–8, 90; Rococo Art and Design in Hogarth's England, Victoria and Albert Museum, 1984, pp.289–290.*

207 *The Concert*

OIL ON CANVAS; PHILIP MERCIER, *c.*1729.

This painting is based on an engraving by Audran of Watteau's L'Enchanteur, which was published by 1729. With the exception of the lady in the left foreground, the figures are in similar positions; the young man playing the hautboy replaces a man in fancy dress, holding a guitar, whereas the lady in the centre of the composition is playing a guitar.

Philip Mercier's paintings of this period reveal an intimate knowledge of the work of the French painter, Jean Antoine Watteau. Sometimes he produced exact copies of Watteau's work, on other occasions, as here, he transformed the composition by varying minor details. It is probable that Mercier spent some time in Paris in the 1720s, and he may have entertained Watteau on the latter's visit to London in 1719–1720.

Philip Mercier was born in Berlin, the son of a Huguenot tapestry worker. He studied under the painter Antoine Pesne in Berlin, toured Italy and France, and settled in London in 1716, where he worked as a dealer and an artist. In 1729, he was appointed Principal Painter and Library Keeper to Frederick, Prince of Wales.

DIMENSIONS: *286 × 343mm.*

PROVENANCE: *Duke of Northumberland.*

EXHIBITED: *Philip Mercier 1689–1760, City Art Gallery, York and Iveagh Bequest, Kenwood, 1969, no.14.*

LITERATURE: *John Ingamells and Robert Raines, A Catalogue of the Paintings, Drawings and Etchings of Philip Mercier, The Walpole Society, Vol.XLVI, 1976–1978, pp.1–70, no.241; Robert Raines, Watteaus and 'Watteaus' in England before 1760, Gazette des Beaux Arts, 1977, p.54.*

205

206

207

208 *Introduction to Singing*
PETER PRELLEUR, 1731.

Peter Prelleur began his career in London as a writing master, and he also played the harpsichord in the Angel and Crown Tavern, Whitechapel. In 1728, he was appointed organist of St. Alban's, Wood Street.

The 'Introduction to Singing' was first published in 1731 as Part I of a much larger work, 'The Modern Musick Master', which also contained instructions for playing the recorder, German flute, hautboy, violin and harpsichord.

The frontispiece to the 'Introduction to Singing' shows a fiddler and a harpist gathered round a punch bowl in a panelled room. A sign over the chimneypiece reads 'Orders of this Club'. In view of Prelleur's connections with Spitalfields, it is tempting to see this as a reference to a musical club which met regularly, but no evidence of such a club has yet come to light.

In 1735, Peter Prelleur was elected the first organist of Christ Church, Spitalfields.

PROVENANCE: *Museum of London.*

LITERATURE: *The New Grove Dictionary of Music and Musicians, 1980, under Prelleur.*

209 *Baucis and Philemon*
OVERTURE AND THE SONGS AND DUETS; PETER PRELLEUR, 1740.

From 1728 until the theatre was closed under the Licensing Act of 1737, Prelleur played the harpsichord and composed for the Goodman's Fields Theatre. He then transferred to the New Wells or Goodman's Fields Wells Theatre in nearby Leman Street. For this new theatre he wrote songs, pantomines and overtures, and this interlude, 'Baucis and Philemon', which includes an overture for strings, obligato, oboes and continuo.

Peter Prelleur also wrote the music for 'Harlequin Hermit or the Arabian Courtesan', a pantomine, which was first performed at Goodman's Fields in 1739. David Garrick's earliest appearance on stage was in the masked pantomine role of Harlequin, as a substitute for Richard Yates, in a production at Goodman's Fields in 1740.

PROVENANCE: *British Library.*

LITERATURE: *The New Grove Dictionary of Music and Musicians, 1980, under Prelleur; Helen R. Smith, David Garrick, 1717–1779, A brief account, 1979, p.12.*

210 *Songs Compleat Pleasant and Divertive set to Musick*
THOMAS D'URFEY, 1719.

The exhibited volume is the first in the three volume standard edition of D'Urfey's own songs. The third volume contains a few of his poems and prologues including one to the Massacre of Paris (St. Bartholomew).

Thomas D'Urfey or d'Urfé was a member of a Huguenot family from La Rochelle that settled in the Exeter area in the late 1620s.

His first play was produced at the King's Theatre in 1676. His later plays were enlivened by sparkling songs which were set to music by his friends, Henry Purcell, Thomas Farmer and Dr. John Blow. These songs were published separately with music in single sheets and later in volumes from 1683.

Alexander Pope said of D'Urfey 'He makes all the merriment in our entertainments'.

DIMENSIONS: *Octavo.*

PROVENANCE: *British Library.*

LITERATURE: *Sir Paul Harvey, The Oxford Companion to English Literature, 1932, p.245; Dictionary of National Biography under D'Urfey.*

211 *Bassoon*
MAPLE AND BOXWOOD; THOMAS CAHUSAC, LONDON, 1769.

This bassoon bears the maker's mark of Thomas Cahusac, of 196, Strand, London, and the date, 1769. It retains its original brass mounts, four flat brass keys on the saddles, an original heavy brass crook, and a bulbous bell which is characteristic of the eighteenth century. It was originally used in the church band of Brailes, Warwickshire.

The family originally came from Cahusac near Albi in the south of France.

ILLUSTRATED: *page 148.*

DIMENSIONS: *1259 × 81mm.*

PROVENANCE: *Brailes Parish Church, Warwickshire; Lyndesay Langwill; Philip Bate, 1976; Faculty of Music, Oxford University.*

EXHIBITED: *Galpin Society Exhibitions, 1951 (94); 1958 (21); 1968 (241).*

212 *Trade card of Thomas and William Cahusac*
NO. 196 OPPOSITE ST. CLEMENT'S CHURCH IN THE STRAND, ENGRAVED BY BARNES, 1800.

This card describes Thomas and William Cahusac as 'Musical Instrument Makers, Wholesale, Retail and for Exportation'.

Thomas Cahusac worked at this address at the sign of the 'Two Flutes and Violin' from 1755 to 1798. His son, William, remained at the same premises till 1802, and later moved to Holborn. William's brother, also Thomas, worked in Reading during the 1780s before joining his father in London in 1789. Thomas Cahusac the younger later worked in the Haymarket and in New Bond Street.

Another trade card of Thomas Cahusac lists the wide range of instruments and equipment that he supplied. Thomas Cahusac the elder married the daughter of Benjamin Banks, a well-known violin maker in Salisbury. (Information kindly supplied by Tony Bingham.)

ILLUSTRATED: *page 148.*

DIMENSIONS: *120 × 79mm.*

PROVENANCE: *Banks Collection, British Museum, Department of Prints and Drawings.*

LITERATURE: *Musical Opinion, December 1936.*

208

The
SONGS and DUETTS
in
Baucis & Philemon

they are now Perform'd at the
New Wells in
Goodman's Fields.

To which is prefix'd,
Overture in Score.

Compos'd by P. Prelleur.

LONDON Printed for the Author, and
the Musick Shops.

Price 3sh.

209

Whilst Durfey's voice his verse do's raise,
When Durfey sings his Tunefull Layes,
Give D'urfeys Lyrick-muse the Bayes.
E. G.

210

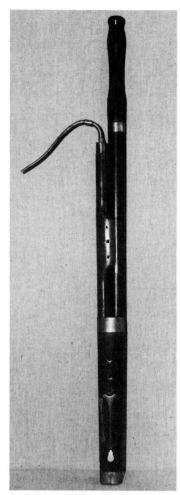

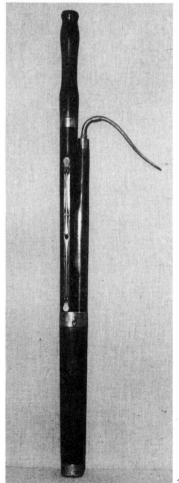

212

211

MEN OF LETTERS
& ANTIQUARIES

Huguenot writers made an important contribution to the assimilation of English philosophical and social opinions by French thinkers. Acting as abbreviators, commentators, journalists, publishers and translators, they facilitated the cross-fertilisation of ideas.

Sir Paul Rycaut's intelligent and important study, 'The History of the Turkish Empire, 1623–1677', was published in 1680. Paul Rapin de Thoyras made English institutions known across the Channel with his 'History of England'.

Many generations have testified to the value of Peter Mark Roget's 'Thesaurus of English Words and Phrases', 1852. Harriet Martineau (1802–1876) and Walter de la Mare (1873–1956) were also of Huguenot descent.

In the eighteenth century, scientific inclinations were satisfied by collecting. The early benefactors of the new British Museum included several Huguenots. Matthew Maty (1718–1776), Librarian of the Museum, made at least twenty donations. William Lethieullier (*d.* 1755) and his cousin Smart (1701–1760) gave Egyptian antiquities, bottled specimens and a stuffed pelican.

Matthew Maty c.1750, oil on canvas, Barthelemy Dupan

DETAIL

216

213 Sir Paul Rycaut (1628–1700)
OIL ON CANVAS; AFTER SIR PETER LELY, c.1679.

The sitter is shown half-length facing to the left.

Sir Paul Rycaut FRS was the grandson of Andrew Rycaut, a grandee of Brabant. He was born at Aylesford, Kent and baptised at St. Christopher le Stocks, although his elder siblings were baptised at the Threadneedle Street Church. He was educated at Trinity College, Cambridge. A member of an embassy to the Porte, he stayed for six years, and became a leading authority on Turkey. In 1668, he published a comprehensive work on the Ottoman Empire giving on the whole 'an animated and faithful picture of Turkish manners'. Samuel Pepys bought a copy at the fantastic price of 55 shillings and noted his appreciation of the work. After spending ten years as consul for the Levant Company at Smyrna, Rycaut published his 'History of the Turkish Empire, 1623–1677'.

In 1685, he was appointed a Privy Councillor, a judge of the admiralty in Ireland, and secretary to Clarendon the new Lord Lieutenant of Ireland, who, after attacks from the Catholic party, praised Rycaut's integrity. He finished his diplomatic career as a resident in Hamburg and the Hanse towns. He was buried at Aylesford, Kent.

Some 1,000 of his letters are preserved in the British Library, the Public Record Office and the Bodleian Library.

DIMENSIONS: 750 × 620mm.

PROVENANCE: National Portrait Gallery.

LITERATURE: Sonia P. Anderson, Sir Paul Rycaut, FRS (1629–1700) His Family and Writings, Proceedings of the Huguenot Society of London, Vol.21 (1965–70), pp.464–491; David Piper, Catalogue of the Seventeenth-century Portraits in the National Portrait Gallery, 1625–1714, 1963, p.306.

214 Paul Rapin de Thoyras (1661–1725)
PORTRAIT ENGRAVING; GEORGE VERTUE, 1734.

The sitter is shown half-length to the right, in armour, his right hand supporting a book. In the foreground, his coat-of-arms is supported by a number of volumes, one of which is inscribed 'History of England'.

Paul Rapin de Thoyras, was born at Castres, the son of an advocate who practised in the chamber of the Edict of Castres in defence of the rights of the Huguenots. His uncle was Paul de Pélisson-Fontanier, the historian of the Académie Française. He was educated at the academies of Puylaurens and Saumur, and trained as an advocate. He came to London in 1686, but then went on to Holland, where he enlisted in a company of French refugees at Utrecht, which formed part of the army with which William of Orange landed in England in 1688. In 1689, he was made an ensign in Lord Kingston's regiment of foot. He fought at the Battle of the Boyne, and was wounded at Limerick.

In 1693, he became tutor to Lord Woodstock, the Earl of Portland's eldest son, with whom he travelled to Germany and Italy. When Lord Woodstock married, William III granted Rapin a pension and he settled at the Hague. He moved afterwards to Wesel, where he died.

This portrait was engraved as a frontispiece to his 'History of England' (*Catalogue number 215*).

DIMENSIONS: 313 × 208mm.

PROVENANCE: Private Collection.

215 A History of England
VOL.I, PAUL RAPIN DE THOYRAS, TRANSLATED BY NICHOLAS TINDAL, 1743.

Rapin's 'History of England' was written for foreigners rather than Englishmen. The first volumes written in French were published in 1723, and the last were completed in 1725, just before his death. By 1749, six editions had been published in French. The history was continued by David Durand (d.1763), the Huguenot minister of the French chapel at the Savoy, and later Les Grecs.

In 1736, a series of portraits, monuments and medals engraved by George Vertue were published to accompany Nicholas Tindal's English translation.

Rapin's History begins with the landing of Julius Caesar and ends with the accession of William and Mary. Rapin's account of William III's expedition to England in November, 1688, is particularly valuable, as he was an eyewitness of the event.

PROVENANCE: Huguenot Library.

LITERATURE: M. Raoul de Cazenove, Rapin Thoyras, sa Famille, sa Vie, et ses Oeuvres, 1866.

216 Matthew Maty (1718–1776)
OIL ON CANVAS; BARTHELEMY DUPAN, c.1750.

The sitter is shown three-quarter length to the right, leaning on the back of a chair, with a notebook in his left hand.

Matthew Maty was descended from a family of ministers who had fled from Beaufort in Dauphiné to Utrecht, Holland, after the Revocation. In 1740, May emigrated to England after completing a dual degree in philosophy and medicine at Leyden. In 1750, he engaged single handed in the issue of a monthly periodical in French, the 'Journal Britannique' (1750–1755) which aimed to acquaint French readers with the best of English literature.

The success of the periodical amongst the intellectual elite led to Maty being elected a Fellow of the Royal Society, and to his appointment as one of the under-librarians at the British Museum. Having completed his catalogue of the Royal Library in 1765, Maty transferred his attention to natural history. His transfer led to the revival of the collections through planned accession and purchase grants.

During the first twenty years of the Museum's life, 1756–1776, he added some two thousand natural history specimens to the Museum's collections, and other antiquities which

ILLUSTRATED: page 149.

DIMENSIONS: 690 × 690mm.

PROVENANCE: British Museum.

LITERATURE: Uta Janssens, Mathieu Maty: A French 'Apostle' of English Letters, Proceedings of the Huguenot Society of London, Vol.XXII (1970–76), pp.211–223; Ibid. Mathieu Maty and the Journal Britannique, 1750–1755, Amsterdam, 1975; A.E. Gunther, The Founders of Science, 1753–1900, 1981.

213

214

215

Maty had evidently acquired through the sale rooms. Between 1758 and 1776, the Benefactor's Book records gifts from Maty on at least twenty different occasions. On 28th May 1762, he presented seventeen busts from the sale of Roubiliac's effects (*Catalogue number 312*).

Maty was a frequenter of Slaughter's Coffee House in St. Martin's Lane, the resort of artists and foreigners, especially Frenchmen. Here Dr. Johnson came to try to learn French. Maty criticised his Dictionary, and was subsequently described by Johnson as 'a little black dog' whom he would throw in the Thames.

Maty married Elisabeth de Boisragon in the Huguenot chapel, Spring Gardens, one of the daughter churches of the Huguenot church of the Savoy. He lived in Holles Street, and from 1752–56, when he worked in Montagu House, in Thrift (or Frith) Street.

217 *Anthony Chamier (1725–1780)*
PORTRAIT, OIL ON CANVAS; SIR JOSHUA REYNOLDS, 1777.

The sitter is shown whole length, seated at a table to the left, and holding a letter.

Anthony Chamier was the grandson of Daniel Chamier, a minister of the Reformed Church, who sought refuge in England after the Revocation. Anthony was baptised in the French Church, Threadneedle Street. He worked initially on the Stock Exchange, but through the influence of family connections was appointed Deputy Secretary at War in January, 1772 and an Under Secretary of State in 1775. He was elected M.P. for Tamworth in 1778. This advancement was attacked by one Junius (probably Philip Francis) in the press.

Chamier was an original member of the Literary Club, and a close friend of Dr. Johnson, who spent his seventieth birthday with Chamier.

Sir Joshua Reynolds was also a close friend, and Chamier sat to the artist on three different occasions, in December 1762, January 1767, and November 1777.

COLOUR PLATE: *page 8.*

PROVENANCE: *Private Collection.*

LITERATURE: *David C. Agnew, Protestant Exiles from France, Vol.II, 1871, pp.245, 294–295; Dictionary of National Biography, under Chamier; James Boswell, The Life of Samuel Johnson, ed. Roger Inkpen, Vol.11, 1907, pp.290, 517, 680, 743, 764.*

218 *Peter Mark Roget (1779–1869)*
PORTRAIT DRAWING, BLACK AND RED CHALK; WILLIAM BROCKEDON, 1835.

The sitter is shown full-face to the shoulders.

Peter Mark Roget was born in Broad Street (Broadwick Street), Soho, the only son of John Roget, a native of Geneva, and a pastor of the French Church, Threadneedle Street. Roget's uncle, Sir Samuel Romilly helped to launch his career.

By 1815, Roget had established his growing practice as a physician in Bloomsbury, and he was acquainted with a variety of distinguished contemporaries, from Jeremy Bentham to Humphrey Davy. Roget became a Fellow of the Royal Society in 1815, and was for twenty years, its Secretary, a Vice President, and a member of Council.

In 1837, this 'busily indefatigable, indispensable man' took an active part in establishing London University, and remained a member of the Senate until his death.

DIMENSIONS: *360 × 260mm.*

PROVENANCE: *National Portrait Gallery.*

LITERATURE: *D.L. Emblem, Peter Mark Roget, The Word and the Man, 1970; K.K. Yung, National Portrait Gallery, The Complete Illustrated Catalogue, 1981, no.2515 (79).*

219 *Roget's Thesaurus*
FIRST EDITION, 1852.

After 1840, Roget retired from professional practice and devoted himself to compiling his useful 'Thesaurus of English Words and Phrases, classified and arranged so as to facilitate the expression of ideas and assist in Literary Composition', which was first published in 1852. This work reached its twenty-eighth edition during Roget's lifetime, and is still widely used. Many generations of literary men and journalists have testified to its usefulness. An edition of 1879 embodying Roget's latest corrections, was edited by his son.

DIMENSIONS: *Octavo.*

PROVENANCE: *London Library.*

220 *Autobiography*
HARRIET MARTINEAU, 1877.

Harriet Martineau (1802–1876) was born at Norwich, the daughter of Thomas Martineau, manufacturer of camlet and bombazine. The family traced its descent from David Martineau, a surgeon who settled in Norwich after the Revocation.

Between 1832–4, Harriet published a series of stories in illustration of political economy. Over six thousand copies were printed and she soon became one of the 'lions' of the day. She lived in Fluyder Street, Westminster and became acquainted with other contemporary literary celebrities. Access to the private papers of Chancellor Brougham enabled her to write effectively on behalf of the projected poor-law reforms.

Harriet Martineau is chiefly remembered for her remarkable illustration of the contemporary state of mind. Her ability to popularise knowledge, with revelations of the current doctrines of political economics, and the school of Malthus, Ricardo and James Stuart Mill, in fiction rather than in dry treatises, met the popular mood.

PROVENANCE: *Guildhall Library.*

LITERATURE: *C. Anthony Crofton, Pedigrees of the Martineau Family, 1972; Mrs. Fenwick Miller, Harriet Martineau, in Eminent Women Series, 1884.*

217

27.11.35

Harriet Martineau

1833.

218

220

221 *Three books by Walter De La Mare (1873–1956)*

a. THE RETURN, 1910, SIGNED BY THE AUTHOR.

The hero of the novel, Arthur Lawford, encounters the Huguenot Nicholas Sabathier, the mainspring of the tragedy.

DIMENSIONS: *Octavo.*

b. MEMOIRS OF A MIDGET, 1921, SIGNED BY THE AUTHOR.

Regarded as a masterpiece among twentieth century novels.

DIMENSIONS: *Octavo.*

c. PEACOCK PIE, 1946, WITH DRAWINGS BY EDWARD ARDIZZONE.

Walter De La Mare, writer, was descended from Jean Baptiste Delamare, who arrived in England in October 1730 from Bolbec, Normandy. One branch of the family were prominent in the Spitalfields silk industry, the other pursued professional and intellectual careers. During the nineteenth century the family provided three Directors of the French Hospital.

In his novels, short stories and poems, De La Mare is ceaselessly concerned with the supernatural and the macabre. His interest in a child's perceptions led him to write many poems for children. His constant theme is the mysteriousness of experience and the awareness that the simplest event is shadowed by the inexplicable.

DIMENSIONS: *Large octavo.*

PROVENANCE: *Private Collection.*

LITERATURE: *Luce Bonnerot, Walter de la Mare, poet and writer of Huguenot extraction, Proceedings of the Huguenot Society of London, Vol. 20 (1958–64), pp. 440–449; R.L. Mégriz, Walter de la Mare; a Biographical and Critical Sketch, 1924.*

222 *Smart Lethieullier (1701–1760)*
PORTRAIT, OIL ON CANVAS; GEORGE KNAPTON *c.*1725.

Smart Lethieullier was a leading scholar and collector of his day. He was descended from a Huguenot family who had come to England from Brabant in 1605, and quickly established themselves as eminent merchants and landowners. Smart's grandfather became Sheriff of London in 1674, and was knighted in the same year. His father, John Lethieullier, bought Aldersbrook House in Essex in 1693; this was Smart's main residence throughout his life. Educated at Eton and Trinity College, Oxford, he was elected a Fellow of the Royal Society and a Fellow of the Society of Antiquaries soon after leaving Oxford, in 1724. He travelled widely in the British Isles, collected fossils, coins and books, and corresponded with like-minded scholarly contemporaries, the Dean of Exeter, Emmanuel de Costa, Dr. Richard Pococke and Peter Collinson. He wrote many learned papers, some of which were published posthumously in 'Archaeologia', the Journal of the Society of Antiquaries. Other writings survive in manuscript (*Catalogue numbers* 223, 224).

Smart was probably responsible for the construction of the chapel and family mausoleum at St. Mary's Church, Little Ilford. In his portrait he holds a half unfurled sketch of a contemporary building façade in the Palladian style. This has yet to be identified, but may have been a projected plan, perhaps designed in part by Smart, for an alteration to one of the many Lethieullier properties, or for a new project which was never realised. Smart and his wife landscaped the grounds of Aldersbrook House (now the City of London Cemetery) and built a 'Hermitage' there to house his collections.

The portrait is likely to date from about the time of his marriage, in February, 1725, to Margaret Sloper. The costume and wig cannot be later than about 1727, and the fine silver waistcoat may have been part of his wedding outfit. (Information kindly supplied by Natalie Rothstein and Avril Hart.)

George Knapton (1698–1778) worked mainly in London, and had been a pupil of Jonathan Richardson the Elder. He specialised in pastels, and the velvety quality of this oil painting simulates a pastel effect. Knapton was a founder member of the Society of Dilettanti in 1736, and published a paper on the recent discovery of Herculaneum in 1740. He became Surveyor and Keeper of the King's pictures in 1765. Lethieullier may well have commissioned his portrait from a young artist whose intellectual bent appealed to him.

DIMENSIONS: *762 × 610mm.*

PROVENANCE: *Smart Lethieullier, by descent to the present owner, Sir Westrow Hulse.*

EXHIBITED: *Georgian Essex 1714–1837, Valence House, Dagenham, 3–17 May, 1958 (321).*

LITERATURE: *C.H.I. Chown, The Lethieullier Family of Aldersbrook House, Essex Review, XXXV, 1926, pp.203–220; XXXVI, 1927, pp.1–21; L.Cust, History of the Society of Dilettanti, ed. S. Colvin, 1898, pp.261–9; Smart Lethieullier, Archaeologia, I, pp.26–29; 56–59; 73–9; II, pp.291–300; H. Walpole, Anecdotes of Painting in England, ed. R.N. Wornum, 1862, II, p.710.*

223 *Catalogue of Fossils*
MANUSCRIPT, 543ff., PEN, INK AND WATERCOLOUR ON PAPER, BOUND IN LEATHER.
COMPILED BY SMART LETHIEULLIER, 1750–1760.

The title page reads 'A Catalogue of the Fossil Shells and other Bodies now Preservd in my Collection Ranged into different Classes with Notes of any particular Accidents attending them And the Places generally where they are found'. This meticulous handwritten and illustrated catalogue of Smart Lethieullier's collection of fossils was completed some time after 1750, as a note refers to a group of fossils given in that year. Lethieullier divided his collection into specific categories, e.g. nautili, bivalves, teeth and palates of fish. The numbered entries correspond with the numbers which were presumably assigned to each fossil (now all lost). He also noted the colour and provenance of each fossil and probably executed the drawings.

The fossils were kept in two large cabinets, although some 'being too heavy for the cabinet, are plac'd elsewhere'. Peter Collinson described it as a 'great collection, which excells most others', and other notable contemporaries visited Lethieullier's home at Aldersbrook House to study it. After Lethieullier's death in 1760, it seems to have disappeared.

PROVENANCE: *Smart Lethieullier; by descent to the present owner; Private Collection.*

LITERATURE: *J. Delair, Collections and Collectors of Note: 27 Smart Lethieullier, 1701–1760, The Geological Curator, II, no.6 (1979), pp.31–2; The Gentleman's Magazine, XXX, 1760, p.443.*

223

222

223

223

224 *Catalogue of Egyptian Antiquities*
MANUSCRIPT *c*.1733–43.

This handwritten unbound list of Lethieullier's Egyptian antiquities is entitled 'A Catalogue of the Ægyptian Antiqs in my Collection'. It consists of twenty-one numbered items. The first four; an urn, two small idols, and a painting on board, are followed by the statement, 'All these 4 Antiqs were brought out of Ægypt by Capt Wm Lethieullier, & presented to me by him'.

Smart himself never visited Egypt, although he was much interested in Egyptology. Captain (later Colonel) Lethieullier was a cousin of Smart's father. Nichols comments in his 'Literary Anecdotes', 'Colonel William Lethieullier … travelled into Egypt and brought over a very perfect mummy … now in the British Museum, the rest having been in Mr Smart Lethieullier's hands'. Smart and William Lethieullier both belonged to the Egyptian Society, founded in London in 1741, which met to dine and discuss Egyptology. Some of the members had been to Egypt, and brought antiquities to be studied by others. The Society flourished for only two years, and last met on March 31st, 1743. During that time Smart attended and contributed to several meetings and was appointed 'Inspector, Controller & Examiner of the Egyptian medals'.

The next eleven entries in his catalogue are followed by a note, 'Most of the foregoing numbers were sent to Dr Woodward from Ægypt by the Revnd Mr Thos Shaw'. The final five entries, which include 'the skull of an Ægyptian mummy Entire & preserv'd with Gums & Spices' and a 'Crocodile in Brass' are not given a provenance, with the exception of 'a comb of brown wood' from Cairo 'sent to Dr Woodward by Mr Coke' and an alabaster head 'brought from Rome by Abbe Sterbini Ao 1732 … formerly in the Cabinet of Cardinal Gualteri'. Mr Coke was also a member of the Egyptian Society.

The manuscript must date from after 1732, and before 1743, when William Lethieullier was promoted from Captain to Colonel. A check of the objects is written in the margin and initialled 'M.H.' (Mary Hulse, Smart's niece and the main beneficiary of his will) and dated 1774.

The present whereabouts of the antiquities listed is not known, and two others, not listed (an obelisk and a marble 'covered in Hieroglyphics'), are illustrated in a contemporary monograph, but have similarly disappeared.

PROVENANCE: *Private Collection.*

LITERATURE: *A.Gordon, An Essay towards Explaining the hieroglyphical Figures on the Coffin of the Ancient Mummy belonging to Capt. William Lethieullier, 1737, plates I, II, and V; J. Nichols, Literary Anecdotes of the Eighteenth Century, V, London, 1812, pp.368–72; Journal of the Egyptian Society, 1741–3, British Library, Add. Ms.52362.*

225 *Tankard*
AMBER MOUNTED IN SILVER GILT, WITH ORIGINAL HINGED LEATHER CASE; NORTH EAST GERMANY, PERHAPS KONIGSBERG; *c*.1650–60.

This lidded tankard is constructed of clear amber carved in low relief, and mounted in silver gilt. The body is composed of ten sections, each one made up of three panels dowelled together. The central cartouche of each depicts a full-length figure in contemporary dress. Above and below these panels are decorative borders of fruit and birds. The foot consists of eight panels carved with stylised flowers and tendrils; inside the base is a hexagonal relief of a naked female figure (Galatea?) astride a dolphin. The seven sections of the domed lid depict two winged and five wingless putti riding sea monsters. Stylised flowers and tendrils surround a central medallion on top of the lid, in which is shown a full-length seated figure of Bacchus (?) raising a goblet. On the underside of the lid is a matching medallion of a half-length figure of a woman pouring wine from a ewer into a goblet, possibly signifying Temperance. Both these medallions differ in technique from the carved clear amber elsewhere on the work. They are of pierced white amber, painted with black dots for the eyes, set against a black backing (probably horn and mica) under a panel of clear amber. Such medallions can be seen on other contemporary ambers, such as the inside of the lid of a tankard in the British Museum (Waddesdon Bequest) and the base of a bowl in the Victoria and Albert Museum.

The silver gilt thumb-piece of the hinged lid is formed of three plumes, the central one beaded. The mounts on the handle are embellished with niello designs of leaves, and a decorative emblem on each side. The amber of the handle is carved as a half-length female figure, but the head is now missing.

Of the ten full-length figures of men and women on the central panels, seven are playing instruments: violin, small lute, harp, flute, rustic fiddle (played by a hunch-back man), curtal (an early form of bassoon) and cello. One woman is singing from a book. The two remaining figures could be dancers, one carrying a plumed fan (?) and the other a fan or chatelaine.

Although it has yet to be identified, the figures almost certainly derive from an engraved source. The dancer bearing a plumed fan (?) is identical with a figure on the tankard in the British Museum referred to above, while the singer and the violin player correspond with figures on a tankard in the Schatzkammer in Munich and the harpist appears on a hexagonal flask in the Darmstadt Landesmuseum. The simplicity of the figures and the folk iconography strongly suggest that they derive from a series of popular prints.

The fruit, birds, and putti on sea-creatures are also dependent on an engraved source, and parallels with other ambers can be cited.

Amber seems at first a strange choice of material for a tankard. It was used primarily because of its exotic appeal. Most amber works of art are made of Baltic amber, which is about 40 million years old. This is washed up on the shore of the Baltic Sea, or mined from the land in North East Germany and Poland. The sixteenth and seventeenth century Kunst- and Schatzkammern often included carved or turned ambers, and a drinking vessel carved of

COLOUR PLATE: *page 9.*

DIMENSIONS: *174mm high, 134mm diameter of base.*

PROVENANCE: *Smart Lethieullier; by descent to the present owner; Private Collection.*

LITERATURE: *O. Pelka, Zum Werk des Bernsteinmeisters Georg Schreiber in Königsberg, Pantheon, XVII, pp.27–29; A. Rohde, Bernstein Ein Deutscher Werkstoff, Berlin, 1937; A. Rohde and U.Stöver, Goldschmiedekunst in Königsberg, Stuttgart, 1959, figs.34–36; S. Schade, Gefässen gegen Gift, Staatliche Kunstsammlungen Kassel Informationen, no.11, November 1982; M. Trusted, Smart Lethieullier's Amber Tankard, Apollo, May, 1985; Ibid., Catalogue of the European Ambers in the Victoria and Albert Museum, forthcoming, 1985.*

225

225

amber was thought, like rhinoceros horn and coconut-shell, to indicate if the liquid it contained was contaminated with poison.

The overall form of the tankard, reflecting contemporary goldsmiths' work, the costume of the figures depicted on it, and the metal mounts all point to a date of about 1650–60. At this time, amber was worked primarily in centres along the Baltic coast, in particular Königsberg and Danzig. One tankard, now destroyed, dated 1617, was signed by a Königsberg amber-worker, Georg Schreiber (active 1617–43). It is probable that the present one comes from a Königsberg workshop influenced by his work, and by the work of another Königsberg artist, Jacob Heise (d.1667). The tankards in the British Museum and the Munich Schatzkammer referred to above may well be products of the same workshop.

226 *The Procession of King Edward VI from the Tower of London to Westminster, 19 February 1547, previous to his coronation*
ENGRAVING, JAMES BASIRE I AFTER S.H. GRIMM, 1787.

The procession winds its way through the City, starting from the Tower, down Cheapside, past the Eleanor Cross and the Conduit, up to St. Paul's and Temple Bar. The procession finished at Westminster; in the engraving the route has been considerably condensed so as to enable the artist to exhibit the whole distance to the spectator.

This engraving was published by the Society of Antiquaries on 1 May 1787 for 'Vetusta Monumenta'. As the Society had decided to commission engravings on an unprecedented scale, James Basire, as engraver to the Society of Antiquaries, persuaded the paper manufacturer Whatman in 1770 to produce a special paper which was given the name, 'antiquarian'. This engraving was printed on 'antiquarian paper'. It was based on a copy by S. H. Grimm of a coeval painting at Cowdray, Sussex, the seat of Viscount Montagu.

A few years later, in 1793, the original painting at Cowdray was destroyed in a fire.

For details of the Basire family (see *Catalogue number 233*).

DIMENSIONS: *655 × 1310mm.*

PROVENANCE: *Museum of London.*

LITERATURE: *Bernard Adams, London Illustrated 1604–1851, no. 36, pp. 85,88.*

227 *Waltham Cross*
ENGRAVING, JAMES BASIRE I(?) AFTER R. SCHNEBBELIE, 1791.

Of the three Eleanor crosses erected in London in the 1290s, Waltham Cross is the only one to survive although it has been considerably restored. The crosses mark the places where the funeral cortège of Edward I's beloved wife, Eleanor of Castile, stopped on its way from Lincoln, where she died, to London, where she was buried.

This engraving was published by the Society of Antiquaries on 23 April 1791. It shows the cross in its pre-restoration state, without its finial and showing signs of advanced deterioration. The monument was often depicted by artists, notably Rowlandson, for its picturesque qualities. It was also of interest to antiquarians for its age and rarity.

DIMENSIONS: *482 × 328mm.*

PROVENANCE: *Museum of London.*

228 *Anglo Norman Antiquities*
ANDRE COLTEE DUCAREL, 1767.

André Coltee Ducarel, DCL (1713–1785) was born in Normandy in 1713. His family later left Caen and settled in Greenwich.

In 1737 he was made a Fellow of the Society of Antiquaries, and was appointed Keeper of Lambeth Palace Library in 1757. Ducarel spent his holidays on antiquarian tours, taking topographical and archaeological notes.

His coins, pictures and antiquities were sold by auction on 30 November 1785, and his books, manuscripts and prints in April, 1786. The greater part of the manuscripts passed into the hands of Richard Gough and John Nichols.

In 1754, he published 'A Tour Through Normandy', and an enlarged account of this was republished under the title of 'Anglo Norman Antiquities considered in a Tour through part of Normandy, illustrated with twenty-seven copper plates'. The volume was dedicated to Bishop Lyttelton, President of the Society of Antiquaries. A French translation was published at Caen in 1823.

PROVENANCE: *British Library.*

LITERATURE: *Irvine R. Gray, Huguenot Manuscripts: A descriptive Catalogue of the Remaining Manuscripts in the Huguenot Library, Huguenot Society Quarto Series, Vol.LVI, 1983, p.184, Ms.T.13. A list of printed books and manuscripts in the Archiepiscopal Library relating to French Protestant History, compiled 1883, with a brief introduction by the donor, referring to three Lambeth Palace Librarians of Huguenot origin, Pierre (recte Paul) Colomiez, Hans de Veille, and Andrew Coltee Ducarel.*

226

227

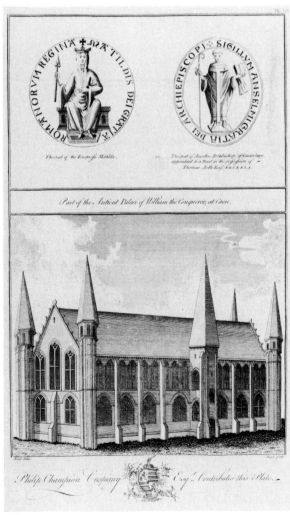

228

A LIST of the WORKS of
JOHN ROCQUE,

Chorographer to His Royal Highneſs the PRINCE OF *WALES*,

Near *Old Round-Court* in the *Strand*, LONDON, and on the *Batchelors-Walk*, DUBLIN.

No.		L.	s.	d.
1	HIS large Survey of London in 24 Sheets	3	3	0
2	Ditto reduced into one large Sheet —	0	5	0
3	An exact Survey of the City of London and 10 Miles round in 16 Sheets, containing all the New Roads, Buildings, &c. to the Year 1759	2	2	0
4	Ditto reduced into one Large Sheet —	0	5	0
5	Ditto of Paris in 7 Sheets, on the same Scale as the Environs of London and Dublin	1	1	0
6	Ditto reduced into one Sheet, to the same Scale as that of London, by which may be seen the beautiful Situation of these two Rivals, their Extent, and by how much London exceeds Paris in Acres, Arpens, &c.	0	5	0
7	An exact Survey of the City and Suburbs of Dublin in 4 Sheets; in which every House is expressed	1	1	0
8	Ditto reduced into one Sheet, with the Division of the Parishes —	0	4	0
9	Ditto and Environs in 4 Sheets; which contains the Harbours, Bays, Soundings, &c.	0	12	0
10	A Plan of the City of Cork —	0	5	0
11	Ditto of Kilkenny —	0	2	6
12	Ditto of the Camp at Turles in Ireland, 1757	0	1	0
13	Ditto of Paris } on the same Scale	0	2	6
14	Ditto of Rome }	0	2	6
15	Ditto of Bristol in 4 Sheets	0	10	6
16	Ditto reduced into one Sheet, with Views of the principal Buildings in the City	0	2	6
17	Ditto of York, with Views	0	2	6
18	Ditto of St. Edmund's-Bury —	0	2	6
19	Ditto of Fort St. George and Madras —	0	1	0
20	Ditto of Trichinapoli in the East-Indies, with the Encampment of the English and French Armies 1754	0	2	6
21	Ditto of Quebec, with all the Fortifications	0	1	6
22	Ditto of Dunkirk, with its Fortifications	0	1	6
23	Plan of St. Malo's, with a Map of the Coast	0	1	6
24	Ditto of Brest, with all the Fortifications, Bay, Harbour, Soundings, &c.	0	1	6
25	Ditto of Port L'Orient and Port Louis	0	1	0
26	Ditto of St. Martin's in the Island of Rhé	0	0	6
27	Ditto of Rochfort, the Island of Aix, the Bay, &c. —	0	1	0
28	Ditto of Toulon, with its Environs —	0	1	6
29	Ditto of Fort St. Philip's in the Island of Minorca, with the French Batteries, from a Survey made by Capt. Nanpierre, Engineer	0	1	6
30	An exact Survey of the Island of Minorca by Dº.	0	2	0
31	A Plan of Gibraltar, with the Fortifications, Spanish Approaches, &c. —	0	2	0
32	Ditto of Metz in Lorrain —	0	2	6
33	Ditto of Thionville ——	0	2	6
34	Ditto of Montpelier —	0	2	6
35	Ditto of Nismes ——	0	2	6
36	Ditto of Dresden — —	0	1	6
37	Ditto of Constantinople			
38	Ditto of the Seraglio			
39	View of Constantinople } — —	0	5	0
40	Ditto of the Seraglio			
41	A Plan of London before the Great Fire, by Hollar — —	0	1	0
42	Ditto after the Fire, as it was designed by Sir Christopher Wren	0	1	6
43	A General Map of the Post-Roads of Europe in 2 Sheets —	0	5	0
44	The Seven First Sheets of a Survey of the Counties of Berks, Oxford and Buckingham	at 3s. each		
45	Ditto, with the Division of the Parishes	0	4	0

No.		L.	s.	d.
46	An exact Survey of the County of Middlesex in 4 Sheets, with the Division of the Parishes	1	1	0
47	Ditto reduced into one Sheet ——	0	2	6
48	Ditto of Shropshire in 4 Sheets ——	0	12	6
49	The British Atlas, or a Set of Maps of all the Counties in England, with 2 General Maps	0	7	6
50	The Quarter Master's or Cromwell's Map of England in 6 Sheets, being the best extant	0	10	6
51	A Plan of Exeter in 2 Sheets	1	1	0
52	Ditto of Calais	0	5	0
53	Ditto of Chebucto-Harbour and Town of Hallifax: These are very scarce.	0	5	0
54	Ditto of Richmond-Gardens in 2 Sheets	0	10	6
55	Ditto reduced into one Sheet ——	0	2	6
56	Ditto of Kensington-Gardens	0	2	6
57	Ditto of Wilton-Gardens, the Seat of the Earl of Pembroke	0	2	6
58	Ditto of Esher-Gardens, the Seat of the late Right Hon. Henry Pelham, Esq;	0	2	6
59	Ditto of Claremont, the Seat of His Grace the Duke of Newcastle, with Views	0	5	0
60	Ditto of the Earl of Lincoln's Gardens	0	2	6
61	Ditto of Windsor, with Views of the Castle and Park —	0	2	6
62	Ditto of Geneva — —	0	2	6
63	Ditto of Lima, Capital of Peru in S. America	0	2	6
64	A Book of Ornaments by Brunitty —	0	7	6
65	Twelve Heads after Raphael ——	0	3	0
66	Twelve Beasts by Audry ——	0	3	0
67	Six Figures of Horses — —	0	1	6
*68	A Survey of the County of Dublin in 4 Sheets	1	1	0
*69	Ditto of the County of Armagh in 4 Sheets	1	1	0
70	An exact Map of the British and French Dominions in North-America, with the Roads, Distances, Limits of Settlement and Forts as they are at present, 1759	0	2	0

A Set of MAPS *of all the different Parts of the World, at* 1 s. 6 d. *each.*

71 The World
72 Europe
73 Asia
74 Africa
75 General Map of America
76 North-America
77 South-America
78 England, with all the Post-Roads
79 Scotland
80 Map of Ireland
81 Spain and Portugal
82 Italy
83 France, with the Post-Roads
84 The United-Provinces
85 The Catholic Low-Countries
86 Germany
87 Switzerland
88 Denmark
89 Sweden and Norway
90 Hungary, 2 Sheets
91 Russia
92 Poland
93 Holy-Land
94 The Mediterranean-Sea
95 Hungary
96 Turkish Empire in Europe.

N.B. *Great Variety of Foreign Maps, Plans, Battles, Sieges, complete Atlas,* &c. (*The First* 32 *Sheets of the large Map of* France, *drawn by the King's Orders, by Messieurs* Cassiny, *at* 5 s. *each.*) *By* De L'Isle, Roberts, Bellin, D'Anville, Broukener, Le Rouge, *the Academy of Berlin,* &c.

246

ENGRAVERS & PRINTSELLERS

A List of the Works of John Rocque, 1759

Engravers of Huguenot origin made special contributions to different aspects of the profession. Isaac Basire (1704–1768) was the first of four different generations of engravers, and his son and grandson worked in close association with the Society of Antiquaries. Paul Fourdrinier specialised in architectural plans. Simon Gribelin, who published pattern books of ornament in the 1680s and 1690s, also engraved designs for book illustration. Francis Vivares was later recognised as the 'Father of English Landscape Engraving'.

John Rocque, Francis Vivares and J.B.C. Chatelain played an important part in the dissemination of the Rococo style in England, by publishing and engraving the latest designs from Paris. Dorothy Mercier, the wife of the painter Philip Mercier, and Celeste Regnier, companion of the Huguenot sculptor, Louis François Roubiliac, both ran print shops which specialised in continental engravings.

Trade card of Isaac Basire, c.1730.

233

229 *The Victory of Namur*

ENGRAVING, SIMON GRIBELIN AFTER A MEDAL BY JOHN FOWLER *c*.1694.
INSCRIBED: TO SAVE THE WORLD, SEE WILLIAM STRIKE LIKE JOVE! AND WATCHFULL
HEAV'N THE MIGHTY WORK APPROVE: FAME SOUNDS HIS PRAISE, FRESH LAURELS GRACE
HIS BROW, NAMUR SUBMITTS, AND ENVY'S TAUGHT TO BOW. NOW LEWIS FROM THIS
MOMENT DATE THY FALL, THE CONQU'ROUR OF NAMUR, WITH EASE MAY CONQUER ALL.
SOLD BY WILLM. CREED AT THE CASTLE, THE CORNER OF FISHER STREET RED LION SQUARE.

Namur was probably William III's most spectacular victory. In 1694 William besieged the
city, regarded as the strongest fortress in Europe, and despite the size of the French army of
100,000, the city surrendered.

Simon Gribelin was the son of Jacob Gribelin, engraver of Blois. His grandfather was
watchmaker to Louis XIII. Simon Gribelin was in England by March 1681, when he received
denization. He was admitted to the Clockmakers' Company in 1686. Gribelin specialised in
engraving silver and smaller items such as snuffboxes and watchcases (*Catalogue number* 379).
He published two pattern books of decorative ornament, the first, 'A Book of Severall
Ornaments' in 1682, the second 'A Book of Ornaments usefull to jewellers watch-makers and
all other Artists', appeared in 1697. Gribelin also engraved designs for book illustration
see *Catalogue numbers* 231, 232.

DIMENSIONS: *164 × 197mm.*

PROVENANCE: *National Portrait Gallery.*

LITERATURE: *Stephen Baxter, William III, 1966, p. 330; Sheila O'Connell, Simon Gribelin (1661–1733) Printmaker and metal-engraver, Print Quarterly, Vol. II, March, 1985, pp. 27–38; Charles Oman, English Engraved Silver, 1150–1900, 1978, pp. 17,72–81.*

230 *A New Book of Ornaments*

SIMON GRIBELIN, REPRINTED BY JOHN BOWLES AND SON, LONDON, BETWEEN 1753
AND 1763.

The plates are compiled from two earlier publications by Gribelin, 'A Book of Severall
Ornaments', 1682 and 'A Book of Ornaments usefull to jewellers, watch-makers and all other
Artists', 1697, which were combined in Gribelin's own lifetime and published as 'A New
Book of Ornaments: Usefull to all Artists' and dedicated to Colonel Parsons, as one book of
12 leaves, which was originally published in 1704.

The fact that this volume was reprinted shows that Gribelin's pattern books were still in
demand seventy years after their first appearance. 'The Daily Post' announced on 21 February
1738 that Gribelin's engravings of 'Raphael Cartoons, Ceiling of the Banqueting House, etc;
A Book of Ornament of Twelve leaves, invented and engrav'd by him, were available from
Mr Pascall, Picture Frame-Maker, at the Golden Head, over against Hanover Street in Long
Acre'. For Pascall see *Catalogue number* 289.

NOT EXHIBITED.

PROVENANCE: *Yale Center for British Art, Paul Mellon Fund.*

231 *De Arte Graphica, Frontispiece*

a. DESIGN FOR FRONTISPIECE, PEN AND INK OVER RED CHALK, SIMON GRIBELIN, *c*.1716.
INSCRIBED: DE ARTE GRAPHICA LIBER.

This design represents the daughter of Dibutades, guided by Cupid, tracing her lover's
outline from his shadow on the wall. The subject, a legend from Pliny, was used in academic
circles to illustrate the origin of painting. The composition is framed in an oval hung with
drapery, with implements of painting on the pedestal below.

b. DE ARTE GRAPHICA (THE ART OF PAINTING),
C.A. DU FRESNOY, TRANSLATED BY JOHN DRYDEN, 1716.

This, the second edition of John Dryden's translation from the original French, is illustrated
with a frontispiece which was engraved and designed by Simon Gribelin. The original design
still survives (*see a. above*). The first edition has a different frontispiece, engraved but not
designed by Gribelin. The volume was published by Bernard Lintot, for whom Gribelin also
designed illustrations to the poems of Alexander Pope (*Catalogue number* 232).

DIMENSIONS: *137 × 97mm.*

PROVENANCE: *British Museum, Department of Prints and Drawings.*

LITERATURE: *Lawrence Binyon, Catalogue of Drawings by British Artists and Artists of Foreign Origin working in Great Britain, Department of Prints and Drawings, British Museum, 1900, Vol. II, p. 248.*

DIMENSIONS: *Octavo.*

PROVENANCE: *British Library.*

232 *The Works of Alexander Pope*

ILLUSTRATED BY SIMON GRIBELIN, 1717.

Simon Gribelin worked in association with the publisher, Bernard Lintot, and provided a
title vignette, eight headpieces, and six illustrated initials for this edition of the works of
Alexander Pope. Pope took great interest and care in the publication of his work, and his
correspondence with Lintot over the production of this volume still survives.

The volume is exhibited open at the headpiece to the 'Rape of Lock'. Adapted from an
earlier illustration to the poem by the Huguenot engraver, Louis du Guernier, the central
medallion shows the East Front of Hampton Court. In the foreground sylphs are engaged in
the various activities which are mentioned in the course of the poem. This vignette is flanked
by two satyrs, who peer at the scene through masks.

Gribelin engraved the illustrations to the second edition of the Earl of Shaftesbury's
'Characteristics', 1712, and his work was highly praised by the author. It is probable that this
successful project led to other commissions of a similar nature. The fine detailed decorative
ornament in Gribelin's book illustrations reveals his background and training in the fields of
jewellery and watchmaking.

DIMENSIONS: *Quarto.*

PROVENANCE: *British Library.*

LITERATURE: *Robert Halsband, The Rape of the Lock and its illustrations, 1714–1896, 1978, p. 22–3, fig. 9; Hans Hammelman, Book Illustrators in Eighteenth Century England, ed. T.S.R. Boase, 1975.*

231 a

229

231 b

230

232

233 Trade card of Isaac Basire

ST. JOHN'S COURT, NEAR RED LYON STREET, CLERKENWELL, c.1730.

Isaac was the son of James Basire, of Wardour Street, Soho, a refugee from Rouen, Normandy. It is possible that his father James Basire was also an engraver (*Catalogue number* 234). Isaac was the first recorded engraver of four generations of the family who worked in the same trade. He was succeeded at these premises by his son John Basire, and a copy of the latter's original bill heading is also in the Heal Collection. Isaac's elder son, James (1730–1802) is best remembered as the master of William Blake, whom he took on as an apprentice in 1772. He worked for the Society of Antiquaries and in particular association with the antiquary Richard Gough (*Catalogue numbers* 226, 227). This association was continued by his son, also James (1769–95); the latter was in turn succeeded by his son, also James Basire (1796–1869).

ILLUSTRATED: *page 161.*

DIMENSIONS: *72 × 101mm.*

PROVENANCE: *Heal Collection, Department of Prints and Drawings, British Museum.*

LITERATURE: *David Bindman, Blake as an Artist, 1977, pp.12–13,41; Dictionary of National Biography under Basire; Richard Godfrey, Printmaking in Britain, Oxford, 1978, p. 66; Wagner, Ms. Pedigree of the Basire Family, Huguenot Library.*

234 A Crocodile and Alligator

ENGRAVINGS, JAMES? AND ISAAC? BASIRE AFTER C. LEMPRIERE, 1739.
INSCRIBED: A YOUNG CROCODILE DRAWN FROM THE LIFE IN LONDON, OCTOBER 1739 AND SIGNED I. BASIRE; A YOUNG ALLIGATOR DRAWN FROM THE LIFE IN LONDON, OCTOBER 1739 AND SIGNED J. BASIRE.

The authorship of these engravings is puzzling. It is possible that they were executed by Isaac Basire (1704–1768) and his son James, although the latter was only nine in 1739.

The animals may have been drawn at the Tower of London, where there was a menagerie at this time.

DIMENSIONS: *137 × 272mm; 132 × 276mm.*

PROVENANCE: *Department of Prints and Drawings, Victoria and Albert Museum.*

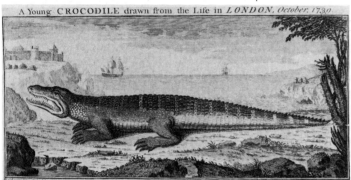 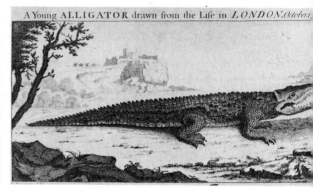

234

235 Triumphal Arch for the Coronation of George II and Queen Caroline

PAUL FOURDRINIER, AFTER WILLIAM KENT, 1727.
INSCRIBED: TRIUMPHAL ARCH ERECTED AND PAINTED ON THE WEST END OF WESTMINSTER HALL FOR THE CORONATION OF HIS MAJTY KING GEORGE THE SECOND AND QUEEN CAROLINE. OCTOBER THE 11TH 1727. WITH THE CEREMONIE OF THE KINGS CHAMPION ATTENDED BY THE LORD HIGH CONSTABLE AND THE EARL MARSHAL. SOLD BY P. FOURDRINIER, PRINTSELLER & STATIONER, THE CORNER OF CRAGGS COURT, CHARING CROSS.

The Fourdrinier family came originally from Caen in Normandy. Paul Fourdrinier was born in Groningen, Holland, and studied under the engraver Bernard Picart, and came to London in 1720. In 1721, he married Suzanne Grolleau, whose family also came from Caen.

He specialised as an engraver of plates for architectural treatises, working for William Chambers (*Catalogue number* 236) and William Kent, for whom, in 1736, he engraved the plans of Houghton, Norfolk, the seat of Sir Robert Walpole. William Kent designed Fourdrinier's trade card which is dated 1731 (photograph only in the Heal Collection), the year in which Fourdrinier moved to Craggs Court, Charing Cross from St. Martin's Lane. Paul Fourdrinier was buried at Mount Nod, Wandsworth, in 1758 (*Catalogue number* 163). He was succeeded by his son and grandson, both named Charles, who continued the stationery business at the same premises until 1811.

Paul Fourdrinier also engraved the plans of Charles Labelye's various designs for Westminster Bridge and the frontispiece to Stephen Riou's 'Elements of Fortification' (*Catalogue numbers* 144, 194).

DIMENSIONS: *360 × 260mm.*

PROVENANCE: *Department of Prints and Drawings, Victoria and Albert Museum.*

LITERATURE: *Richard Edwards, The Rise and Fall of the Fourdriniers, The Paper Maker, October 1968, pp. 59–61; Rev. F.G. Lee, Pedigree of Fourdrinier and Grolleau, Miscellanea Genealogica et Heraldica, July 1880, pp. 385–386. Hugh Phillips, Mid-Georgian London, 1964, p. 102.*

Triumphal Arch Erected and Painted on the West end of Westminster Hall
for the Coronation of his Maj.ty King George the Second and Queen Caroline.
October the 11th. 1727.
With the Ceremonie of the Kings Champion attended by the Lord High Constable and the Earl Marshal

236

235

236

236 *Designs of Chinese Buildings, Furniture, Dresses, Medicines and Utensils*

JOHN FOUGERON, PAUL FOURDRINIER, CHARLES GRIGNION AND E. ROOKER AFTER
WILLIAM CHAMBERS, 1757.

These twelve plates after William Chambers' designs were engraved by three craftsmen of
Huguenot origins. (For Paul Fourdrinier and Charles Grignion see *Catalogue numbers* 235,
284). John Fougeron was possibly the son of Daniel Fougeron, both of whom received
naturalisation in April, 1693. Another John Fougeron was naturalised in 1700.

ILLUSTRATED: *page 165.*

DIMENSIONS: *394 × 260mm.*

PROVENANCE: *Department of Prints
and Drawings, Victoria and Albert
Museum.*

LITERATURE: *Hugh Honour,
Chinoiserie, 1961, pp.154–6;
David C. Agnew, Protestant Exiles
from France, Index Volume, 1874,
pp.55,65.*

237 *Trade card of William De La Cour, Drawing Master*

AT THE SIGN OF THE GOLDEN HEAD, KATHERINE STREET, STRAND, R. WHITE AFTER
DE LA COUR, c.1740.

William De La Cour was a designer and a drawing master of considerable range and ability.
In 1740, he produced the stage designs for a production of G.B. Pescetti's opera 'Busiri' at the
King's Theatre, London. From 1741, he published a series of pattern books, the first of
which was engraved by Francis Vivares (*Catalogue number* 244), the last, by Jacob Bonneau
(*Catalogue number* 294). He also ran his own shop at the above address, where his stock
included artists' supplies and engraved ornament.

In 1753, The Public Advertiser announced the sale of 'the Household Furniture, Pictures,
Plate, China and Linen of Mr. De la Cour' as he had been invited to establish an academy in
Dublin. De La Cour later settled in Edinburgh, where he worked as a decorative painter. His
self-portrait of 1765 is in the Scottish National Portrait Gallery.

DIMENSIONS: *165 × 125mm.*

PROVENANCE: *Heal Collection,
Department of Prints and Drawings,
British Museum.*

EXHIBITED: *Rococo Art and Design
in Hogarth's England, Victoria and
Albert Museum, 1984, D29d, p. 63.*

LITERATURE: *John Fleming, Enigma
of a Rococo Artist, Country Life,
Vol.131, 24 May 1962, pp.1224–6.*

238 *The 4th Book of Ornaments*

FRONTISPIECE, WILLIAM DE LA COUR, 1743; INSCRIBED: THE 4TH BOOK OF ORNAMENTS BY
DE LA COUR, PUBLISHD ACCORDING TO ACT OF PARLIAMENT AUG.ST YE 20TH, 1743.

William De La Cour published eight different books of ornament in the 1740s. The first three
books were dedicated to the Earl of Middlesex, the Earl of Holderness and the Duke of
Rutland. Michael Snodin noted that all three noblemen were keen supporters of the Opera,
for which De La Cour painted scenery.

DIMENSIONS: *558 × 407mm.*

PROVENANCE: *Department of Prints
and Drawings, British Museum.*

LITERATURE: *Rococo Art and Design
in Hogarth's England, Victoria and
Albert Museum, C.11, p. 45.*

239 *Views of London Churches*

HENRY ROBERTS AFTER J.B.C. CHATELAIN, 1750.

The full title reads 'Fifty small Original and Elegant Views of the most Splendid Churches,
Villages Rural Prospects and Masterly Pieces of Architecture adjacent to London design'd for
the Improvement of Such Gentlemen and Ladies as have a Taste for Drawing and Colouring,
or are delighted with the several Exhibitions of the Diagonal Mirror'. The prints in this
volume are hand coloured.

J.B.C. Chatelain was of Huguenot parentage, and was born in London. He is said to have
held a commission in the French army, under his assumed name Chatelain, his real surname
being Philipe. He abandoned his career in the army and turned to drawing and engraving,
and he also boosted his income by working as a drawing master. In 1737 he produced
'A New Book of Landskips Pleasant & useful to learn to Draw without a master', which was
published by John Rocque. In 1750, with the assistance of Francis Vivares (*Catalogue number*
244), he etched six of his own drawings of 'Views of the River Thames'. Chatelain also
travelled round Britain producing drawings and watercolours of country houses and provincial
cities.

Chatelain engraved a title page and some of the plates for 'A Book of Ornaments Containing
Divers elegant Designs for the use of Goldsmiths, Chasers, Carvers etc. from the Drawings
of Messrs. Germain, Meissonnier, Sigr Cattarello'.

Chatelain died at the White Bear Inn, Piccadilly, much reduced in circumstances. His burial
in the poor ground of St. James's Workhouse in Poland Street was attended by Francis
Vivares. He died a Roman Catholic.

DIMENSIONS: *Octavo.*

PROVENANCE: *Museum of London.*

LITERATURE: *Hans Hammelman,
Book Illustrators in eighteenth-century
England, ed. T.S.R. Boase, 1975,
p. 24; Men and women of Soho, 1903,
270–273; Peter Ward Jackson, English
Furniture Designs, 1958, p. 34,
pls.19,346; Hugh Phillips,
Mid-Georgian London, 1964, p. 272;
J.T. Smith, Nollekens and His Times,
1829, Vol.1, pp.158–9; Rococo Art
and Design in Hogarth's England,
Victoria and Albert Museum
Exhibition Catalogue, 1984,
pp.43,124,245.*

240 *View of South Sea House*

ENGRAVING BY J. FOUGERON AFTER S. WALE, NO DATE.

This building was once the premises of 'The Governor and Company of Merchants of Great
Britain trading to the South Seas and other parts of America'. The Company became
notorious for the collapse of a highly speculative scheme known as the 'South Sea Bubble'.

No biographical information has come to light about this engraver, but Fougeron was
certainly a Huguenot name (*Catalogue number* 236).

DIMENSIONS: *142 × 86mm.*

PROVENANCE: *Museum of London.*

237

238

239

A View of St. Mary le Bone Church
Publish'd according to Act of Parliament Nov.t 3 1750

240

South Sea House

241 Matthew Liart (c.1736–c.1782)

MEZZOTINT PORTRAIT, PHILIP AUDINET, c.1780.

The sitter is shown half-length facing three quarters to the right.

Matthew Liart was the grandson of a Huguenot refugee, who worked as a respectable periwig-maker and barber, and built his own house in the south west corner of Compton Street and Crown Street (then Hog Lane) close to the French church of Les Grecs. Matthew's father was a maker of 'survelois' or 'saveloys', 'a relishing kind of sausage' much in demand by the French residents in Soho.

Matthew Liart was apprenticed to Simon Francis Ravenet. Liart was later employed by John Boydell to engrave plates after Old Master paintings.

Philip Audinet (1766–1837) was born in Soho in 1766, where he was educated by his uncle, Rev. Samuel Audinet. He supplied J.T. Smith with biographical details of Matthew Liart, and apparently owned a 'spirited portrait' of Liart by Laurenson.

Audinet earned his living by engraving the plates for Harrison's 'Biographical Magazine', and Bell's 'Shakespeare' and 'British Theatre'.

DIMENSIONS: *155 × 115mm.*

PROVENANCE: *Given to the Victoria and Albert Museum by Mr. Brian Connors, 1965.*

LITERATURE: *J. Chaloner Smith, British Mezzotinto Portraits, 1878–1883, Vol. II; J.T. Smith, Nollekens and His Times, Vol. II, 1828, pp. 54–55, 317.*

242 Trade card of Regnier, printseller

AT THE SIGN OF THE GOLDEN BALL, NEWPORT STREET, LONG ACRE, c.1750.

There were several engravers of this name working in London during the eighteenth century. In 1710, Von Uffenbach, a German visitor, recorded a visit 'to Longacre to the house of a Frenchman, called Regnier, who is said to be one of the most elegant and best seal-engravers in England'. In 1712, a James Regnier advertised in the Daily Courant as a seal-engraver. In 1727, Jacques Regnier supplied the 2nd Duke of Montagu with a print.

This trade card probably advertises the shop which was run by a member of the same family, a Miss Celeste Regnier, by 1762. She was the fourth wife of the Huguenot sculptor, Louis François Roubiliac. A portrait of Miss Celeste Regnier, shown holding a volume of prints (by F.X. Vispré, who also painted Roubiliac) was sold at Christie's 20 March, 1953 (120).

DIMENSIONS: *250 × 170mm.*

PROVENANCE: *Heal Collection, Department of Prints and Drawings, British Museum.*

LITERATURE: *Tessa Murdoch, Louis François Roubiliac and his Huguenot Connections, Proceedings of the Huguenot Society of London, Vol. 24 (1983), pp. 26–45, fig. 2 and plate V.*

243 Trade card of Dorothy Mercier, printseller

AT THE SIGN OF THE GOLDEN BALL IN WINDMILL STREET, c.1762.

This trade card is inscribed on the verso with a bill dated June, 1765.

Dorothy Mercier was the second wife of the painter Philip Mercier (1689–1760, *Catalogue number* 207), whom she married in 1735. After her husband's death in 1761, she looked after the miniatures at the Society of Arts' annual exhibition and received ten guineas from their Charity List. In 1762, she set up as a Printseller and Engraver in Little Windmill Street, and in 1764 she was appointed stationer to the Society of Artists.

Dorothy Mercier's stock included artists' supplies, Italian, French and Flemish Prints, Fans and also 'Flower Pieces in Water Colours Painted by herself from the life'.

DIMENSIONS: *255 × 165mm.*

PROVENANCE: *Banks Collection; Department of Prints and Drawings, British Museum.*

LITERATURE: *Ambrose Heal, London Tradesmen's Cards of the XVIII century, 1925, pl. 78; John Ingamells and Robert Raines, A Catalogue of the Paintings, Drawings and Etchings of Philip Mercier, The Walpole Society, Vol. XLVI, 1976–78, p. 7.*

244 Francis Vivares (1709–1780)

PORTRAIT ENGRAVING.

INSCRIBED: FRANS. VIVARES, NATUS IN PAGO STI. JOHANNIS DE BRUEL IN ROUERGUE 11.0 JULII 1709. GENEVAM MISSUS 1711. UNDE ANGLIAM PETIT AN:AET:18:ET LONDINI ARTEM AENEIS EXCUDENDI TABULIS DIDICIT' FRANS VIVARES & CALDWAL SCULP. PUBLISHED BY F. VIVARES ACCORDING TO ACT OF PARLIAMT. APRIL 4, 1776.

Francis Vivares was the third son of John Vivares, a 'nouveau converti' (in order to remain in France he had abjured his Protestant faith). In 1711, he moved with his family to Geneva and in 1727 he came to England where he learnt engraving with the Swiss Joseph Wagner (1706–1780). Vivares became a close friend of the engraver and surveyor John Rocque, and in 1743 the latter stood godfather to Vivares' son John, at the Huguenot Church of Spring Gardens.

Francis Vivares ran a printshop in Great Newport Street (*Catalogue number* 245).

His obituary in the Gentleman's Magazine described him as 'the celebrated landscape engraver' and he is now regarded as one of the founders of the English school of landscape engraving.

After his death, the printselling business was carried on by his son Thomas.

DIMENSIONS: *211 × 165mm.*

PROVENANCE: *National Portrait Gallery.*

LITERATURE: *Richard T. Godfrey, Printmaking in Britain, 1978, pp. 40,43–4; Henry Vivarez, Pro Domo Mea, Un Artiste Graveur au XVIIIe siècle, François Vivares, 1904 (reproduced as frontispiece).*

241

242

243

244

245 *A Catalogue of Prints Ingraved*
FRANCIS VIVARES, *c.* 1760

Vivares ran a printshop at the Golden Head, Newport Street, where he sold 'all Sorts of Italian, French and Flemish Prints of the best Masters . . . all sorts of the best Drawing Paper & French & Italian Chalk & Lead Pencils, and Prints for Hanging Rooms'. He also supplied ornamental pattern books which included 'Trophies, Flowers, Nosegays and Birds,' and would have been widely used by artists and craftsmen working in many different fields.

Vivares is known to have engraved plates for Mathias Lock's 'A New Drawing Book of Ornaments' in 1740, and De La Cour's 'First Book of Ornament' in 1741.

DIMENSIONS: *330 × 210mm.*

PROVENANCE: *Department of Prints and Drawings, British Museum.*

LITERATURE: *Terry Friedman, Two eighteenth century catalogues of ornamental pattern books, Furniture History, Vol. XI, 1975, pp. 68–75.*

246 *A List of the Works of John Rocque*
LONDON, 1759.

This document lists the range of maps, surveys and engravings that Rocque supplied at his premises near Old Round Court on the north side of the Strand. These items were also available on the Batchelor's Walk in Dublin, where his brother-in-law, Bernard Scalé, was based from 1756. Rocque's earliest surviving work consists of surveys of gentlemen's estates, including Kensington Palace and Gardens, and Drumlanrig (*Catalogue numbers* 247, 248).

John Rocque played an important part in the dissemination of the Rococo style by publishing in England in the 1730s the latest books of engraved ornament from Paris. In 1759, he still supplied 'A Book of Ornaments' by Brunetti, which had first been published in London in 1736, and for which he himself had engraved several plates.

Rocque's reputation was largely based on his Survey of London and its Environs, which first appeared in the 1740s. This list shows that he also produced maps of other English cities and counties, as well as plans of French ports and continental cities.

ILLUSTRATED: *page* 160.

DIMENSIONS: *299 × 182mm.*

PROVENANCE: *Heal Collection, Department of Prints and Drawings, British Museum.*

LITERATURE: *Alistair Laing, Rococo at the V & A, The Burlington Magazine, July 1984, pp. 450–451; Hugh Phillips, Mid-Georgian London, 1964, p. 102, fig 156; Rococo Art and Design in Hogarth's England, Victoria and Albert Museum Exhibition Catalogue, 1984, pp. 38,46.*

247 *Survey of Drumlanrig*
ENGRAVING, HAND COLOURED, JOHN ROCQUE.
INSCRIBED: A PLAN OF THE GARDEN AND PLANTATION OF DRUMLANGRIG IN SCOTLAND. THE SEAT OF HIS GRACE THE DUKE OF QUEENSBURRY (SIC) TO THE MOST NOBLE PRINCE CHARLES, DUKE OF QUEENSBURRY & DOVER. THIS PLAN IS MOST HUMBLY INSCRIBED BY HIS GRACE'S MOST HUMBLE SERVANT J. ROCQUE.

ILLUSTRATED: *page* 174.

DIMENSIONS: *565 × 680mm.*

PROVENANCE: *Duke of Buccleuch and Queensberry, Drumlanrig, Dumfries.*

248 *View of Kensington Palace and Gardens from the East*
SURVEYED, DRAWN AND ENGRAVED BY JOHN ROCQUE, 1736.
INSCRIBED: TO THE QUEENS MOST EXCELLENT MAJESTY, THIS PLAN OF YE ROYAL PALACE AND GARDENS OF KENSINGTON IS MOST HUMBLY INSCRIBED BY YOUR MAJESTY'S MOST DUTIFUL LOYAL & OBEDIENT SUBJECT JOHN ROCQUE.

The inscription is contained in an ornamental Rococo cartouche which is flanked by gardener's implements.

DIMENSIONS: *290 × 505mm.*

PROVENANCE: *Museum of London.*

LITERATURE: *Hugh Phillips, John Rocque's Career, London Topographical Record, Vol. XX, pp. 9–25.*

249 *A Map of London and the adjacent country 10 miles round as Survey'd and Published in 16 Sheets reduc'd into one sheet*
SURVEYED AND PUBLISHED BY JOHN ROCQUE, 1748.
INSCRIBED: TO THE MOST HIGH PUISSANT & NOBLE PRINCE, JOHN DUKE OF MONTAGU &C. GRAND MASTER OF THE MOST HONOURABLE ORDER OF THE BATH, MASTER GENERAL OF THE ORDNANCE, MASTER OF THE GREAT WARDROBE & KNIGHT OF THE MOST NOBLE ORDER OF THE GARTER &C. THIS PLAN IS MOST HUMBLY INSCRIB'D BY HIS GRACES MOST DEVOTED & OBEDT HUMBLE SERVANT JOHN ROCQUE.

John Rocque's first Survey of London was published between 1741 and 1745 by John Pine, who had employed Rocque as his surveyor. Rocque later produced this companion map of London and the surrounding countryside, which was engraved by Richard Parr. It was dedicated to John, 2nd Duke of Montagu. In 1762, Rocque published a comparative plan of London and Paris which was dedicated to the same patron.

The original idea for this map came apparently from the engraver George Vertue. In 1738, William Oldys recorded in his diary for March 3rd, 'Went to Leicester Square . . . and saw Mr. Vertue there, and had some discourse about his grand design of an ichnographical survey or map of London and all the suburbs, but Mr. Rocque and he are not yet come to an agreement.' By 1759 (*Catalogue number* 246) the map had been updated to include 'all the New Roads, Buildings etc'.

NOT EXHIBITED.

ILLUSTRATED: *pages* 172–3.

DIMENSIONS: *540 × 255mm.*

PROVENANCE: *Museum of London.*

LITERATURE: *Hugh Phillips, John Rocque's Career, London Topographical Record, Vol. XX, 1959, pp. 9–25.*

A Catalogue
of Prints Ingraved by Francis Vivares.

Sold at the Authors Print Shop, ÿ Golden Head, in Newport Street, near Leicester Fields.

NB. Those without the Price are unfinish'd.

Titles.	Painters Names.	Price.
Landships	Fran. Milly	
Ditto	G. Lambert	} 0-7-6
Ditto	Patel	
Ditto	Wooton	} 0-7-6
Ditto and Ruin	Patel	0-4-0
Ditto	Patel	0-4-0
One Romantick View in Yorkshire		0-6-0
Second Ditto		
Landships	Martorelli	0-6-0
Ditto	G. Poussin	
Landskips and Figures	Zucarelli	} 0-6-6
Ditto	Zuccarelli	
Ruin	P. Pannini	} 0-6-6
Ditto	P. Ditto	
Landskips and Figures	Zuccarelli	} 0-6-6
Ditto	Zuccarelli	
Landskips	C. Lorraine	} 0-7-0
Ditto	G. Poussin	
Landskip and Figures	Fo. Simonini	} 0-7-0
Ditto its Companion	Fo. Simonini	
The Rural Lovers	T. Gainsborough	} 0-7-0
The Hop Pickers	G. Smith	
Landskips and Ruins	Patel	} 0-8-0
Ditto	C. Lorrain	
	T. Gainsborough	0-..0
	T. Gainsborough	0-..0
The Happy Peasant	P. Bergham	0-1-6
The Morning	A. Cnyp	0-1-6
The Evening	A. Cnyp	0-1-6
The Dutch Fisher Men	Van Goyen	0-1-6
Two small Ruins and Figures	Berg	0-2-0
The Topers	D. Teniers	0-0-6
Two small Landskips	Zuccarelli	0-2-0
Two Ditto	Zuccarelli	0-2-0
Six Landskips	Rembrandt	0-2-6
Books of Figures	Rembrandt	0-1-6
Books of Heads	Rembrandt	0-1-6
Two Landskips	Wouverman	0-..0
Two Views of Charanton	Boucher	0-1-0
The Handsom Cook Maid	Boucher	} 0-1-0
The Carefull Mother	Boucher	
The 5 Senses	D. Teniers	0-1-0
Two Dogs	D. Teniers	0-0-6
A Cat	C. Nicher	0-0-6
A Dog	Huet	0-0-6
A Drawing Book 12	Raphael	0-3-0
Ditto 12	Watteau	0-1-6
Ditto 12	Le Clerc	0-0-6

Books	Leaves	Painters Names	Price
Ruins	4	Mar. Ricci	0-2-0
Ruins	6	Piranesi	0-2-0
Large Cattel	6	Bergham	0-1-0
Small Cattel	6	Ditto	0-0-6
Small Cattel	6	Ditto	0-0-6
Cattel and Figures	4	Ditto	0-1-0
Horses	6	Stoup	0-1-6
A Book of Wild Baists	6	Snyder &c	0-..0
A Ditto	6	Ditto	0-..0
Small Fancies	4	Watteau	0-1-0
The Seasons	4	Ditto	0-1-0
The Seasons	4	Coypel	0-1-0
Chinese figures	4	Watteau	0-0-6
A Book of Masks	12	Toro &c	0-2-0
Books of Flowers	6	Fauquier	0-0-9
Ditto	6	Ditto	0-0-9
Ditto	6	Ditto	0-0-9
Ditto	6	Ditto	0-0-9
New Book of Flowers	24	Tepser	0-3-0
New Book of Flowers	6	Petty	0-1-0
Book of Trophies Deadgame	6	C Huet	0-1-6
Books of Ornament	12	Bruneti	0-1-6
Ditto of Chanys	6	Pirote	0-1-0
Books of Ornament	24	Angelo Rossi	0-8-0
Ditto of Trophies	6	R. Chrpentier	0-1-0
Ditto of Ornament	6	Eisen	0-0-9
Ditto of Chanys	6	Gliziere	0-1-0
Ditto Ornament	6	Babel	0-1-0
Ditto	12	Nilson	0-1-0
Ditto	6	Pariset	0-1-0
Ditto	6	C. de la Touche	0-1-6
A Book of Nosegays	6	Aug. Heckel	0-4-0
New Book of Flowers	6	Dodd	0-1-0
Ditto Drawn from Nature	6	Aug. Heckel	0-1-0
Book of Birds	12	Barlon	0-1-6
Ditto	12	Le Clerc	0-0-6

No. Books of Small Landskip after F. Vivares Drawing &c

No.		Leaves	Painters Names	Price
a	Ditto	6		0-0-6
b	Ditto	6		0-0-6
c	Ditto	6	Le Clerc	0-0-6
d	Ditto	6		0-0-6
e	Ditto out Lines	6		0-1-0
f	Ditto	6	Le Clerc	0-0-6
g	Ditto	6	Le Clerc	0-0-6
h	Ditto out Lines	6		0-1-0
i	Landskip and Ruins	6		0-1-0
k	Ditto	6	Perelle	0-1-0
l	Landskips	6	Ditto	0-1-0
m	Landskips ovals	6	Le Prince	0-1-0
n	Ditto Ovals	6	Le Prince	0-..0
o	Landskips & figures	8	Cochin	0-0-9
p	Landskips	6	Waterlo	0-1-0
q				0-0-6
r				0-0-6
s				0-0-6
t				
u				
v				
w				
x				
y				
z				
A Drawing Book in the Manner of Chalk No 1		6	Vanloo	0-1-6
Ditto No 2		6	Natoir	0-1-6
Ditto No 3		6	Eisen	0-1-6
Ditto No 4		6	Boucher	0-1-6
A Madona Head			Vien	0-1-0

Sells all sorts of Italian French and Flemish Prints of the best Masters. Likewise all sorts of the best Drawing Paper & French & Italian Chalk & Lead Pencils.

To be had all sorts of the Best Borders, Festoons and Trophies, &c. Likewise all sorts of Prints for Hanging Rooms.

The area covered by
Rocque's 'Map of London
and the adjacent Country
10 Miles Round', 1748

249

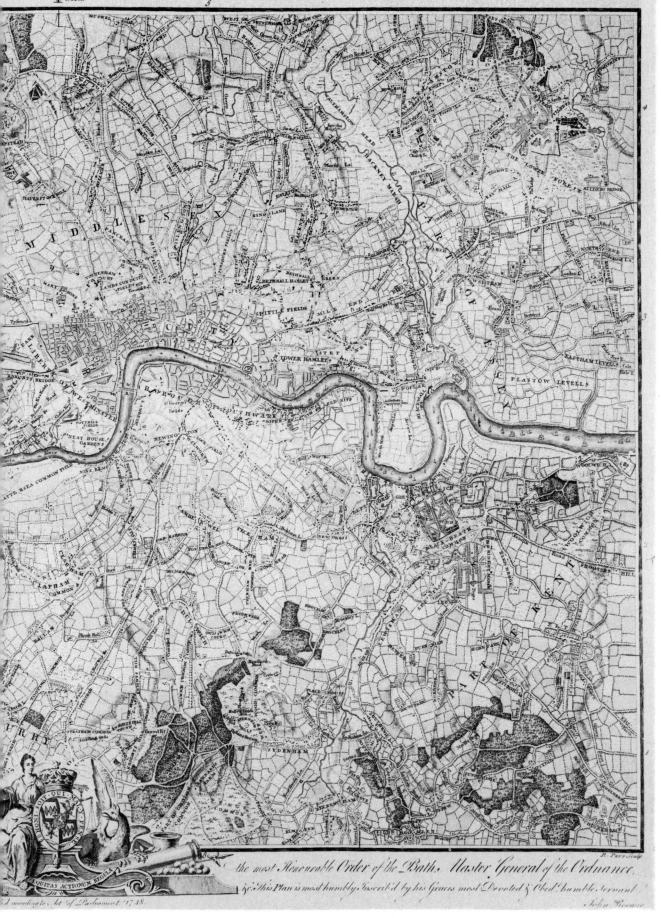

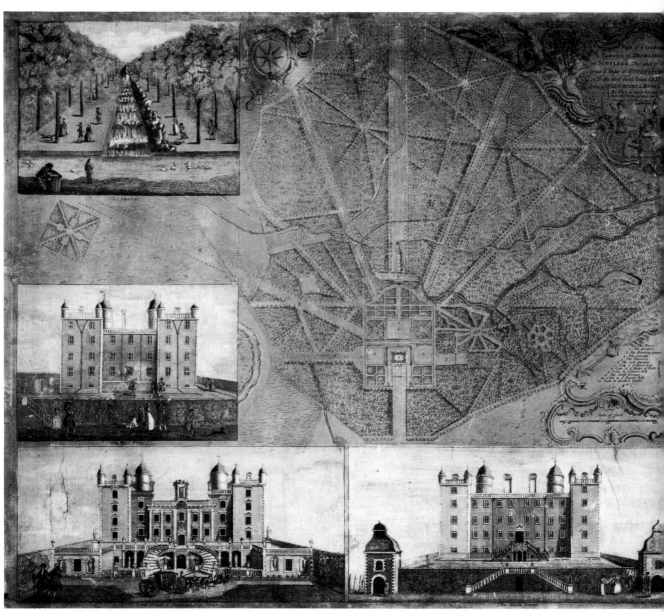

247

PRINTERS, PAPER MAKERS, BOOKSELLERS & BINDERS

In France, the Huguenots were excluded from printing and selling books. As a result, printers and booksellers moved to Holland and to England, where there was a demand for foreign literature, and scope for the introduction of new printing methods.

Thomas Vautrollier settled in London in the late sixteenth century, and printed English and Latin editions of Calvin's 'Institutes'. In the early eighteenth century, Jacques Christophe Le Blon introduced a new method of colour printing for which he was awarded a patent in 1719.

The Huguenots contributed to the improvement in the manufacture of paper in England. They set up new mills under the authority of the White Paper Maker's Company. At South Stoneham, near Southampton, Gerard de Vaux took on Henry Portal as an apprentice in 1707. In 1712, Portal set up his own mill and by 1724 was manufacturing the paper on which the Bank of England notes were printed.

In London, the refugee booksellers settled mainly in the Strand. François Vaillant, formerly bookseller to the Protestant Academy at Saumur, opened a bookshop in the Strand in 1686; the shop remained in family ownership for almost eighty years. Prominent bookbinders included Jean de Planche in the late sixteenth century, and Robert Riviere, of Huguenot descent, who set up as a binder in London in 1832.

Bere Mill, Hampshire, where Henry Portal first set up his paper manufactory

250 *Mulberry (Morus nigra)*
WATERCOLOUR AND BODYCOLOUR, JACQUES LE MOYNE DE MORGUES, *c.* 1566.

Jacques Le Moyne de Morgues (*c.* 1530–1588) was born at Dieppe. Little is known of his early life, but in 1564 he accompanied Laudonnière's expedition to Florida, as cartographer and artist. He returned to Paris, and in 1572 he escaped from the Massacre of St. Bartholomew and took refuge in London. He settled at Blackfriars, and in the Return of Aliens, 1583, was recorded as a member of the French church in Threadneedle Street.

This is one of fifty-nine watercolours representing flowers, fruit and insects, which were originally bound in a small folio volume, acquired by the Victoria and Albert Museum for its sixteenth-century French binding rather than its contents.

COLOUR PLATE: *page 10.*
DIMENSIONS: *275 × 185mm.*
PROVENANCE: *Purchased by the Victoria and Albert Museum, 1856.*
LITERATURE: *Paul Hulton, The Work of Jacques Le Moyne de Morgues, A Huguenot Artist in France, Florida and England, 1977, Vol. I, p.160, no. 22 verso, Vol. II, pl. 28c.*

251 *La Clef des Champs*
JACQUES LE MOYNE DE MORGUES, 1586.

The book is opened at the illustrations of the Musk Rose and German Iris (Hulton, *op.cit.,* 1977, pp. 63, 64).

It contains ninety-six coloured wood-cuts of beasts, birds and plants, which were intended as models for the painter, engraver and embroiderer. It is probable that Le Moyne supervised the production of the volume and even the colouring of the cuts, as this often follows closely the original drawings which are in the British Museum and on which some of the woodcuts are based.

The book was printed in Blackfriars where Le Moyne de Morgues lived from 1572, when he first arrived in London, until his death in 1588. It may have been printed on the press of the Huguenot scholar printer, Thomas Vautrollier.

The volume contains a dedication and a sonnet to Madame de Sidney, presumably Lady Mary Sidney, wife of Sir Henry Sidney, Lord Deputy of Ireland, and mother of Sir Philip Sidney. Only three copies of La Clef des Champs are known to exist today.

DIMENSIONS: *Small Quarto.*
PROVENANCE: *Samuel Cooper; British Library.*
LITERATURE: *Paul Hulton, The Work of Jacques Le Moyne de Morgues, A Huguenot Artist in France, Florida and England, 1977, Vol. I, pp.3,4,11,186–200; Vol. II, pls. 64–90.*

252 *The Four Gospels, 1571*
BINDING BY JEAN DE PLANCHE.

This Anglo-Saxon edition of the Four Gospels was edited by John Fox, and printed privately by Archbishop Parker at Lambeth. It is bound in brown calf, with inlaid corners, border pieces and central ornament in gilt white leather. The initials I.D.P. are contained in small cartouches on the L-shaped white cornerpieces.

DIMENSIONS: *Quarto.*
PROVENANCE: *Cracherode Collection; British Library.*
LITERATURE: *Howard M. Nixon, Some Huguenot Bookbinders, Proceedings of the Huguenot Society of London, Vol. 23 (1977–82), pp. 319–329, pl. XIII.*

253 *Trade card of Paul and Isaac Vaillant, booksellers*
AT THE SIGN OF THE SHIP, STRAND, 1720–1739.

Paul (1671–1739) and Isaac (1679–1753) were the sons of François Vaillant, a refugee from Saumur, who settled in premises in the Strand, opposite Southampton Street, in 1686 as a foreign bookseller. His daughter Suzanne (1669–1749) married Nicholas Prevost (*d.* 1748) who worked in the family bookshop (see *Catalogue number* 72). Paul Vaillant published the printed accounts of the distribution of the Royal Bounty, 1705–1708 (see *Catalogue number* 84). Paul's son, also Paul (1716–1803), became Sheriff of the City of London, 1759, and was a liveryman of the Stationers' Company for 64 years.

The Vaillant family gained the monopoly of the publication of the French translation of the Anglican Liturgy in the third quarter of the eighteenth century. Paul Vaillant the younger visited Paris on at least two occasions to superintend Abbé Olivet's edition of Cicero, 1739–40 and the Abbé Brotier's edition of Tacitus, 1759. His bookshop became the rendezvous of the literary figures of the day. In 1770, the bookshop was taken over by Peter Elmsly.

DIMENSIONS: *123 × 77mm.*
PROVENANCE: *Heal Collection, Department of Prints and Drawings, British Museum.*
LITERATURE: *D.N. Griffiths, The French Translations of the English Book of Common Prayer, Proceedings of the Huguenot Society of London, Vol. 22 (1971–76), pp. 90–114; Hugh Phillips, Mid-Georgian London, 1964, p.155, fig. 214; Timperley's Manual of Printers, p. 811; W.B. Vaillant, The Vaillant Family, 2nd edition, 1928.*

254 *Theodosia Whichcote, Letitia Vaillant, Frances Vaillant and Paul Vaillant*
MINIATURE PORTRAITS, ATTRIBUTED TO JOSEPH DANIEL, *c.*1790.
INSCRIBED: THEODOSIA WHICHCOTE 1735–1827, MARRIED PAUL VAILLANT 14TH AUG. 1760; PAUL VAILLANT 1716–1803 J.P. AND SHERIFF OF LONDON, 1759 DIED AT 52, PALL MALL; LETITIA VAILLANT 1770–1852, MARRIED LT COL. WILLIAM HUTCHINSON 49TH FOOT; FRANCES VAILLANT 1776–1845 DIED UNMARRIED.

The miniatures are contained in their original gilt wooden frame.

Theodosia Whichcote (1735–1827) was originally engaged to Adam Vaillant, but married instead his father Paul (1716–1803) as his second wife in 1766.

Paul Vaillant (1716–1803) was described in his obituary as 'an opulent and respectable bookseller.' He owned two houses in Pall Mall in addition to a house in Twickenham. He is commemorated by a memorial in the church of St. Clement's Danes, in the Strand.

The other two miniatures represent Paul Vaillant's daughters, Letitia, who married Lt.Col. William Hutchinson of the 49th Foot, and Frances who died unmarried.

COLOUR PLATE: *page 11.*
DIMENSIONS: *Frame, 339 × 174mm.*
PROVENANCE: *Private Collection.*
LITERATURE: *W.B. Vaillant, The Vaillant Family, 2nd edition, 1928.*

Lat. IRIS.
Gal. FLEVR DE FLAMBE
Ang. FLOWER DE LVCE.

251

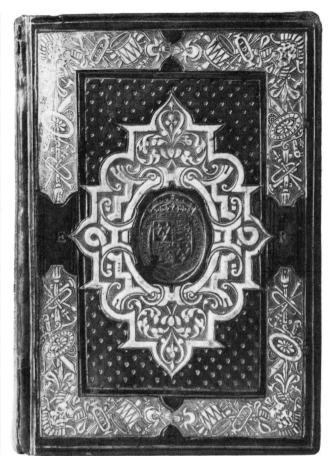

252

This book is to be had at
Paul and Isaac Vaillant's
at the Ship in the Strand
London.

253

254

255 *Coloritto or the Harmony of Colouring in Painting*
JACQUES CHRISTOPHE LE BLON, 1723–6.

J.C. Le Blon (1667–1741) is generally regarded as the inventor of the modern system of chromolithography and similar processes of colour printing.

This manual was intended for the use of painters and all lovers of painting. The text is printed in both French and English and illustrated with colour plates demonstrating Le Blon's printing method. In the introduction to the manual, Le Blon states that he is using his method to produce anatomical tables in conjunction with the King's anatomist, Mr. St. André.

Le Blon is recorded as working in London from 1717 till 1733. In 1719, he was granted a patent for 'Multiplying pictures and draughts by natural colours with impression', which is presumably a reference to the method used in the publication of this manual. On the strength of the patent, he formed a company with the help of Colonel John Guise, which he named 'Picture Office', but this was dissolved in 1723. Le Blon was a versatile man, and in June, 1727, he was granted another patent for making or weaving tapestry in the loom (*Catalogue number* 462).

DIMENSIONS: *Quarto.*

PROVENANCE: *British Library.*

LITERATURE: *Information kindly supplied by O.M. Lilien who is preparing a book on J.C. Le Blon.*

256 *Inventory of Goods, The White Paper Makers' Company*
MANUSCRIPT, 3FF. 1696.

In 1686, James II granted a patent to a group of fifteen men for the production of white paper, which was till then mainly imported from Holland, Italy, Germany and France. The Company obtained mills in Kent, Surrey, Hampshire and Devon, and these included four mills in South Stoneham, just north of Southampton. In 1697, these mills were sold, and prior to this transaction, the Company had an inventory made of the site.

The inventory gives a detailed picture of the plant, and mentions a total of six men employed there. It was compiled by Daniel Roussillon, a Huguenot refugee, who in 1688 had been sent on a recruiting drive to the Dutch papermaking province of Gelderland. His name appears in the registers of the French church, Southampton in 1691 and 1693, although by 1712, he was a churchwarden in the parish church, South Stoneham, where he was eventually buried in 1719.

A number of refugees who settled in Southampton, were closely associated with the local papermaking industry. Gerard de Vaux, who came from Castres, in Languedoc, ran one of the mills in South Stoneham, and in 1707, took Henry Portal as an apprentice.

PROVENANCE: *Southampton Record Office.*

LITERATURE: *Sir William Portal, The Art of Papermaking, The Hampshire Chronicle, 30 March 1912; J.H. Thomas, The Company of White Paper Makers: An Inventory of Plant, The Journal of the Society for Post-Medieval Archaeology, Vol. II, 1977, pp. 22–35.*

257 *Paper, fragment made by Portals*
BRITANNIA WATERMARK, 1754.

In 1724 Henry Portal agreed to manufacture the paper on which the Bank of England notes were printed (*Catalogue number* 420). By this date, Portal had expanded from his own humble start at Bere Mill, and had another larger mill at Laverstoke. In 1719, he took his former master's son, John de Vaux, as an apprentice.

In 1885, a papermaking machine of the type developed by the Fourdrinier family (*Catalogue number* 259) was introduced.

Portals continue to manufacture the paper used for Bank of England notes.

PROVENANCE: *Portals Ltd.*

LITERATURE: *Sir Francis Portal, Portals, the Church, the State, and the People, leading to 250 years of papermaking, 1962.*

258 *Trade card of Baker & Fourdrinier, stationers*
AT THE SIGN OF THE GLOBE NEXT DOOR TO THE GENERAL POST OFFICE IN LOMBARD STREET, *c.*1757.

Henry Fourdrinier, the elder son of the engraver, Paul Fourdrinier (fl. 1720–d. 1758) (*Catalogue numbers* 235, 259) was apprenticed to William Baker of Lombard Street and became his partner after 1757. By 1793, the firm had become Fourdrinier, Bloxam and Walker at 11, Lombard Street.

Their trade card shows that they supplied 'all sorts of Merchants', & other Account Books, Paper, Parchment, Stamps, & all Stationary Wares'.

DIMENSIONS: *166 × 135mm.*

PROVENANCE: *Heal Collection, Department of Prints and Drawings, British Museum.*

LITERATURE: *The Fourdrinier family and Cardinal Newman, Proceedings of the Huguenot Society of London, Vol. VIII, pp. 291,391; Rev. F.G. Lee, Pedigree of the Fourdrinier and Grolleau Families, Miscellanea Genealogica et Heraldica, July, 1880, pp. 385–386.*

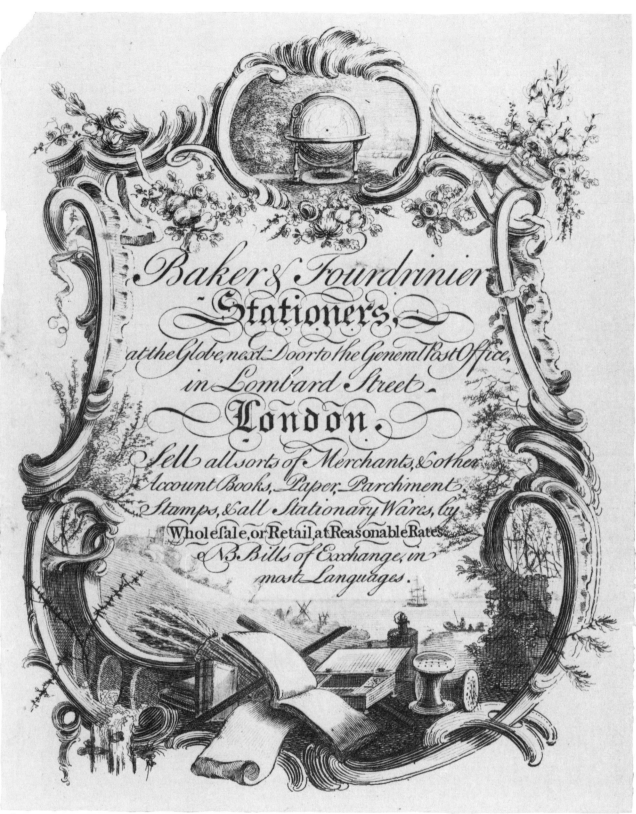

Baker & Fourdrinier
Stationers,
at the Globe, next Door to the General Post Office,
in Lombard Street
London.

Sell all sorts of Merchants, & other
Account Books, Paper, Parchment
Stamps, & all Stationary Wares, by
Wholesale, or Retail at Reasonable Rates.
N.B. Bills of Exchange, in
most Languages.

258

259 *The Fourdrinier Family*
PORTRAIT GROUP, OIL ON METAL, ATTRIBUTED TO JOHN DOWNMAN, *c*.1785.

This painting shows in the centre, Henry Fourdrinier (1730–1799) a paper manufacturer and wholesale stationer in Lombard Street (*Catalogue number* 258). The monumental urn to the right records the death of his wife, Jemima (née White) in 1781.

His two sons Henry (1766–1854) and Charles (1767–1841) are standing to the far left of the composition. In the foreground, are Henry's two youngest children, John Rawson (born 1770) and Sealy (1772–1847). Henry's only daughter, Jemima, who is standing beside her father, married John Newman in 1799. Their son, John Henry, born in 1801, became a Catholic convert and eventually a Cardinal of the Catholic church.

With his brother Sealy, Henry Fourdrinier the younger devised new methods for the production of paper, and in 1807 patented the invention of a machine for making continuous paper. For the first time, paper of any size could be produced at a greatly increased speed. The brothers were forced to spend £60,000 on protecting their patent, and this led to their bankruptcy. Their patent was extended for an additional fourteen years. In 1814, Fourdrinier supplied two papermaking machines to the Tsar Alexander I for an annual stipend of £700 for a period of ten years. This money was never forthcoming.

In recognition of their important invention, Parliament rewarded the brothers with £7,000 in 1840, and members of the Paper Trade raised a subscription from which they paid the family an annual income.

COLOUR PLATE: *page 12.*

DIMENSIONS: *465 × 615mm.*

PROVENANCE: *Private Collection.*

LITERATURE: *Dictionary of National Biography, under Fourdrinier; The Fourdrinier Family and Cardinal Newman, Proceedings of the Huguenot Society of London, Vol. 8 (1901–04), pp. 291,391; Rev. F.G. Lee, Pedigree of the Fourdrinier and Grolleau Families, Miscellanea Genealogica et Heraldica, July, 1880, pp. 385–386.*

260 *Trade card of Robert Riviere & Son Limited, Bookbinders*
BURLINGTON BUILDINGS, HEDDON STREET, REGENT STREET, W.I., *c*.1929.

The card indicates that Riviere had specialised in the restoration of ancient books and bindings by special appointment to Her Majesty Queen Victoria, H.R.H. The Prince of Wales, and H.R.H. The Princess of Wales.

Robert Riviere (1808–1882) was the son of Daniel Valentine Riviere, and a descendant of the gunsmith, Isaac Riviere (*Catalogue number* 326). He was apprenticed to Messrs Allman, Booksellers of Princes Street, Hanover Square and in 1829, started his own business as a bookseller in Bath. He bound books as a hobby at first, but finding binding profitable, he moved in 1832 to Great Queen Street, London, and set up as a bookbinder.

He soon gained considerable patronage, and in 1840, he moved to 196, Piccadilly, where he remained until just before his death.

His most important commissions were in 1851 for the binding of a thousand copies of the large illustrated catalogue of the Great Exhibition and the restoration and binding, in 1870, of the original Domesday Book.

Riviere's business was continued by his son at 29–33 Heddon Street until at least 1929.

DIMENSIONS: *100 × 140mm.*

PROVENANCE: *Banks Collection, Department of Prints and Drawings, British Museum.*

LITERATURE: *Bernard Quaritch, Examples of Modern Bookbinding designed and executed by Robert Riviere & Son, 1919; Michael Riviere, Notes on the Huguenot Family of Riviere in England, privately printed, 1965.*

261 *Five bindings by Robert Riviere*
a. BIOGRAPHIA LITERARIA, SAMUEL TAYLOR COLERIDGE, FIRST EDITION, 1817, BINDING *c*. 1832; INSCRIBED: BOUND BY R. RIVIERE, 24 UNION STREET, BATH.

Bound in sprinkled brown panelled calf, with a border of triple fillet lines and a single pin head roll ending in a circled star at the corners. The inner panel has a double fillet border with a single pin head roll and decorative tools at the corners.

The spine has five raised bands, with decorative panels in between. The lettering pieces are in the second and fourth panels on red and olive, and the volume is dated at the tail.

Both the edge and the inside edge of the boards are decorated with an ornamental roll. The end papers and the edges of the pages are marbled with the French shell pattern. The binding has a matching blue and white silk headband.

b. CHRISTOBEL AND KUBLA KHAN, SAMUEL TAYLOR COLERIDGE, FIRST EDITION, 1816, BINDING *c*. 1880.

Bound in brown calf, with an antique French triple line border, ending in decorative circles at the corners. The spine has a run up gilt back, five raised bands, and panels with decorative bands and centre tool bouquet of flowers, with leafy corner tools, stars and open rings. There is a green lettering piece in the second panel and the tail is dated. The edges of the boards are decorated with a double line.

The inside edges are decorated with an ornamental roll, the top edge of the paper is gilt, and the end papers are marbled in a red feather design. The matching headband is worked in blue, yellow and red silks.

c. THE NATURAL HISTORY AND ANTIQUITIES OF SELBORNE, GILBERT WHITE, 1837, BINDING, *c*. 1840.

Bound in full green morocco with an all over fanfare design, with a three line antique French border ending at the corners in a decorative star within a circle, and with an outer decorative roll. The board edges are decorated with an ornamental roll and the inside edges with a wavy line and daisy roll.

The spine has five raised bands with a wavy decorative pallet, and run up gilt back, and decorative panels with a central rosette, leaves, thistles and circles with stars. The lettering piece is in the second panel. All the page edges are gilt. The plain pale yellow end papers are complimented by the red and yellow headband.

ILLUSTRATED: *page 182.*

DIMENSIONS: *Octavo.*

DIMENSIONS: *Octavo.*

ILLUSTRATED: *page 182.*

DIMENSIONS: *Octavo.*

259

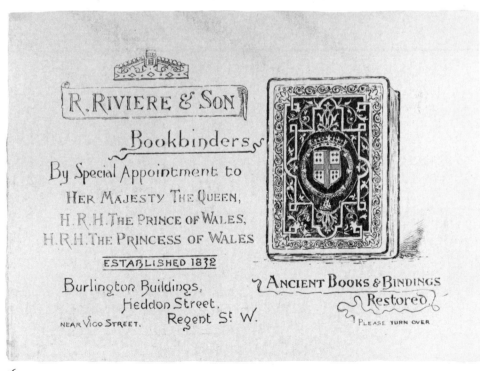

260

d. THE ANTIQUITIES OF OXFORDSHIRE, JOSEPH SKELTON, 1823–6, *c*. 1880.

Bound in three quarter red morocco and buckram, the leather borders are decorated with a double fillet and inner ornamental roll.

    The spine has six raised bands with decorative panels, each with a centre tool, corner tools and ornamental circles. The lettering piece is in the second panel, and the volume is dated at the tail. The upper edges of the pages are gilt.

DIMENSIONS: *Large folio.*
PROVENANCE: *a.b.c. & d.*
Michael Riviere Esq.

e. CATALOGUE OF THE GREAT EXHIBITION, VOL. 2, 1851.

A blue morocco panel binding, the panels decorated at the corners with foliate scrollwork, with an outer border of three small and one large fillet.

    The spine has five bands, with decorative panels, and lettering pieces in the second and fourth panel. The inside has a three line outer fillet and decorative border. All the edges are gilt and the pale yellow plain endpapers are complimented by a blue and white machine made headband. This is one of a thousand copies of the Great Exhibition catalogue which were bound in Robert Riviere's workshop.

DIMENSIONS: *Large folio.*
PROVENANCE: *Museum of London.*

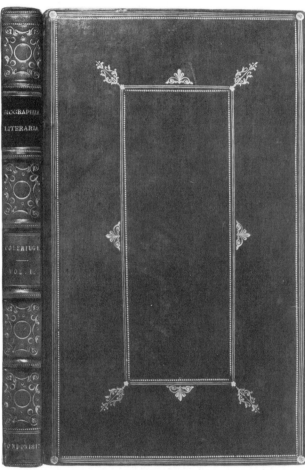

261 *a*

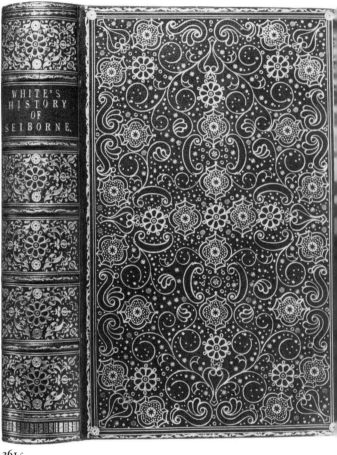

261 *c*

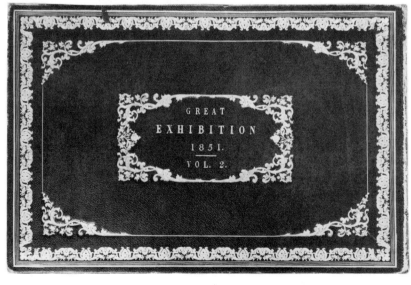

261 *e*

HUGUENOTS &
ENGLISH ARCHITECTURE

As Architect to William III, Daniel Marot designed his state coach and the interior furnishings and garden layout at Hampton Court Palace. There, Marot's parterre design was complemented by wrought ironwork made by the Huguenot gatesmith, Jean Tijou. Marot also worked for Ralph, later 1st Duke of Montagu (William III's Master of the Wardrobe) at Montagu House, London.

Marot was the first to introduce to English architecture the idea that everything in a room should be designed by the same hand. This practice was taken up by two great designer architects of the later eighteenth century, William Kent and Robert Adam.

Daniel Marot's influence can be seen in a number of country houses built after 1688. Less well known Huguenot architects, Samuel Hauduroy and Jean de Bodt, produced designs for Dyrham Park, Avon and Wentworth Castle, Yorkshire. The refugee stone carver, Nadauld, worked in conjunction with William Talman and John Vanbrugh on ornamental sculpture for the exterior of Chatsworth and Castle Howard.

Plate 7 of 'A New Booke of Drawings', Jean Tijou, 1693

262

262 A New Booke of Drawings

JEAN TIJOU, LONDON, 1693.

The publication of this book by the refugee ironsmith from St. Germain, revolutionised wrought iron work in England. His designs relied closely on earlier French sources published by Jean de Mortin, *c.* 1640 and Hugues Brisville in 1663. The gates in plate 7 (exhibited) are based on gates executed by Luchet, the master ironsmith, at Versailles in 1678.

Although Tijou's daughter Eleanor married the Catholic painter Louis Laguerre (he designed the frontispiece to this book), Tijou was evidently a Huguenot, for in the 1780s, his son Thomas applied for places at the French Protestant Charity School on behalf of his granddaughters, Elizabeth and Henrietta Green (*Catalogue number* 117).

Many of the designs in this book were executed. Tijou worked in conjunction with Sir Christopher Wren at St. Paul's Cathedral, and at Burghley, Chatsworth and Hampton Court, where he had his own smithy. Between 1691 and 1700, Tijou was paid £4,500 for his work at Hampton Court, although his son later claimed that because the ironwork there was not finished until the reign of Queen Anne 'only part was paid for'.

ILLUSTRATED: *page 183.*

PROVENANCE: *British Library.*

LITERATURE: *Gervase Jackson Stops, The Sources of Tijou's Designs, Country Life, 28 January 1971, pp. 182–3; ibid. English Baroque Ironwork II, The Influence of Tijou, Country Life, 4 February 1971, pp. 262–266; Ifor Edwards, Ironwork Master of St. Paul's, Country Life, 23 February 1961, pp. 386–7.*

263 Masks from the Fountain Screen, Hampton Court

TWO, WROUGHT IRON, JEAN TIJOU, *c.* 1695.

These masks, one female with an ionic headdress, the other a bearded male mask, formed the uppermost ornament on the gates of the Fountain Screen adjacent to the river at Hampton Court. Each mask was originally supported by scrolls with acanthus leaves and garlands, over a moulded stand and a richly embossed cloth of estate, which was in turn upheld by two large lateral scrolls, which formed the main part of the screen below.

Five of these masks were included in Tijou's 'New Booke of Drawings', pls. 16,19 and 20. These originals have been replaced on the Fountain Screen by reproductions.

DIMENSIONS: *Female mask, 315 × 240mm; male mask, 275 × 270mm.*

PROVENANCE: *Department of Education; On loan to the Victoria and Albert Museum.*

LITERATURE: *J. Starkie Gardner, A Complete Survey of the Artistic Working of Iron in Great Britain from the Earliest Times, Vol. III, 1922, p. 50, figs. 25,26.*

NOT EXHIBITED: *right hand mask.*

263

264 Design for the Parterre at Hampton Court

DANIEL MAROT, PEN AND WASH, 1689; INSCRIBED: MAROT FECIT AOUST 1689.

This drawing is a preliminary design for the parterre at Hampton Court. It was published with Marot's other engravings for garden designs, and inscribed 'Parterre d'Amton Court inventé par D. Marot'.

In 1689 John Evelyn wrote, 'I went to Hampton Court about business . . . a spacious garden with fountaines was beginning in the park at the head of the canal'. It is possible that Marot was in England in 1689, although this drawing could have been executed in Holland. Marot was certainly in England in the 1690s as his children were baptised at the Huguenot church in Leicester Fields in June 1695 and June 1696. There was, however, some considerable delay before Marot received payment for this work. On 21 March 1698, Caspar Frederick Henning (paymaster of the money for the use and service of His Majesty's gardens at Hampton Court and Newmarket) wrote to the Council of Nassau Demesne suggesting that Mr. Marot should be paid 236 pounds 11 shillings 11 pence sterling.

The disparity between the date of the drawing and the date of payment is explained by the fact that Queen Mary's early death in December 1694 turned King William's thoughts from the refurbishment of Hampton Court. It was only with the destruction of Whitehall Palace by fire in January, 1698, that work on the gardens at Hampton Court was put in hand.

Jan Kip's large engraved views of Hampton Court published in 'Britannia Illustrata', 1707, show the parterre as executed.

DIMENSIONS: *197 × 514mm.*

PROVENANCE: *Museum Boymans, Rotterdam.*

EXHIBITED: *William and Mary and Their Time, Victoria and Albert Museum, 1950 (72).*

LITERATURE: *Arthur Lane, Daniel Marot: Designer of Delft Vases and of Gardens at Hampton Court, Connoisseur, Vol. CXXIII, 1949, pp. 19–25; Oliver Millar, The William and Mary Exhibition, The Burlington Magazine, Vol. XCII, 1950, p. 234, fig. 19.*

265 Design for a ceiling

PEN AND INK, WITH TOUCHES OF PINK AND YELLOW WASH. ATTRIBUTED TO DANIEL MAROT; INSCRIBED: CORNICHE, *c.*1695.

This design is for a ceiling with a central oval and six surrounding compartments. The oval contains two cloud-borne putti supporting a shield and royal crown. Two of the corner cartouches contain bacchic scenes.

The drawing is attributed to Marot on stylistic grounds by comparison with other signed drawings. The design may have been intended for Hampton Court Palace.

DIMENSIONS: *290 × 230mm.*

PROVENANCE: *John D. Crace; presented to the Royal Institute of British Architects, 1911.*

LITERATURE: *Catalogue of the Drawings in the Royal Institute of British Architects, 1969–1976, under Marot.*

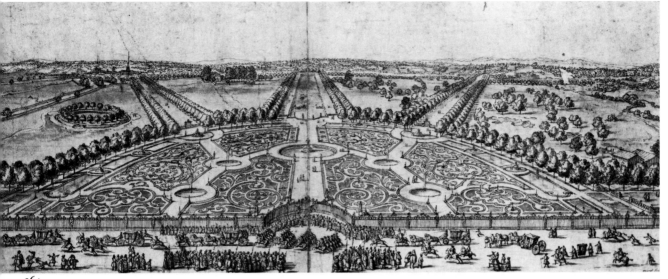

264

262

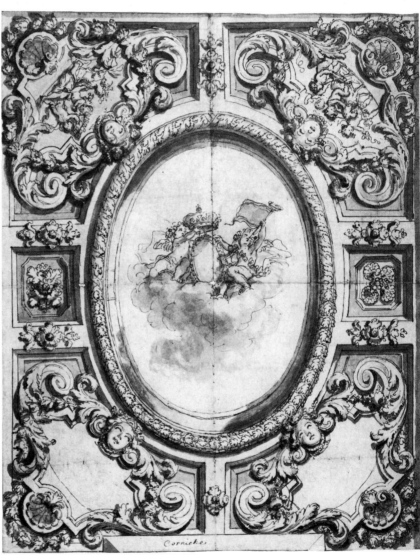

265

266 *State Bed from Melville House*
ATTRIBUTED TO FRANCOIS LAPIERRE, 1690S, PHOTOGRAPH.

Constructed on a pine frame, the bed is upholstered in crimson silk Genoa velvet, lined with white Chinese silk damask, and embroidered with crimson silk braid. The design relates closely to State Beds in Daniel Marot's 'Nouveaux Livres d'Appartements', published in Amsterdam in 1702, and may derive from drawings by Marot before the engravings were circulated.

The Huguenot upholsterer François Lapierre worked for the Duke of Devonshire, the Duke of Montagu and for the Royal Household. In 1689, Lapierre charged £230 for furnishing the Duke of Schomberg's apartment at St. James's.

PROVENANCE: *Victoria and Albert Museum.*

LITERATURE: *Lisa Clinton, Victoria and Albert Museum Masterpieces, 21, The State Bed from Melville House, 1979; Peter Thornton, Seventeenth Century Interior Decoration in England, France and Holland, 1978, pp. 49,342n, pl. 97.*

267 *Designs for Architecture, Interiors, Paintings etc*
DANIEL MAROT; INSCRIBED: J'AI ACHETE CE LIVRE RARE A PARIS, 1785 PRIX 6505 FF.

These designs were first published in The Hague in 1702, under the title 'Oeuvres du Sieur D. Marot, architecte de Guillaume III, roy de la Grande Bretagne, contenant plusieurs pensées utiles aux architectes, peintres, sculpteurs, orfèvres'. The second enlarged edition was published in Amsterdam, 1712.

This particular volume contains designs for perspectives, chimney-pieces, ceilings, paintings, embroidery, clocks, apartments, trellises, gardens, vases, monuments and mausolea. The exhibited design for a chimney-piece in the 'Nouvelles Cheminées à Panneaux de Glace à La Manière de France', is close to that in the King's Dressing Room at Hampton Court.

Although Daniel Marot described himself as an architect, he was the first such in England to design the whole range of interior features as well. Trained at the Court of Versailles under the designer Jean Berain, Marot was largely responsible for disseminating the Louis XIV style in England. His influence is to be seen particularly in English furniture of the period, but also in silver and ceramics.

PROVENANCE: *Victoria and Albert Museum.*

LITERATURE: *Jessen, Das Ornamentwerk des Daniel Marots, Berlin, 1892; M.D. Ozinga, Daniel Marot, 1938.*

268 *State Coach for William III*
DESIGNED BY DANIEL MAROT, 1698.

The body of the coach is decorated with features typical of Marot's ornamental vocabulary: shells, oak leaves, boars' heads, female masks and lambrequins. Two dogs at the base of the carriage are surmounted by a mace decorated with ribbons, the lower section of the coach has painted panels, and the outer window frames are surmounted by standing caryatid male figures, supporting the cornice. The coachman's seat is supported by rampant lions at the rear, and resting above the main junctions of the wheel and cog are female figures representing the Four Seasons.

This elaborate coach was made for William III in the Hague in 1698. It was first used in its present capacity as the coach of the Speaker of the House of Commons by Charles Abbot, Speaker, 1802–1817, who recorded a payment to Lord Redesdale for the coach of £1,060. It is normally housed at Whitbreads Brewery in Chiswell Street, and is used by the Speaker of the House of Commons in the Coronation and Jubilee processions.

Designs by Marot for a Dutch state coach are in the Rijksmuseum and the Cooper Hewitt Museum, New York.

COLOUR PLATE: *page 12.*

PROVENANCE: *William III; Lord Redesdale; The Speaker, Charles Abbot, 1802; The Rt. Hon. the Speaker.*

LITERATURE: *M.D. Ozinga, Daniel Marot, 1938, pl.19; Robert C. Smith, Five Furniture Drawings in Sienna, Furniture History, Vol. III, 1967, pl. 8.*

269 *Ralph, Duke of Montagu (1638–1709)*
PORTRAIT, OIL ON CANVAS, MICHAEL DAHL.

Ralph Montagu was British Ambassador in France between 1666 and 1678. From 1682 to 1685 he spent a period of exile in Montpellier, in order to avoid the English reaction to his implication in the popish plots. Abel Boyer, the Huguenot historian, indicates that Montagu only returned to England at the end of James II's reign. In Montpellier, which was a Huguenot stronghold, Montagu would have been acutely aware of the persecution of the French Protestants (*Catalogue number* 22).

On his return to England, he became a patron of the Huguenot refugees, including the stonecarver Gideon du Chesne, the woodcarvers and gilders, John and Thomas Pelletier, the carpenter Peter Rieusset, the upholsterers Remy George and François Lapierre and the tailor Joseph Boucher.

John, 2nd Duke of Montagu, who succeeded his father in 1709, continued this tradition, and from 1727 to 1746 made an annual contribution to the Soupe, the Huguenot charity in Spitalfields (*Catalogue numbers* 85, 86).

DIMENSIONS: *1000 × 800mm.*

PROVENANCE: *The Duke of Buccleuch and Queensberry at Boughton House, Kettering.*

267

266

269

266

270 *Nine Estimates for Furniture for Hampton Court Palace*
SIGNED BY RALPH, EARL OF MONTAGU, 1699.

Ralph, Earl of Montagu, resumed his office as Master of the Wardrobe in 1689, after a period of voluntary exile in France. These estimates were prepared in 1699 for the furnishings at Hampton Court Palace. They included the State Bedchamber, Presence Chamber and Withdrawing Room and rooms for members of William III's household.

'The Estimate for the Goodes to be furnished to compleat the furniture for the Crimson Velvet Bed sold to his Matie by the Rt. Hon: the Earl of Jersey' for the state bedchamber (exhibited) includes red window and case curtains, a white satin quilt and bolster, a rich suite of white bed feathers, and '4 very fine black and white fern top sprigs with white and scarlet down at the bottom of the sprigs'. The total estimated cost is given as £423 3s. 6d.

It is probable that the upholsterer who provided these furnishings was the Huguenot François Lapierre. According to the Lord Chamberlain's accounts, Lapierre provided the damask beds for the 'Gentlemen and Groomes of his Majty Bedchamber at Hampton Court' in 1693–4, for which the estimate is also contained in the exhibited volume.

PROVENANCE: *Victoria and Albert Museum.*

271 *Panels, oil on canvas, three from a set of five*
DESIGNED BY DANIEL MAROT, c.1690.

These panels were originally intended for the walls of a state drawing room or closet at Montagu House. The subjects depicted show scenes from the loves of the gods: Apollo and Daphne, Diana and Endymion, Venus and Adonis, Jupiter and Io, and the Triumph of Galatea.

The variable but generally high quality of the painting suggests that like most of the decoration at Montagu House, it was a team effort. The baskets of fruit would have been painted by Jean Baptiste Monnoyer (d. 1699), the mythological scenes by Charles La Fosse (1636–1716), and the trompe l'oeil picture frames by Jacques Rousseau (1630–1693). The painters of these panels appear to have observed the directions on Daniel Marot's designs (*Catalogue number* 272) very faithfully.

George Vertue records in 1722, 'the late Duke Brought from France three excellent painters to adorn & beautify this House. Monsieur Lafosse History painter, Monsieur Rousseau for landskip and Architecture & Baptist for fruit & flowers . . . these three great masters have happily united their thoughts & skill to a great perfection'.

COLOUR PLATE: *page 13.*

DIMENSIONS: *Double panel 2237 × 1775mm; three single panels 2237 × 1208mm.*

PROVENANCE: *Montagu House, London; The Duke of Buccleuch and Queensberry, Boughton House, Kettering.*

LITERATURE: *Gervase Jackson Stops, Daniel Marot and the 1st Duke of Montagu, Nederlands Kunsthistorisch Jaarboek, 1981, pp. 244–262, figs.7–12.*

272 *Designs for two painted panels*
PEN AND INK WITH TRACES OF PENCIL; ATTRIBUTED TO DANIEL MAROT, c. 1690.

These designs relate directly to two of the five panels (*Catalogue number* 271) which were probably painted for a cabinet or small closet at Montagu House, the London home of Ralph, 1st Duke of Montagu.

The central vignettes show two different versions of the same story, Apollo and Daphne. The inscriptions refer to the colours 'rouge, violet, bleu, or ver'; to the identification of the birds 'pigone . . . paroque' and to the dimensions of the panels; another inscription refers to a 'screen that I have made'. These are in the same handwriting as other signed drawings by Daniel Marot.

These designs are contained in a miscellaneous volume with several other drawings in Marot's hand.

DIMENSIONS: *400 × 122mm.*

PROVENANCE: *E. Parsons, bought by the Victoria and Albert Museum, 1879.*

LITERATURE: *Gervase Jackson Stops, Daniel Marot and the 1st Duke of Montagu, Nederlands Kunsthistorisch Jaarboek, 1981, pp. 244–262, fig. 6.*

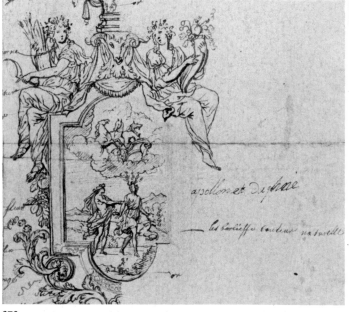

272   271

272

271

HUGUENOTS & ENGLISH ARCHITECTURE 189

273 *Design for an Overmantel*
PEN AND GREY WASH, BOUJET, *c.*1700.

This design incorporates the coat of arms of George Booth, 2nd Earl of Warrington, and relates to the overmantel in the Hall at Dunham Massey. The draughtsmanship of an illuminated pedigree drawn up for the 2nd Earl of Warrington, still at Dunham Massey, is close to this design, and it is probable that Boujet was one of the many Huguenot craftsmen whom Warrington is known to have patronised.

Another design for a pediment in the Metropolitan Museum of Art bears the same signature, but there is as yet no further information on this draughtsman.

DIMENSIONS: *251 × 362mm.*

PROVENANCE: *Smythson Collection; Royal Institute of British Architects.*

LITERATURE: *Mark Girouard, The Smythson Collection of the Royal Institute of British Architects, Architectural History, Vol. V, 1962, pp. 64,181–2; John Hardy and Gervase Jackson Stops, The Second Earl of Warrington and the Age of Walnut, Apollo, Vol. CVIII, July, 1978, pp. 22–39, reproduced fig. 2.*

273

274 *Design for a Staircase*
PEN, BROWN INK AND GREY WASH, SAMUEL HAUDUROY.
INSCRIBED: CETTE RAMPE DESCALIER EST PLUS SOLLIDE ET DESSIGNE DANS L'ORDRE D'ARCHITECTURE ET POUR LA MODE DU TEMP C'EST CE QUE L'ON DOIT FUIR (?) LE PLUS QU'IL LE PEUT CAR LES MODES CE CHANGES ET JAMAIS CEUX CY, *c.*1690.

This design for a staircase balustrade was intended for the Hall on the garden front at Dyrham, a Tudor house, which was rebuilt by William Blathwayt, Secretary of State to William III. Samuel Hauduroy designed the new garden front, although the other façade was built to the designs of William Talman. It is probable that Blathwayt chose Hauduroy because he was conscientious, penniless and therefore cheap. A letter from Hauduroy in the Blathwayt archives complains that he received only six guineas for designing the façade and master plan.

Samuel Hauduroy was probably a relative of the decorative painter Mark Anthony Hauduroy who also worked at Dyrham, at Knole, and at Wrest Park. The latter worshipped at the Huguenot church in Berwick Street, Soho.

DIMENSIONS: *245 × 155mm.*

PROVENANCE: *Gloucester County Record Office.*

LITERATURE: *Mark Girouard, Dyrham Park, Avon, Country Life, Vol. CXXXI, 15–22 February, 1962, pp. 335–339; 396–399; John Kenworthy Browne, Dyrham House, Avon, National Trust Guide Book, 5th edition, 1978, p. 24.*

275 *Section of Gallery, Wentworth Castle*
PEN, INK AND WATERCOLOUR, JEAN DE BODT, *c.*1708.
INSCRIBED: ONE END OF A GALLERY ETC J. TALMAN.

This is one of two drawings for Wentworth Castle, near Barnsley, Yorkshire, which probably constitute the original design for the house which was built for Lord Raby. The inscription is misleading; both drawings were in the collection of John Talman and as a result were originally attributed to the architect William Talman.

The designs probably date from 1708, the year in which Lord Raby acquired the old seventeenth-century house. Lord Raby was British Ambassador in Berlin from 1703 to 1711. The design was probably commissioned in Berlin, for although Jean de Bodt came to Ireland in 1690–1, as an engineer in the artillery train that accompanied William III, and was in England in 1697, by 1700 he had been appointed Chief Architect to the Elector of Brandenburg.

De Bodt's name is not recorded in any of the contemporary correspondence, but in a letter to Richard Bentley, August 1756, Horace Walpole described the East Wing as 'a pompous front screening an old house; it was built by the last Lord on a design of the Prussian architect Bott . . . the one pair of stairs is engrossed entirely by a gallery of 180 feet, on the plan of that in the Colonna Palace at Rome'.

Jean de Bodt was born in Paris of a German father from Mecklenburg, and a Huguenot mother, Rose Louvint de Veral.

DIMENSIONS: *437 × 384mm.*

PROVENANCE: *John Talman; Francis St. John of Thorpe Hall, Peterborough; Victoria and Albert Museum.*

LITERATURE: *John Harris, Bodt and Stainborough, Architectural Review, CXXX, 1961, pp. 34–5; The Letters of Horace Walpole, ed Toynbee, Vol. III, 1903, p. 443.*

One End of a Gallery &c

275

276 *Design for the frieze on the West Front, Chatsworth*
BLACK CHALK ON PAPER, NADAULD, 1702.

This drawing is connected with the carvings in stone on the West Front at Chatsworth, for which Nadauld was paid in 1702. Such ornamental carving was usually supervised by the architect in charge, but six working drawings by Nadauld at Chatsworth indicate that he was responsible for developing his own designs. Nadauld is recorded as working at Chatsworth from April 1700 to 1704, as a stonecarver, producing ornamental details for the façades and garden sculpture, much of which has survived. He also worked in plaster, executing an exquisite relief of putti on horseback in the West-Sub-Vestibule.

By 1705, Nadauld is recorded at Castle Howard, with his compatriots Gideon du Chesne (who also worked at Boughton) and Daniel Hervé or Harvey (who worked at Wentworth Castle). Again, Nadauld was responsible for both the decorative features in the interior and the garden statuary.

Nadauld may be identified with the Mr. Nadue who was paid in 1698 for plastering work done in the Queen's closet in the Water Gallery at Hampton Court.

Although the name recurs in the Huguenot church registers and a family pedigree is preserved in the Huguenot Library, it has not been possible to identify the sculptor further.

DIMENSIONS: *150 × 490mm.*

PROVENANCE: *Trustees of the Devonshire Collection, Chatsworth.*

LITERATURE: *Geoffrey Beard, Decorative Plasterwork in Great Britain, 1975, pp. 43,231.*

ST MARTIN'S LANE ACADEMY

Louis Chéron, a Huguenot artist from Paris, attended the first official art academy in London, which opened in 1711 in Sir Godfrey Kneller's house in Great Queen Street. It was modelled on the Royal Academy of Painting and Sculpture which had opened in Paris in 1648. In 1718, Kneller's Academy split into two groups, one of which was managed by Louis Chéron, and met in a 'Great Room' in St. Martin's Lane. Evening sessions were held by lamplight, and provided the opportunity to draw from the living model, and in 1722, a female model was introduced for the first time.

In the 1730s, the Academy was associated with the painter William Hogarth. The sculptor, Louis François Roubiliac taught there in the 1740s. A smaller drawing school in Covent Garden run by Hubert Gravelot, was attended by Thomas Gainsborough and the Huguenot Charles Grignion. From the 1730s, students practised by drawing from the fully clothed lay figure, as well as the living model.

Life drawing, black chalk on paper, Louis Chéron, c.1720

277 *Drawing class at a London academy*
OIL ON CANVAS, ARTIST UNKNOWN, EARLY EIGHTEENTH CENTURY.

This painting may represent the first official art academy in Britain, which opened in Sir Godfrey Kneller's house in Great Queen Street, Lincoln's Inn Fields, in October 1711. Kneller's Academy was attended by Louis Chéron (*Catalogue number* 278), the engraver Louis Du Guernier and the decorative painter Pierre Berchet (all of whom were Huguenots). George Vertue noted that Berchet 'drew in the academy very well both at London & at Paris'.

Kneller's Academy continued to meet in Great Queen Street till 1718, although in 1716, the painter James Thornhill succeeded Kneller as Governor.

DIMENSIONS: *292 × 355mm.*

PROVENANCE: *Private Collection.*

LITERATURE: *Michael Kitson, Hogarth's Apology for Painters, The Walpole Society, Vol. XLI, 1966–1968, p. 65, pl. 43(2).*

278 *Louis Chéron (1600–1725)*
PORTRAIT ENGRAVING, AUBERT, *c.*1676.
INSCRIBED: MASTER OF VANDERGUTCH (SIC), BUT NOT IN ENGLAND.

The inscription is in Horace Walpole's hand, and refers to the engraver, G. Vandergucht, who frequently engraved Louis Chéron's designs for book illustration.

Louis Chéron was the son of Henri Chéron, an enamel painter, and his sister, Elizabeth Sophie, was a painter and poetess who abjured her Protestant faith.

Chéron studied at the Academy of Painting and Sculpture in Paris, and won a scholarship to Rome in 1676, where he drew from the paintings of Raphael and Giulio Romano. On his return to Paris he painted in 1687 and 1690 two altarpieces for the Goldsmiths' Guild, which were presented to the Cathedral of Notre Dame, Paris.

Chéron joined the Huguenot congregation at the Savoy Chapel in 1693, when he was described as from Paris. He was encouraged to come to England by Ralph, 1st Earl of Montagu, and he worked mainly as a decorative painter and teacher. According to George Vertue, Chéron was 'much imitated by the Young people & indeed on that account by all lovers of Art much esteem'd & from thence rais'd his reputation'.

DIMENSIONS: *123 × 95mm.*

PROVENANCE: *National Portrait Gallery.*

LITERATURE: *Pierre Auzas, Les grands Mays de Notre Dame de Paris, Bulletin de la Societé de l'Histoire de l'Art Français, 1949, pp. 85–88; Edward Croft-Murray, Decorative painting in England, 1537–1837, Vol. I, 1962, pp. 243–5; Le Livre des Conversions et des Reconnaissances faites à L'Eglise française de la Savoye, 1684–1702. Huguenot Society Quarto Series, Vol. XXII, 19, p.13.*

279 *Seated male nude*
BROWN WASH AND PENCIL ON GREY PAPER LOUIS CHERON.
INSCRIBED: L.CHERON D., *c.*1720.

A seated male nude shown facing left supporting his chin with his right arm, with his legs crossed.

This is an example of the drawings executed by Chéron and his students at the St. Martin's Lane Academy. Thirty-five similar drawings by Chéron, on a larger scale, are in the British Museum, Department of Prints and Drawings. They are preserved in an album which was bought at the sale of Chéron's effects by the Earl of Derby.

DIMENSIONS: *244 × 188mm.*

PROVENANCE: *Covent Garden Gallery, 1982; Private Collection.*

LITERATURE: *Edward Croft-Murray, Catalogue of British Drawings in the Department of Prints and Drawings, The British Museum, 1960, under Chéron.*

280 *The marriage of Charles I*
LOUIS CHERON, 1725.

This is one of a series of nine paintings representing the life of King Charles I which were painted by members of the St. Martin's Lane set on the one hand, and contemporary artistic circles in France, on the other. As Charles I was married by proxy, Chéron avoided the problem of having to conform to the likeness of the King as painted by the five other artists involved in the project. All the paintings and one additional design were engraved and advertised for publication in 1728.

This painting appears to be unfinished. The legs of the rather incongruous figure of Hymen, to the left of the betrothed couple, have breeches outlined only in beige ground, and the silk stockings on the left leg of the King's proxy, Claude Lorraine, Duc de Chevreuse, fail to cover the knee.

DIMENSIONS: *620 × 755mm.*

PROVENANCE: *Private Collection.*

LITERATURE: *Robert Raines and Kenneth Sharpe, The Story of Charles I, Part I, Connoisseur, Vol.184, September 1973, pp.35–46; II, Vol.185, July 1974, pp.192–5.*

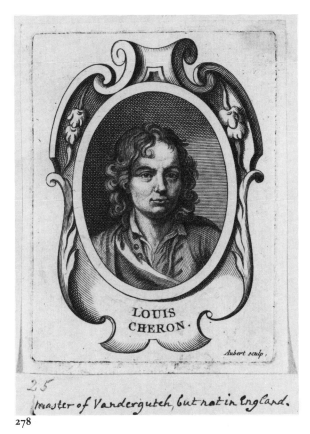

278

279

280

281 Life drawing class said to be the St Martin's Lane Academy
OIL ON CANVAS, ARTIST UNKNOWN, c.1740.

This painting may represent the St. Martin's Lane Academy in the 1740s. The exact location of the Academy has never been proved, although it was probably in a house in St. Martin's Lane. It may, however, represent an Italian or French academy. Judging from this painting, the room could accommodate between thirty and forty students.

The teachers included the French designer Hubert Gravelot (1699–1773), the painter Francis Hayman (1708–1776) and the Huguenot sculptor Louis François Roubiliac.

An advertisement in 1745 indicates that the Academy of Painting and Sculpture met during the winter for the 'Study of Drawing'. Subscriptions were taken in advance at the Half Moon Tavern in the Strand. One student who enrolled in January, 1749, noted, 'there are a man and a woman for models. The man poses three days, the woman two'. The last evening of the drawing classes that season was on 17th March. (Information kindly supplied by Kim Sloan).

NOT EXHIBITED.

DIMENSIONS: *1350 × 980mm.*

PROVENANCE: *Royal Academy of Arts.*

EXHIBITED: *Royal Academy Art Treasures, 1963(2).*

LITERATURE: *Hugh Phillips, Mid-Georgian London, 1964, pp.113, 278, fig.135; George Vertue, Note Books, III, The Walpole Society, Vol. XXII, pp.160–1; ibid., Vol. XLI, pl. 43(1).*

282 Trade card of Joseph Sympson
AT THE DOVE, RUSSELL COURT, DRURY LANE
ATTRIBUTED TO JOSEPH SYMPSON, c.1730–c.1747.

The trade card shows an artist drawing a male model from life, and proclaims that the subject of the trade card has had a formal artistic education, as does the latinisation of the engraver's Christian name.

The list of the members of the St. Martin's Lane Academy in 1724 included two engravers of this name, described as senior and junior respectively.

As the trade card indicates, the Sympson family also worked as engravers of silver and seals. Joseph Sympson is known to have worked for the goldsmiths Augustin Courtauld, Simon Margas and William Lukin, as his engraving on silver is occasionally signed.

DIMENSIONS: *165 × 163mm.*

PROVENANCE: *Heal Collection, Department of Prints and Drawings, British Museum.*

LITERATURE: *Tessa Murdoch, The Courtaulds: Silversmiths for Three Generations, 1708–1780, The Proceedings of the Silver Society, Vol.III, Number 4, 1984, pp. 88–96, fig.4; Charles Oman, English Engravers on Plate III, Apollo, July, 1957, pp.286–289; Ibid., English Engraved Silver, 1150–1900, 1978.*

283 Roubiliac's lay figure, c.1740

The figure is made of cork covered with silk stockingette. The head, of carved and painted wood, is of a type suited to either sex. The figure retains its original box, which contains a male and female costume and a military uniform which was made for a smaller figure. The male costume (exhibited) consists of a tricorn hat, wig, buff coloured frock coat, black breeches, shoes and stockings. The figure was restored by John Wragg in 1793 for Richard French. A letter from Mr. Wragg to the owner has been preserved with the lay figure, and is also in the Museum's collection.

From 1745, Louis François Roubiliac taught sculpture at the St. Martin's Lane Academy maintained by the painter William Hogarth. Roubiliac also had students and apprentices of his own. The sculptor Nicholas Read learnt drawing and modelling privately from Roubiliac, and another apprentice Edward Keyt was bound to the sculptor in 1747.

ILLUSTRATED: *page 198.*

DIMENSIONS: *760mm high.*

PROVENANCE: *Louis François Roubiliac; Richard French by 1793; J.J. Linzell; Ernest S. Makower; given to the London Museum, 1929; Museum of London.*

EXHIBITED: *Polite Society by Arthur Devis, Preston Art Gallery and National Portrait Gallery, 1983–4,(55).*

LITERATURE: *K.A. Esdaile, The Times, 1st October 1929; Ibid., Roubiliac, Some unrecorded details connected with his life and work, The Archeological Journal, Vol.86, 1929, pp.178–187; Twenty-five years of the London Museum, 1937, Plate LXXXI.*

284 Study of a standing male figure in a tricorn hat
BLACK CHALK, HEIGHTENED WITH WHITE ON BLUE PAPER, ATTRIBUTED TO CHARLES GRIGNION, c.1740.

The subject is shown facing right, and holding a cane in his right hand. The drawing is attributed to Grignion on stylistic grounds by comparison with documented examples in the Ashmolean and the British Museum (*Catalogue number 365*).

The artist was the son of the Huguenot refugee watchmaker Daniel Grignion. He studied in Paris, and under Gravelot in London, probably at the latter's drawing school at the sign of the Pestle and Mortar in Covent Garden, where his fellow pupil was Thomas Gainsborough. Here he would have practised drawing from dolls such as the lay figure (*Catalogue number 283*).

ILLUSTRATED: *page 198.*

DIMENSIONS: *405 × 226mm.*

PROVENANCE: *With Colnaghi's, 1980; Private Collection.*

LITERATURE: *English Drawings and Watercolours, Colnaghi's, November–December 1979, no.15.*

281

At *Josephus Sympson's* WAREHOUSE, *At the* Dove *in* Russell-Court *in* Drury-Lane, LONDON. *Are Sold all Sorts of* English, Italian, *and* French-Prints; *likewise all Sorts of* Frames & Glasses *for Prints or Pictures. Also all Sorts of* Engraving *undertaken and perform'd, as* Stone-Seals, Steel *and* Silver-Seals, Plate *and* Copper-Plates *either in* Heraldry, History *or* Writing *at reasonable Rates.*

282

284

283

FURNITURE & WOODWORK

Daniel Marot's engraved designs were particularly influential for furniture produced in the first two decades of the eighteenth century, and were used by cabinet makers and woodcarvers, the Pelletier family for example, and upholsterers. Marot had close family connections with the furniture trade, and his wife's family, the Goles, although of Dutch origin, were cabinet makers to the French court.

The second generation Huguenots continued the tradition of carving and gilding and played an extremely important part in the development of rococo carving and framemaking. It has recently been discovered that the framemaker, James Pascall, made the elaborate suite of rococo furniture for Temple Newsam House, Leeds.

Pages from the scrapbook of Gideon Saint (1729–99), woodcarver

Huguenot craftsmen also developed the use of papier-mâché for ornament, and by 1784, the woodcarver William Collett was forced to apply for his son's admission to the French Protestant Charity School, Westminster, due to the resulting decrease of opportunities within his craft.

METROPOLITAN MUSEUM OF ART

285 Side table

CARVED AND GILT WALNUT, JEAN PELLETIER, c.1695.

This gilded side table is supported on four column legs with ionic capitals joined at the base by scrolled stretchers which support a vase full of flowers in the centre. The surfaces are decorated with foliate scrollwork and acanthus motifs. The top is decorated in gesso with Ralph Montagu's monogram and an Earl's coronet. The table must therefore date between 1689 when Montagu received his Earldom and 1704, when he was made a Duke by Queen Anne.

As Master of the Wardrobe, Montagu was in a position to recommend craftsmen for Royal commissions and as a result, Jean Pelletier's name occurs in the Lord Chamberlain's accounts from 1690. In 1700, Pelletier carved four gilt frames for marble tables and six pairs of large stands for Hampton Court Palace.

COLOUR PLATE: *page 14.*

NOT EXHIBITED.

DIMENSIONS: *1040 × 700 × 820mm.*

PROVENANCE: *Duke of Buccleuch and Queensberry; Boughton House, Kettering.*

LITERATURE: *John Cornforth, Boughton House, Northamptonshire, Country Life, 10th September 1970, pp.624–628, fig.8; Percy Macquoid and Ralph Edwards, The Dictionary of English Furniture, Vol.III, 1927, p.29.*

286 Receipt issued by René and Thomas Pelletier

PHOTOGRAPH OF ORIGINAL, 1712.

René Pelletier of the Parish of St. Martin's in the Fields, engraver, and Thomas Pelletier of St. Paul's Covent Garden, carver and gilder, were the sons of Jean Pelletier, the maker of the gilt side table (*Catalogue number* 285).

The Pelletier family had undertaken work to the cost of £2382 for Ralph, Duke of Montagu, and on his death in 1709, £924 was still outstanding. This receipt confirms that the debt had been paid by November, 1712, and it is contained in the Ms. volume of Bills and Vouchers paid by the Executors of Ralph, Duke of Montagu.

Although the Pelletier family worked mainly as carvers and gilders, providing picture frames, they also supplied more elaborate furniture such as the 'large walnut tree Cabinet with abundance of drawers to it & shelves within the upper body for My Lord Monthermer's prints' in 1704. The previous year Pelletier had supplied 192 glasses for the sash windows in the nine rooms of the state apartments at Boughton House.

PROVENANCE: *The Duke of Buccleuch and Queensberry, Boughton House, Kettering.*

287 Fire screen

CARVED AND GILT WALNUT, ATTRIBUTED TO JEAN PELLETIER, c.1690.

A gilt cheval fire screen, supported on scrolled feet, with ornately carved cresting and stretcher. The cresting is surmounted by a vase of flowers, flanked by birds supporting garlands in their beaks. The outer columns are surmounted by flaming urns. This screen has been attributed to Jean Pelletier by comparison with a fully documented example at Hampton Court Palace.

The sliding panel is of modern damask.

DIMENSIONS: *1205 × 685mm.*

PROVENANCE: *National Trust, Knole.*

LITERATURE: *Knole, Kent, National Trust Guide Book, 1978, p.32; Percy Macquoid and Ralph Edwards, The Dictionary of English Furniture, Vol.III, 1927, fig.2, p.71.*

288 Hall bench

WALNUT, IN THE STYLE OF DANIEL MAROT, c.1700.

This is the largest and grandest of a series of seven hall benches at Dunham Massey, the seat of the Earls of Warrington. A putto riding a lion in the central cartouche and the lion arm rests are allusions to the crest of the Earls of Warrington. The shell motif, and the cloth of estate below it, relate closely to Daniel Marot's designs for furniture and textiles.

The style of the ornament on this bench is also similar to designs by the mysterious Mr. Boujet and the remodelling of the chimney piece in the Great Hall at Dunham Massey (*Catalogue number* 273).

DIMENSIONS: *2180 × 490 × 1350mm.*

PROVENANCE: *National Trust, Dunham Massey.*

LITERATURE: *John Hardy and Gervase Jackson Stops, The Second Earl of Warrington and the Age of Walnut, Apollo, Vol.CVIII, July 1978, pp.32–39, fig.5.*

289 Candlestand

GILT PINE AND WALNUT, JAMES PASCALL, 1745.

This is one of a set of eight stands which were made for Henry, seventh Viscount Irwin, who between 1738 and 1745 was creating the 'handsommest apartment in England', the long gallery at Temple Newsam. The stands originally flanked four console tables. The ornament of this suite of furniture was inspired by the story of Pan and Syrinx from Ovid's 'Metamorphoses'. Syrinx, in order to escape from Paris' pursuit, was transformed into reeds.

The triangular top is thus supported on a stem of garlanded bulrush fronds, and a bust of Syrinx. The tripod feet are also carved with watery rocaille.

James Pascall was a picture frame maker at the Golden Head over against Hanover Street in Long Acre. The bill for this astonishing suite of furniture has only recently come to light, and shows that a hitherto unknown craftsman of Huguenot origin was capable of the highest standards of production.

DIMENSIONS: *1260 × 660 × 660mm.*

PROVENANCE: *Temple Newsam House, Leeds.*

EXHIBITED: *Rococo Art and Design in Hogarth's England, Victoria and Albert Museum, 1984, L.7.*

LITERATURE: *Christopher Gilbert, The Temple Newsam Suite of early-Georgian Gilt Furniture, Connoisseur, CLXVII, February, 1968, pp.844–8, fig.5; Christopher Gilbert, Furniture at Temple Newsam House and Lotherton Hall, 1978, p.293; David Hill, Archives and Archaeology at Temple Newsam House, Leeds Art Calendar, no.89, 1981, pp.26–32; David Hill, James Pascall and the Long Gallery Suite at Temple Newsam, Furniture History, Vol.XVII, 1981, pp.70–74, fig.49–56.*

285

289

288

290 *Letter and Account for the Long Gallery Suite, Temple Newsam*
JAMES PASCALL, 1746.

On the 9th August, 1746, James Pascall submitted a bill for 20 chairs, 4 settees, a couch, a pair of console tables with enriched gesso tops, and a pair of marble-topped side tables, eight candlestands, and a pair of girandoles, with a covering letter to Viscountess Irwin. The total cost came to £364.16.0.

The letter explained that 'the two Stands Extraordinary well done as is ye Whole jobb now' had been sent the previous day, 'They are not the worse for having been in hand so long'. He assures his client that 'I am as carefull in charging as possible … there is Upholsters and Cabinett Makers in town would have charged 100 pound more than what I have, but as I am ye Maker my Self and does Everything at ye first hand I can doe what they Cannot'.

James Pascall lived and worked on the Bedford Estate in Covent Garden. He occupied two houses in Long Acre and Bow Street, and a plan of his workshop survives amongst the estate papers.

A Jacques Pascal, possibly identical with this craftsman, stood witness with Augustin Courtauld to the marriage of Judith Marie Pascall on 23 April 1718 at the Huguenot Church of Le Tabernacle, Milk Alley (Huguenot Society Quarto Series, Vol. XXIX, p. 23).

DIMENSIONS: *432 × 406mm.*

PROVENANCE: *Leeds District Archives.*

LITERATURE: *David Hill, James Pascall and the Long Gallery Suite at Temple Newsam House, Furniture History, Vol.XVII, 1981, pp.70–74.*

291 *Frame*
CARVED AND GILT WOOD, PAUL PETIT, 1740.

This frame, a documented example of the work of the Huguenot carver and gilder, Paul Petit, surrounds one of a group of six copies after the Raphael cartoons by Joseph Goupy. This represents the death of Ananias, and is executed in bodycolour on parchment. This set of copies was probably originally painted for James Brydges, 1st Duke of Chandos, as the back of the frame bears his seal with his coat of arms and that of his second wife Lydia van Hatten, whom he married in 1736. It is probable that the set was given to Frederick, Prince of Wales, by Chandos' eldest son, Henry Brydges, who was Frederick's First Gentleman of the Bedchamber, 1728 and his Master of Horse in 1735.

On May 20th, 1740, Paul Petit was paid five guineas for 'seven smal frames carv'd all round with a top and bottom rise – carving gilt in oyl gold a Mahogany panel to dito to ye seven cartoons painted by Mr. Goupy.' They were to be seen in Leicester House in 1749, when George Vertue described the Princesses' Drawing Room as 'adorned with the limnings only of Mr. Jo. Goupy in curious carvd frames and Glasses consisting mostly of several most valuable pictures in Collection there that he has copied and Imitated … a set of the 7 cartons after Raphael in a Frame'. The smaller frames were evidently displayed in a larger ornamental surround, and judging from the contemporary description, hung against a mahogany panel.

Although Joseph Goupy was a member of a family from Nevers in France, and may well have been of Huguenot origin. Goupy became Cabinet Painter to Frederick, Prince of Wales in 1736.

COLOUR PLATE: *page 14.*

DIMENSIONS: *498 × 653mm.*

PROVENANCE: *Baron Kielmansegg; James Brydges, 1st Duke of Chandos; Frederick, Prince of Wales; Mr. Forman, 1800; Rev. Alfred Chandler; W.E. Gladstone; Christie's 23 June 1875 (630); Lord Downe, sale, (six of the set), Sotheby's, 19 June 1973 (284–9); Dr. David Bindman. (Information kindly communicated by Frances Carey).*

292 *Trade card of Joseph Duffour*
AT THE GOLDEN HEAD IN BERWICK STREET, SOHO, *c.*1737–1756?

Joseph Duffour's name occurs in the accounts of Frederick, Prince of Wales in 1737–8, when he was paid seven guineas for a frame for a 'Picture of Liberality and Modesty' and for '12 Frames for pictures of Cupid & Psyche'. In 1738, he was paid by John, 2nd Duke of Montagu 'for carving work'. In 1745–6, his name occurs in the accounts of Charles, 5th Lord Baltimore, Gentlemen of the Bedchamber to the Prince of Wales, and from 1751–3 his name is listed in the bank ledgers of the painter Thomas Hudson. The latter evidently recommended his framer to the Goldsmiths' Company, for in 1762, Duffour was paid for gilding the frame to Hudson's painting 'Benn's Club of Aldermen', which had been commissioned by the Company.

Duffour's trade card indicates that he was the original maker of 'Papie Mâchie'. Papier-Mâché was used mainly for ceiling and wall decoration, and became increasingly popular during the 1760s and 1770s.

In 1772, Duffour's shop was occupied by René Stone, who described himself as frame-maker to his Majesty near the French church in Berwick Street. It is probable that Stone was also of Huguenot origin, and that his name had been anglicised from Pierre or La Pierre.

DIMENSIONS: *111 × 141mm.*

PROVENANCE: *Heal Collection, Department of Prints and Drawings, British Museum.*

293 *Trade card of Henry Jouret, picture frame maker*
AT THE ARCHITRAVE FRAME IN GRAFTON STREET, ST ANN'S, SOHO, MATHIAS LOCK, *c.*1750.

Jouret's trade card claimed that he made frames for paintings, prints and drawings, and also varnished prints for interior decoration. The card was designed and engraved by Mathias Lock.

Henry Jouret may be connected with Mr. Joris who appears in the accounts of Frederick, Prince of Wales as the assistant of Paul Petit (*Catalogue number* 291).

DIMENSIONS: *148 × 112mm.*

PROVENANCE: *Heal Collection, Department of Prints and Drawings, British Museum.*

LITERATURE: *Morrison Heckscher, Lock and Copland, A Catalogue of the Engraved Ornament, Furniture History, Vol.XV, 1979, plate 13. (Kindly communicated by Michael Snodin).*

291

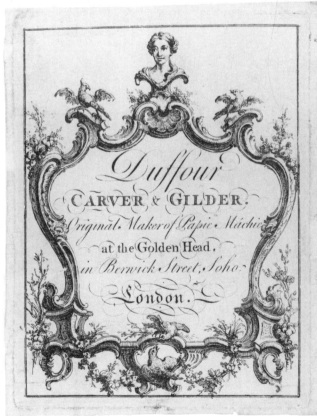

292

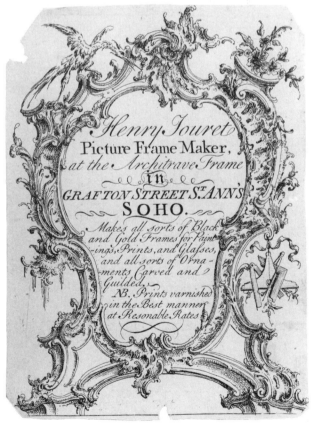

293

294 *Trade card of Daniel Bernardeau, wood turner*
AT THE SIGN OF THE GOLDEN COFFEE MILL, ST. MARTIN'S COURT,
NEAR LEICESTERFIELDS, JACOB BONNEAU, *c.*1740.

Daniel Bernardeau is described as late apprentice to Mr. Storer at Snow Hill. This trade card indicates that he specialises in bowling green bowls and mahogany stands for china dishes, as well as 'all sorts of oval frames'.

The engraver Jacob Bonneau is recorded as working in the 1740s. He also produced trade cards for John Duncan, bookseller in 1743 and Peter Bonneau, razor maker, presumably a relative. Bonneau engraved the plates for William De La Cour's 'Eighth Book of Ornaments', 1747. His son, Jacob, practised as a fashionable drawing master.

Jacob Bonneau the elder was probably one of five children of Pierre Bonneau, an engraver of Rennes, who escaped from France in 1687 and abjured Catholicism on his arrival in Jersey. He later settled in London.

DIMENSIONS: *121 × 135mm.*

PROVENANCE: *Heal Collection, Department of Prints and Drawings, British Museum.*

LITERATURE: *Rococo Art and Design in Hogarth's England, 1984, pp.45, 63, 73, 133; Hans Hammelman, Book Illustrators in 18th Century England,* ed. T.S.R. Boase, *1975, pp.19–20.*

295 *Petition from Mr Collett to the French Protestant Charity School, Westminster*
PHOTOGRAPH OF ORIGINAL, 1784.

William Collett, 'a sober painstaking man who being burthened with a large family finds it very difficult to get a livelyhood, his profession of carver being greatly hurt by the new invented works in papier-mâché, & grown so scarce as not to find sufficient for a constant employ'. As a result, he was forced to apply for his son's admission to the French Protestant Charity School, Westminster.

PROVENANCE: *Huguenot Library.*

LITERATURE: *Irvine R. Gray, Huguenot Manuscripts; A Descriptive Catalogue of the Remaining Manuscripts in the Huguenot Library, Huguenot Society Quarto Series, Vol.LVI, 1983, p.110.*

294

295

SCULPTURE

At the end of the seventeenth century, Huguenot refugee carvers were able to meet a growing demand for likenesses in exotic materials, such as ivory and tortoiseshell. David Le Marchand and Jean Obrisset were trained in Dieppe, a centre for such specialist work. Ivory medallion portraits were worked up from wax models, as were medals, although the latter had the advantage of being easily reproduced, and the eighteenth century saw an increasing demand for series of medals, representing important historical figures or eminent contemporaries as epitomised in the work of Jean and Jacques Antoine Dassier from Geneva. By the mid century, the sculptor Louis François Roubiliac, who had settled in London by 1730, was supplying more substantial portrait busts in marble, but these too could be reproduced in plaster or terracotta on demand at a considerably lower cost. Meanwhile, the modeller Isaac Gosset had discovered a composition that 'imitates ivory' and was reproducing likenesses in wax for a mere 'guinea apeece'.

Queen Mary II, ivory, Jean Cavalier

296 *Charles II on Horseback*

IVORY RELIEF, JEAN CAVALIER, 1684.
INSCRIBED ON THE REVERSE: I. CAVALIER F. 1684.

This relief portrait shows the King in armour, crowned with laurels, wearing a billowing cloak, on horseback, facing to the right. The royal steed stands in a landscape strewn with flowers. On the reverse the sculptor has begun to carve a tree and a flower.

This is one of the earliest signed pieces by Jean Cavalier, about whose origin and training little is known. Terry Friedman has suggested that he may have been trained in Paris under Michael Mollart.

DIMENSIONS: *152mm high.*

PROVENANCE: *Christie's 29 April 1980 (170); Temple Newsam House, Leeds.*

LITERATURE: *Terry Friedman, Cavalier's Charles II on Horseback, Leeds Art Calendar, No.88, 1981, pp.4–13.*

297 *Samuel Pepys*

IVORY MEDALLION PORTRAIT, JEAN CAVALIER, LONDON, 1688.
INSCRIBED: SAM. PEPYS CAR. ET.IAC ANGL.REGIB. A SECRETIS ADMIRALIAE, (AND ON THE REVERSE) J. CAVALIER FECIT AO.D 1688.

The medallion shows the diarist in profile to the right with a long flowing wig, and wearing a lace cravat.

It is interesting to compare this medallion with Cavalier's ivory relief of Sir Godfrey Kneller in the National Portrait Gallery, *c.*1690. Kneller apparently persuaded Pepys to sit to the medallist in January 1690, and was evidently in close contact with Cavalier that year (*Catalogue number* 299).

DIMENSIONS: *85mm diameter.*

PROVENANCE: *Samuel Pepys, by descent to John Pepys Cockerell; acquired by the Worshipful Company of Clothworkers, 1931.*

EXHIBITED: *Carvings in ivory, Burlington Fine Arts Club, 1923(222); Royal Westminster, 1981(97).*

LITERATURE: *Penelope Hunting, Royal Westminster, 1981, p.51, illustrated; J. Douglas Stewart, Sir Godfrey Kneller, National Portrait Gallery, 1971, pp.16–17; J. Verbeck, A Dutchman portrayed in Sweden by a French Ivory Carver, Antiek, VIII, no.1, June–July, 1973, pp.35–42.*

298 *Queen Mary II*

IVORY MEDALLION PORTRAIT, JEAN CAVALIER, LONDON, 1686.
INSCRIBED: ON THE REVERSE, CAVALIER F. 1686.

The medallion shows the Queen, bust length, in profile to the right. Her hair is elaborately dressed with strings of pearls which are also looped around the edge of her low-necked dress. There are similar ivory relief portraits of Queen Mary at Cassel and at Berlin (the latter is dated 1690).

DIMENSIONS: *90mm high.*

PROVENANCE: *Purchased at Sotheby's, 1929, by the Victoria and Albert Museum, Department of Sculpture.*

LITERATURE: *A. Julius, Jean Cavalier, 1926, p.125, no.6; Volbach, Die Elfenbeinbildwerke, 1923, no.J.720, p.77; Victoria and Albert Museum, Review, 1929, p.10.*

299 *William III*

IVORY MEDALLION PORTRAIT, JEAN CAVALIER, LONDON, C.1690.
INSCRIBED: GVLIELMVS.III.D.G.MAG.BRIT.FR. & HI.REX.

The medallion shows the King, bust length in profile facing to the right, wearing a long curled wig, dressed in armour with an embossed harness and a cloak across the shoulder and chest. It is signed on the arm with the initial C.

Other portraits by Cavalier of William III are in Berlin (Volbach, Die Elfenbeinbildwerke, 1923, p.76, illustrated plate 77) and Cassel (A. Julius, Jean Cavalier, 1926, p.140). In a document of 1690, Cavalier is described as medallist to William III. In March 1690, Cavalier shared the sittings given to Kneller for the state portrait of William III.

DIMENSIONS: *90mm high.*

PROVENANCE: *Bequeathed by Dr. W.L. Hildburgh in 1938; Victoria and Albert Museum, Department of Sculpture.*

LITERATURE: *Terry Friedman, Cavalier's Charles II on Horseback, Leeds Art Calendar, no.88, 1981, pp.4–13, fig.3; A. Staring, De Portretten van den Koning-Stadbouder, Nederlands Kunsthistorisch Jaarboek, III, 1950–1, pp.184–6; Victoria and Albert Museum Review, 1938, p.5, fig.7.*

300 *Receipt for a pair of medallion portraits*

JEAN CAVALIER, LONDON, 1690.

This bill reads, 'Recd. of ye Earl of Dorsett by ye hands of Richd. Downing ye sume of twenty guineas; for two meddals one of my Lord & ye other my Lady'. These medals probably represented Charles, 6th Earl of Dorset, and his second wife, Mary, daughter of the 3rd Earl of Northampton who died in 1691, but unfortunately they have not been traced. It is probable, judging by the price, that they were ivory medallion portraits, but it is conceivable that they were cast in bronze, although no other examples in bronze are recorded by Cavalier today. Both ivory and bronze medallions would have been based on a wax original which was probably modelled from the life.

In December, 1690, William III granted Cavalier a 'Pass and letters of recommendation to travel abroad and return'. By 1693, Cavalier is recorded in Copenhagen, and later in Sweden. He appears to have died during a voyage to Persia in 1698 or 1699.

PROVENANCE: *Kent County Record Office, Sackville Papers, A191/1.*

LITERATURE: *A. Julius, Jean Cavalier, 1926, p.145.*

296

297

299

301 *Charles I*

HORN PORTRAIT PLAQUE, OVAL, JEAN OBRISSET, LONDON, NO DATE.

The King is shown in profile to the right, in armour. The portrait is based on the medal of Charles I by John Roettiers, of *c*.1670.

The Obrisset family came from Dieppe, where in 1676 a Jean Aubrisset was recorded as an ivory worker with an open shop. He was probably a relative of the Jean Obrisset, above, who worked in London, 1705 to 1728, specialising in pressed horn and tortoiseshell. In 1691, a Jean Obrisset, described as a turner in ivory, stood godfather to Judith, a daughter of Jean Obrisset, carver ('graveur') at the French church of Hungerford Market.

DIMENSIONS: *68mm long.*

PROVENANCE: *Given to the London Museum by P.A.S. Phillips, 1920; Museum of London.*

LITERATURE: *Medallic Illustrations, I, no. 200, p. 346; P.A.S. Phillips, John Obrisset, Huguenot Carver, Medallist, Horn and Tortoiseshell Worker and Snuffbox maker with examples of his works dated 1705 to 1728, 1931, pp. 59–60, illustrates similar examples.*

302 *Queen Anne*

TORTOISESHELL PORTRAIT PLAQUE, OVAL, JEAN OBRISSET, LONDON, 1705.
INSCRIBED: OB 1705.

The Queen is shown in profile to the left wearing both the Order of the Garter and the Bath. P.A.S. Phillips suggested that Obrisset's portrait of Queen Anne was based on a painting by Sir Godfrey Kneller.

DIMENSIONS: *72mm long.*

PROVENANCE: *Given to the London Museum by P.A.S. Phillips, 1920; Museum of London.*

LITERATURE: *P.A.S. Phillips, John Obrisset, Huguenot Carver, Medallist, Horn and Tortoiseshell Worker and Snuffbox maker with examples of his works dated 1705 to 1728, 1931, p.64 for similar examples.*

303 *Miracle of the Man with the Withered Hand*

IVORY RELIEF, DAVID LE MARCHAND, LONDON.
INSCRIBED: D.L.M. IN. & SC, NO DATE.

David Le Marchand was the son of Guillaume Le Marchand, who painted a Nativity and a Christ Crucified for the Church of St. Jacques and the Convent des Minimes, Dieppe, in the first decade of the eighteenth century. This relief is probably one of Le Marchand's earliest works, as the subject, probably based on an engraving, would be associated with painting, and may have been inspired by Le Marchand's family background.

It is not known when Le Marchand first came to Britain, but by 1696 he is recorded as working as an ivory carver in Edinburgh.

Le Marchand specialised in ivory relief portraits although he also executed busts in the round.

DIMENSIONS: *140 × 205mm.*

PROVENANCE: *Phillip Andrews; National Museum of Wales.*

LITERATURE: *Charles Avery, David Le Marchand, ivory carver, 1674–1726, Proceedings of the Huguenot Society of London, Vol. 24 (1984), pp. 113–118; Ambrose Millet, Ivories et Ivoiriers de Dieppe, 1906, p. 16.*

304 *Samuel Pepys (1633–1703)*

IVORY MEDALLION PORTRAIT, DAVID LE MARCHAND, LONDON.
INSCRIBED: BENEATH THE SHOULDER D.L.M.F., NO DATE.

A profile bust to the right of Samuel Pepys, the diarist.

It is interesting to compare this medallion with that by Jean Cavalier of the same sitter (*Catalogue number* 297).

DIMENSIONS: *132 × 106mm.*

PROVENANCE: *A.W. Franks; presented to the British Museum, 1884.*

LITERATURE: *O.M. Dalton, Catalogue of the Ivory Carvings in the British Museum, 1909, no.458; A. Maskell, Ivories, 1905, pl.lxvi.*

305 *The Rt Hon Thomas Brodrick (1654–1730)*

IVORY MEDALLION PORTRAIT, DAVID LE MARCHAND, LONDON.
INSCRIBED: D.L.M. BELOW THE RIGHT SHOULDER.

A profile bust to the right of Thomas Brodrick PC, the eldest son of Sir St. John Brodrick of Midleton, County Cork. Thomas Brodrick represented his home county in Parliament, 1703, and was later M.P. for Stockbridge, 1713, and Guildford, 1722. He was joint Comptroller of the Army Accounts, 1708, and was appointed a member of the Privy Council to George I, 1714.

DIMENSIONS: *100 × 75mm.*

PROVENANCE: *A.W. Franks, presented to the British Museum, 1882.*

LITERATURE: *O.M. Dalton, Catalogue of the Ivory Carvings in the British Museum, 1909, no.460, pl.CIII; S.R. Houfe, A Whig Artist in Ivory, David Le Marchand, Antique Collector, April 1971, pp.66–70.*

301

302

303

306 *Bust of unknown lady*
IVORY, DAVID LE MARCHAND, 1701; INSCRIBED: LE MARCHAND FE. 1701.

DIMENSIONS: *152mm high.*
PROVENANCE: *Colonel Nelthorpe.*

This lady is probably a member of the Nelthorpe family, who although they were based in Lincolnshire had strong London connections at this period. Richard Nelthorpe (1667–1731) worked as a goldsmith in Lombard Street, London and John Nelthorpe (b.1663) was an Aleppo merchant. The most likely sitter would be Anne (née Hobson) who married Henry Nelthorpe in 1694. Henry died in 1698, and the next year his widow remarried Paris Slaughter (d.1703). Although there were no children by this second marriage, Anne had two sons by Henry Nelthorpe. Thus, although this bust was probably commissioned by Paris Slaughter, it subsequently passed to the Nelthorpes. Anne Slaughter's great uncle was Adlard Stukeley, a relative of William Stukeley, who also sat to Le Marchand (see *Catalogue number* 310).

On the other hand, this bust may represent the wife of the goldsmith, Richard Nelthorpe but her identity has not yet been revealed. (Information kindly supplied by Mr. John Lord from Lincolnshire Archives Office, NEL 17/6/17 and NEL 17/6/29.)

307 *John Churchill, 1st Duke of Marlborough (1650–1722)*
IVORY MEDALLION PORTRAIT, DAVID LE MARCHAND, LONDON.
INSCRIBED: D.L.M.F. UNDER THE SHOULDER, NO DATE.

DIMENSIONS: *130 × 108mm.*
PROVENANCE: *Henry Oppenheimer; E.L. Paget; Sotheby's 11.10.1949(84) illustrated pl.XII; bt. A. Spero; given to the Victoria and Albert Museum by Dr. W.L. Hildburgh, F.S.A.*
EXHIBITED: *Carvings in Ivory, Burlington Fine Arts Club, 1923(221) illustrated.*
LITERATURE: *M.H. Longhurst, English Ivories, 1926, no.LXXVII, pl.54.*

An oval bust in high relief, probably representing John Churchill, 1st Duke of Marlborough. The sitter faces right, and wears a draped cloak over his open shirt and jacket.

David Le Marchand also executed two portrait busts of Marlborough's daughter, Anne Churchill, Countess of Sunderland, one of which is in the same collection.

307

308 *Matthew Raper (1704–1778)*
IVORY RELIEF PORTRAIT, DAVID LE MARCHAND, LONDON, 1720.
INSCRIBED: EFF.MATHEI RAPER JUNI AETAT. SUAE 15.0 AN. AD VIV. SCULP. D.L.M. 1720.

DIMENSIONS: *205 × 160mm.*
PROVENANCE: *C.L. Grindwater; Acquired by the Victoria and Albert Museum, 1959.*
LITERATURE: *Charles Avery, David Le Marchand – ivory carver, 1674–1726, Proceedings of the Huguenot Society of London Vol. 24 (1984), pp.113–118, fig.9; Terence Hodgkinson, An Ingenious Man for Carving in Ivory, Bulletin of the Victoria and Albert Museum, Vol.1, no.2, April 1965, pp.29–32, fig.2; John Kerslake, Sculptor and Patron, Two Portraits by Highmore, Apollo, Vol.95, Jan–June, 1972, pp.25–29.*

Matthew Raper was the son of Matthew Raper, silk merchant of Wendover Dean, Buckinghamshire, who became a Director of the Bank of England in 1738. The Rapers were evidently important patrons of Le Marchand, commissioning the bust of Newton in 1718, and a relief of Sir Christopher Wren.

This relief shows the young Matthew Raper standing in a library and demonstrating a proposition in geometry. He later became a mathematician, scholar and Fellow of the Royal Society. In 1765 he presented Le Marchand's bust of Newton and a relief of Sir Christopher Wren to the British Museum.

309 *Michael Garnault (d.1746)*
IVORY MEDALLION PORTRAIT, DAVID LE MARCHAND, LONDON, NO DATE.

NOT EXHIBITED.
DIMENSIONS: *144 × 115mm.*
PROVENANCE: *Christie's 13 December 1976; Private Collection.*
LITERATURE: *Charles Avery, David Le Marchand – ivory carver, 1674–1726, Proceedings of the Huguenot Society of London, Vol. 24 (1984), pp.113–118, fig.6; Sir William Job Collins, Note on the Garnault Pedigree, Proceedings of the Huguenot Society of London, Vol. 17 (1944), p.269; Wagner, Pedigree of the Garnault family, ibid, Vol. 11 (1915–17), pp.149–151.*

The sitter is shown in profile to the right.

Michael (d.1746) was the son of Pierre Garnault, goldsmith, a refugee from Châtellerault in Poitou. Michael worked as a jeweller and was associated with the jeweller and banker Jaques Louis Berchère (1670–1753) (*Catalogue numbers* 57, 348) and his son-in-law Louis Baril (1692–1761) to whom he left bequests in his will. He purchased Bulls Cross (later Bowling Green House) Enfield, in 1724, and was eventually buried in the church at Enfield with his wife, also of Huguenot extraction, Anne Piozet.

Michael Garnault's name has recently been discovered on an inventory of plate and jewels dated 3 October 1711 for the 2nd Duke of Bedford. The inventory is also signed by Francis Child and suggests that Garnault may have had connections with that banking house. His brother Aimé Garnault (1717–82) became Treasurer of the New River Company.

306

306

308

310

310 *Sir Christopher Wren*

IVORY MEDALLION PORTRAIT, DAVID LE MARCHAND, LONDON, c.1723.

INSCRIBED: ON A LABEL ON THE REVERSE, BUST OF SIR CHRISTOPHER WREN ARCHITECT BORN OCT. 20, 1633, DIED 1724 (SIC) AGED 91 YEARS, IN IVORY, BY DENIS LE MARCHANT FOR MY DEAR DAUGHTER MARGARET H. WILLETT.

The sitter is shown in profile to the right.

According to the antiquary George Vertue, 'Mr. Willett has another head of a gentleman, pretty large with the initial letters D.L.M.'

The previous year Le Marchand executed an ivory portrait of the antiquary William Stukeley, who noted in his diary for 11 July 1722, 'I sat to Mr. Marchand cutting my profile in basso relievo in Ivory'. In June, 1726, Stukeley records the death of one of his most intimate friends, 'the famous cutter in ivory, Monsr. Marchand, who cut my profile'. Le Marchand died at the French Hospital.

ILLUSTRATED: *page 211.*

DIMENSIONS: *127 × 92mm.*

PROVENANCE: *H. Willett; Mrs. Vosey until c.1940; S.R. Hawkswell; Sotheby's 4 July 1966 (54); D. Peel; purchased by the National Portrait Gallery, 1966.*

LITERATURE: *National Portrait Gallery, Annual Report of the Trustees, 1967, pp.32–3; The Family Memoirs of the Rev. William Stukeley, M.P. The Surtees Society, 73 (1882), pp.67,131.*

311 *Arabella Aufrère (d.1804)*

BUST, MARBLE, LOUIS FRANCOIS ROUBILIAC, 1748.

INSCRIBED: ARABELLA AUFRERE MDCCXLVIII L.F. ROUBILIAC FECIT.

The sitter was the daughter of William and Arabella Bate of Foxton, Derbyshire. Her mother died at the age of twenty-six, and so Arabella Bate was brought up by her aunt, the Countess of Exeter. The latter had commissioned a monument to her parents, Thomas and Margaret Chambers, from Roubiliac, which was erected in All Saints, Derby in 1737. In 1746, the sitter married George Aufrère, younger son of Israel Antoine Aufrère, the Huguenot minister of the Savoy Chapel (*Catalogue number* 63). It is probable that this bust was commissioned to celebrate their marriage. Their only daughter, Sophia, married in 1770 Charles Anderson Pelham, later 1st Earl of Yarborough (*Catalogue numbers* 460, 461).

The bust is a most sensitive rendering of the personality of the sitter, and effectively captures the texture of her dress, particularly in the delicacy with which the lace bodice and the braid which supports the hair are executed. Such sensitivity to the rendering of texture might well be expected from a sculptor associated with Lyons, centre of the silk trade. It would have been particularly appreciated by George Aufrère, who judging by his bills for muslin and holland to the Countess of Exeter, was a draper of some standing.

DIMENSIONS: *690mm high.*

PROVENANCE: *George Aufrère, by descent to the present owner, the Earl of Yarborough.*

EXHIBITED: *British Portraits, Royal Academy, 1956 (534); Rococo Art and Design in Hogarth's England, Victoria and Albert Museum, 1984 (S9) p. 293.*

LITERATURE: *Tessa Murdoch, Louis François Roubiliac and his Huguenot Connections, Proceedings of the Huguenot Society of London, Vol.XXIV, No.1, 1983, pp.26–45; Margaret Whinney, Sculpture in Britain, 1530–1830, 1963, p.113.*

312 *Two from a group of seventeen busts bought at the sale of Roubiliac's effects and presented to the British Museum by Dr Maty*

LOUIS FRANCOIS ROUBILIAC.

a. PHILIP STANHOPE, 4TH EARL OF CHESTERFIELD (1694–1773), BUST, PLASTER CAST, LOUIS FRANCOIS ROUBILIAC, c.1745.

INSCRIBED: (ON THE SIDE) STANHOPE.

This plaster cast is similar to a bronze in the Victoria and Albert Museum which is truncated higher on the shoulders and on the neck. Another plaster cast is in the Yale Center for British Art. The sale of Roubiliac's effects included two terracottas and three plasters of this sitter, although the whereabouts of the other three are not known.

This plaster is based on the marble bust of Lord Chesterfield which is signed 'L.F. Roubiliac Sc.iT ad Vivum, dated, MDCCXLV, and inscribed: PHILIP EARL OF CHESTERFIELD twice Embassador extraordinary to the states General Lord Steward of the Household & Lord of the Bed-chamber to KING GEORGE the 2. Lord Lieutenant of Ireland & Knight of the most noble Order of the Garter'. The bust was recorded by Mrs. Esdaile, but has only very recently reappeared at Christie's (3 April 1985) (c).

Dr. Whinney thought that Lord Chesterfield may himself have suggested the classical idiom of this bust, for in May, 1745, he wrote to his son enthusiastically about the bust of Cicero he had just added to his library. Gordon Balderston has suggested that this was probably a version of the Hellenistic marble that is now in the Uffizi. A plaster cast of Cicero was included in the sculptor's posthumous sale of 1762 (Second Day's Sale, Thursday May 14th (44)). It was also presented by Dr. Maty to the British Museum.

Lord Chesterfield had very close associations with the Huguenot community in Soho. He was educated by Mr. Jouneau, minister of the Huguenot Church in Berwick Street. He used a Huguenot tailor, Andrew Regnier, who was probably a relative of Roubiliac's fourth wife, and a Huguenot cook, Vincent la Chapelle. Dr. Maty was his physician and later his biographer as he published in 1777 a collected edition of Chesterfield's writings. Richard Chenevix was his private chaplain, until as Lord Lieutenant of Ireland, Chesterfield was able to obtain for Chenevix the appointment of Bishop of Waterford. Chesterfield said of the sculptor, 'Roubiliac only was a statuary, the rest stone-cutters'.

NOT EXHIBITED.

DIMENSIONS: *650mm high; 195mm wide.*

PROVENANCE: *Roubiliac's Posthumous sale, 13 May 1762 (9) or 14 May (18) or 15 May (20); Dr. Maty, presented to the British Museum, 28 May 1762.*

LITERATURE: *K.A. Esdaile, The Life and Work of Louis François Roubiliac, 1928, p.103, pl. XXIII; Margaret Whinney, English Sculpture 1720–1830, Victoria and Albert Museum, 1971, p. 86. Gordon Balderstone, Apollo, March, 1985.*

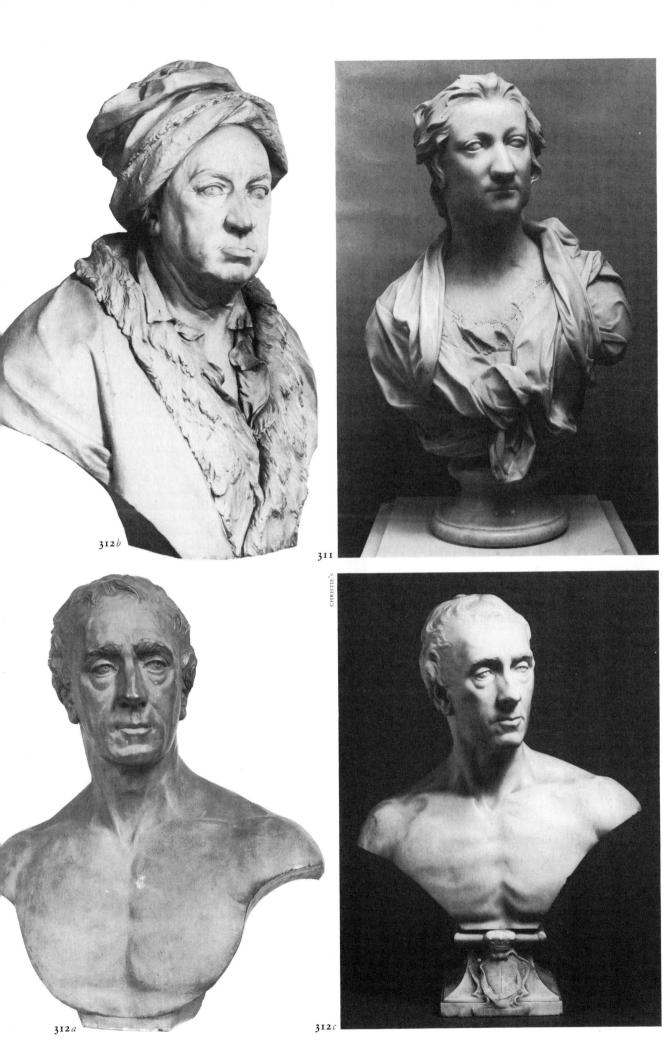

312*b*

311

312*a*

312*c*

b. MARTIN FOLKES (1690–1754), BUST, PLASTER CAST, LOUIS FRANCOIS ROUBILIAC, *c*.1749.

This plaster bust is probably a cast from the original terracotta, which was sculpted from the life as a prelude to the marble. The marble bust was commissioned by the 9th Earl of Pembroke and Roubiliac was paid £35 in full for the bust in November 1749.

The plaster is considerably larger than the finished marble and differs in that it includes extra details such as button holes in the shirt collar. It is probable that the marble was deliberately made smaller as it was the fourth of a series of busts commissioned from Roubiliac in 1747. The others are of the 9th Earl, his Countess and Sir Andrew Fountaine.

These two busts were presented by Dr. Matthew Maty, under-librarian of the British Museum, after the sculptor's death in 1762. The official minute in the early volume of the Museum Registers records the gift on 28 May 1762;
'The following busts of great Men and Authors, being casts and models of the late Mr. Roubiliac; purchased by Dr. Maty at his sale and presented by him to this Museum: viz. Socrates, Plato, Demosthenes, and Tully: from the antique. Marcus Aurelius: from a cast brought from Rome. King Charles the First, Oliver Cromwell and Shakespear; models in terracotta. Milton, Pope, Dr. Mead, Mr. Folkes, and Lord Chesterfield; casts in plaister. Ray, Willoughby, Dr. Barrow and Dr. Bentley; original models in terracotta from which the marble Busts in Trinity College, Cambridge were executed.'
It is probable that Dr. Maty purchased these busts with a view to displaying them in the library of the British Museum, then at Montagu House. The nucleus of the new British Museum Library was that formed by Sir Robert Cotton. The Cotton Library was originally arranged in fourteen presses, each of which was surmounted by a bust. These included the twelve Roman Emperors, and each press was named after one of these personages, a nomenclature which is still retained. The acquisition of a further seventeen busts would have been a useful method of creating further nomenclature for additional presses for a collection that was steadily increasing in size.

Dr. Maty was an exact contemporary of Roubiliac's and worshipped at the Huguenot Chapel in Spring Gardens (an annexe of the Savoy) where the sculptor's daughter Sophie was christened in 1744. He wrote a poem inspired by Roubiliac's statue of Handel in Vauxhall Gardens which was published in the 'Mercure de France', November, 1750 (see *Catalogue number* 216).

ILLUSTRATED: page 213.

DIMENSIONS: *660mm high.*

PROVENANCE: *Roubiliac's Posthumous Sale, 15 May 1762 (15); Dr. Maty, presented to the British Museum, 28 May 1762.*

EXHIBITED: *Rococo Art & Design in Hogarth's England, 1984 (S12) p. 294.*

LITERATURE: *K.A. Esdaile, The Life and Work of Louis François Roubiliac, 1928, pp.102–5,111,182; M.I. Webb, Roubiliac Busts at Wilton, Country Life, Vol.119, 19 April 1956, pp.804–5.*

313 *Isaac Gosset (1713–1799)*
PASTEL, ATTRIBUTED TO JEAN ETIENNE LIOTARD, *c*.1772.

Isaac Gosset was the sixth son of Jean Gosset, a Huguenot who settled in St. Hélier, Jersey. Isaac came to London and was brought up by his uncle, Matthew Gosset, a wax-modeller and frame-maker. Isaac became one of the best known wax modellers of the period, producing likenesses of many eminent figures of the time, including a series of the Royal Family.

In 1773, he became a Director of the Society of Artists, and exhibited there regularly from 1760 to 1778 he was made a Director of the French Hospital in 1764.

DIMENSIONS: *755 × 625mm.*

PROVENANCE: *By family descent to the present owner; Private Collection.*

LITERATURE: *Mary H. Gosset, A family of Modellers in Wax, Proceedings of the Huguenot Society of London, Vol. 3 (1888–1891), p. 547; E.J. Pyke, A Biographical Dictionary of Wax Modellers, 1973, pp. 56–59.*

314 *Bible belonging to the Gosset family*
PUBLISHED IN GENEVA, 1678.

The Bible is inscribed with the dates of birth of Isaac's five brothers, John (1699–1719), Abraham (1701–1785), Jacob (1703–1788), Pierre (1705–1728), and Gedeon (1706–1785). It belonged to Pierre Gosset in 1725, and in 1777 was passed to his youngest daughter Mary, who noted (still in French) that it had belonged to 'mes venerable ancetres pere & Mere'.

PROVENANCE: *By family descent to the present owner; Private Collection.*

LITERATURE: *Mary H. Gosset, ibid., p. 546.*

315 *Tools used by Isaac Gosset*
IVORY.

Gosset's contemporary George Vertue noted the increasing popularity of wax models, and the success of the 'Ingenious Mr. Gosset' in this field, who had even had the honour of 'his Majestyes setting to him'. From his working model, Vertue describes how Gosset, 'molds or casts off, in the same composition of white wax – and sells each head in oval frames for one guinea apeece'. The original model was sold at 4 guineas. The resulting duplicates were used to produce further moulds and plaster reproductions which were 'sold all over the town and Country – at a small price'. Isaac Gosset was so successful that he did not mind this cheaper reproduction of his portraits.

PROVENANCE: *By family descent to the present owner; Private Collection.*

LITERATURE: *E.J. Pyke, A Biographical Dictionary of Wax Modellers, 1973, reproduced pl.113.*

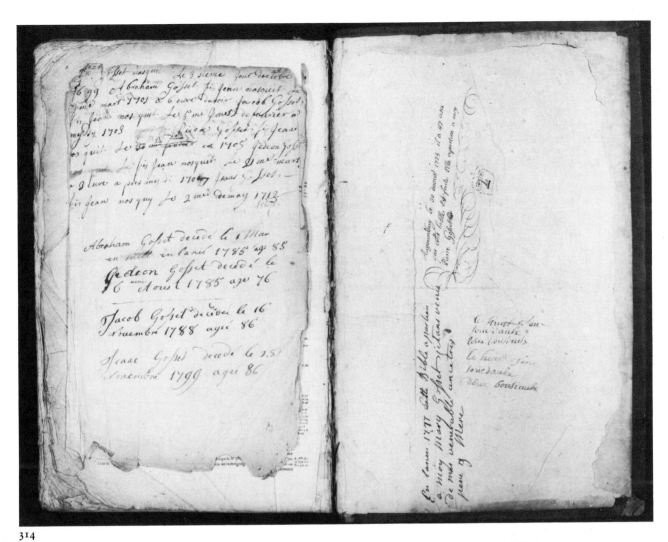

314

315

313

316 *Nine medallion portraits of members of the Murray and Stanhope families*

WAX, ISAAC GOSSET, LONDON, 1745.

a. LADY GRIZEL BAILLIE (1665–1746).

Inscribed: on a label on the reverse, 'The Lady Grizel Baillie (1665–1746) Daughter of 1st Earl of Marchmont & 1st Lord Polwarth m. George Baillie 1692 A poetess and a very gallant woman (see D.N.B. Vol.II, p.413) Grandmother of Grisel Countess S. By Gosset, 1745'. The wooden back to the frame is also inscribed, 'Right Honble Lady Grizel Baillie Gosset 1745'.

The sitter is shown in profile to the left with her head covered.

DIMENSIONS: *98 × 80mm.*

b. HON. GEORGE BAILLIE (*d.*1738).

Inscribed: on a label on the reverse, 'Hon. George Baillie, (brother of Grisel, Countess Stanhope by Gosset, 1745)', and on the wooden back to the frame, 'Honble George Baillie. Gosset?'

The sitter is shown in profile to the right, in late seventeenth-century dress. This represents George Baillie, the husband of Lady Grizel Baillie (*a*) rather than the brother of the Countess Stanhope as implied by the later inscription on the back. The Hon. George Baillie died in 1738, and this wax is apparently based on a contemporary portrait at Mellerstain.

DIMENSIONS: *111 × 78mm.*

c. GRISEL, LADY MURRAY (1693–1759).

Inscribed: on a label on the reverse, 'Grisel Baillie, Lady Murray, elder sister of Rachel, Lady Binning, and aunt of Grisel, Countess Stanhope. Married Sir Alexander Murray of Stanhope, Co. Durham by Gosset 1745', and on the wooden back to the frame, 'Grisel Baillie, Lady Murray Gosset fecit. 1745'.

The sitter is shown in profile to the right with her head covered.

DIMENSIONS: *97 × 75mm.*

d. RACHEL, LADY BINNING (1696–1773).

Inscribed: on the label on the reverse, 'Rachel, Lady Binning, Gosset 1745. She died 1773 (Mother of Grisel, Countess Stanhope)'.

The sitter is shown in profile to the right with her head covered.

DIMENSIONS: *101 × 79mm.*

e. GRISEL, COUNTESS STANHOPE (1719–1811).

Inscribed: on the label on the reverse, 'Grisel, Countess Stanhope (1719–1811) by Gosset 1745', and on the wooden back to the frame, 'Griselda Countess Stanhope Gosset fecit, 1745'.

The sitter is shown in profile to the left, wearing a low-necked dress and pearls.

DIMENSIONS: *98 × 80mm.*

f. THOMAS, EARL OF HADDINGTON (1721–1794).

Inscribed: on a label on the reverse 'Thomas, 7th Earl of Haddington (1721–1794) by Gosset 1745 (brother of Grisel, Countess S)', and on the wooden back to the frame 'Thomas Earl of Haddington Gosset 1745'.

Thomas, Earl of Haddington, was the son of Rachel, Lady Binning. The sitter is shown in profile to the left.

DIMENSIONS: *98 × 78mm.*

g. PHILIP, 2ND EARL STANHOPE (1714–1786).

Inscribed: on a label on the reverse, 'Philip, 2nd Earl Stanhope, 1714–1786 by Gosset, 1745', and on the wooden back of the frame, 'Philip Earl Stanhope Gosset fecit 1745'.

The sitter is shown in profile to the right wearing a tie wig.

DIMENSIONS: *98 × 78mm.*

h. HON. RACHEL HAMILTON (*d.*1797).

Inscribed: on a label on the reverse, 'The Hon. Rachel Hamilton, d. unmarried 1797 by Gosset, 1745', and on the wooden back of the frame 'Hon. Miss Rachel Hamilton, Gosset Fecit, 1745'.

The sitter is shown in profile to the right wearing a low-necked dress and pearls.

DIMENSIONS: *100 × 78mm.*

i. PHILIP, 4TH EARL OF CHESTERFIELD (*c.*1694–1773).

Inscribed: on the wooden back to the frame, 'Philip, Earl of Chesterfield, Gosset fecit, 1745'.

The sitter is shown in profile to the left, wearing the Order of the Bath.

DIMENSIONS: *100 × 78mm.*

This group of wax portraits represents members of the Murray and Stanhope families and was probably commissioned on the occasion of the marriage of Philip, 2nd Earl Stanhope (*g*) and Grisel Hamilton (*e*), daughter of Rachel, Lady Binning (*d*). The other waxes represent the bride's grandparents, Hon. George Baillie (who died in 1738) and Lady Grisel Baillie (*a,b*); her mother, Rachel, Lady Binning (*d*); her aunt, Grisel Baillie, Lady Murray (*c*); her brother, Thomas, Earl of Haddington (*f*) and her sister Hon. Rachel Hamilton (*h*). The other sitter (*i*) represents Philip, 4th Earl of Chesterfield, a cousin of her husband.

Both Lady Grizel Baillie and Grisel Baillie, Lady Murray, sat to Roubiliac in the mid 1740s and Gosset's waxes of these two sitters bear a very close resemblance to the Roubiliac busts. It is probable that Gosset based the waxes of these two sitters on Roubiliac's originals which he must have seen in the sculptor's studio before they were sent to Scotland. (Information kindly communicated by Malcolm Baker.)

PROVENANCE: *By descent in the Stanhope family; The Administrative Trustees of the Chevening Estate.*

LITERATURE: *E.J. Pyke, A Dictionary of Wax Modellers, 1973, pp.56–7.*

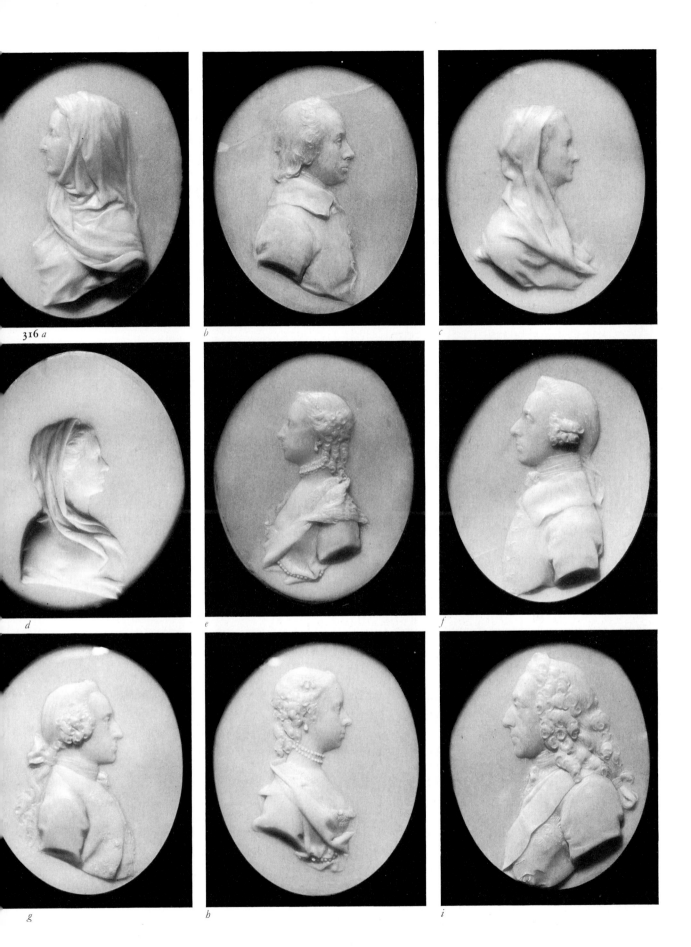

316 *a*

b

c

d

e

f

g

h

i

317 *France Duroure (1715–1808)*

PORTRAIT ENGRAVING, BASED ON WAX MEDALLION PORTRAIT BY ISAAC GOSSET.

Francis Duroure was Secretary to the French Hospital 1765–85; Deputy Governor, 1785–97 and a Director 1764–1799. Gosset's other sitters of Huguenot descent included Mr. and Mrs. Clerimbault and the Rev. Mr. Dubourdieu. These last three waxes are now in the Royal Collection at Windsor Castle. The whereabouts of the original wax of Duroure is unrecorded.

DIMENSIONS: *267 × 204mm.*
PROVENANCE: *French Hospital.*

318 *Eighteen from a set of thirty-three medals of the Kings of England*

JEAN DASSIER, 1731.

a. EDWARD I.

Obverse: Bust of Edward I, three-quarter profile to left, inscribed: EDOUARD. I.D.G.ANG.ET.HIB.REX., signed J.D.
Reverse: a Temple of Fame inscribed: NAT.1230.COR.1279.MORT.1307.

DIMENSIONS: *39mm diameter.*

b. EDWARD II.

Obverse: Bust of Edward II in profile to right, inscribed: EDOUARD.II.D.G.ANG.ET.HIB.REX.
Reverse: Assassination of Edward II, inscribed: NAT.1284.COR.1307.MORT.1327.

DIMENSIONS: *39mm diameter.*

c. EDWARD III.

Obverse: Bust of Edward III in profile to the left, in armour wearing a helmet wreathed in laurels, inscribed: EDOUARD.III.D.G.ANG.FR.ET.HIB.REX., signed J.D.
Reverse: Temple of Mars flanked by putti, inscribed: NAT.1312.COR.1327.MORT.1377.

DIMENSIONS: *39mm diameter.*

d. HENRY IV.

Obverse: Bust of Henry IV in profile to left, inscribed: HENRICUS.IV.D.G.ANG.FR.ET.HIB.REX.
Reverse: Figure of skeleton on sarcophagus with bas relief and inscription NATUS.1366 CORONAT.1399 MORT. 1413.

DIMENSIONS: *39mm diameter.*

e. HENRY VI.

Obverse: Bust of Henry VI in profile to left, inscribed: HENRICUS.VI.D.G.ANG.FR.ET.HIB.REX.
Reverse: Figure in Tabernacle supporting heart and chain, inscribed: NAT.1421 COR.1422.MORT.1471.

DIMENSIONS: *39mm diameter.*

f. EDWARD IV.

Obverse: Bust of Edward IV in profile to right, inscribed: EDOUARD.IV.D.G.ANG.FR.ET.HIB.REX., and signed I.D.F.
Reverse: Figure of Fortune standing on a globe between two pillars, inscribed: NAT.1441.COR.20 IUN.1461.MORT.9.APRIL.1483.

DIMENSIONS: *39mm diameter.*

g. HENRY VII.

Obverse: Bust of Henry VII three-quarters to left, inscribed: HENRICUS.VII.D.G.ANG.FR.ET.HIB.REX.
Reverse: Bas relief of Justice, Peace and Plenty, inscribed: NAT.1457 COR.30 OCT.1485 M.22 APRIL 1509.

DIMENSIONS: *38mm diameter.*

h. HENRY VIII.

Obverse: Bust of Henry VIII full face to right, inscribed: HENRICUS.VIII.D.G.ANG.FRA.ET.HIB.REX., and signed I.D.
Reverse: Figure of Fame seated outside a tabernacle in which symbols of Faith are being destroyed, inscribed: NAT.1491.COR. 24 IUN. 1509.MORT. 28 IAN.1547.

DIMENSIONS: *39mm diameter.*

i. EDWARD VI.

Obverse: Bust of Edward VI three-quarters to the left, inscribed: EDOUARD.VI.D.G.ANG.FR.ET.HIB.REX.
Reverse: Cupid with a winged serpent, inscribed: NAT.12.OCTOB.1537.COR.20 FEBR.1547.MORT.6.IUL.1553.

DIMENSIONS: *39mm diameter.*

j. MARY TUDOR.

Obverse: Bust of Mary Tudor full face to right, inscribed: MARIA.D.G.ANG.FR.ET.HIB.REGINA.
Reverse: Figure of Faith seated in a tabernacle supporting a papal tiara, inscribed: NATA.18.FEBR.1516.COR.1 OCTOB.1553.MORT.17 NOV.1558.

DIMENSIONS: *39mm diameter.*

318a

a

b

b

c

c

d

d

e

e

f

f

g

g

h

h

i

i

j

j

k. ELIZABETH I.

Obverse: Bust of Elizabeth I three-quarters to left,
inscribed: ELISABETH.D.G.ANG.FR.ET.HIB.REGINA., signed I.D.
Reverse: Relief showing storm at sea flanked by Light and Victory,
inscribed: NATA 7 SEPT. 1533. COR.15. IAN.1559. M.24 MART.1602.

l. JAMES I.

Obverse: Bust of James I in profile to right,
inscribed: IACOBUS.I.D.G.M.BR.FR.ET.HIB.REX.
Reverse: Two putti support coat of arms, the right-hand corner of which is being added,
signifying union of Scotland and England,
inscribed: NAT.19.JUN.1556.CORON.25 IUL.1603.MORT.27 MART.1625.

m. OLIVER CROMWELL.

Obverse. Bust of Cromwell in profile to left,
inscribed: OLIVARIUS CROMWELL and signed I.DASSIER.F.
Reverse: Group of putti flanking monument which is inscribed:
ANGLIAE SCO.ET.HIB. PROTECTOR.NAT.3.APRIL.1603.MORT.3.SEPT.1658.

n. CHARLES II.

Obverse: Bust of Charles II in profile to right,
inscribed: CAROLUS II.D.G.M.BR.FR.ET.HIB.REX., signed I.DASSIER.
Reverse: Monument inscribed by a figure of Mercury,
NAT.29.MAI 1630 C.23 APR.1661 M.16.FEBR.1685., signed I.DASSIER.F.

o. WILLIAM III.

Obverse: Bust of William III in profile to right in armour,
inscribed: GULIELMUS III.D.G.M.BRI.FR.ET.HIB.REX., signed I.D.
Reverse: Plinth with seated figure of Fame carrying banner inscribed: ETERNITAS
flanked by figures of Peace and Hercules,
inscribed: NAT.4.NOV.1650 CORONAT.11 APRIL 1689. MORT 5 MART.1702.

p. MARY II.

Obverse: Bust of Mary II in profile to right,
inscribed: MARIA.II.D.G.MAG.BR.FR.ET.HIB.REGINA., signed I.D.
Reverse: Putto with extinguished torch accompanied by Fame and a mourning figure with
a lighted candle inscribed: NATA.10.FEBR.1662.COR.11.APR.1689.MORT.29.DEC.1694.

q. GEORGE I.

Obverse: Bust of George I in profile to right in armour,
inscribed: GEORGIUS.I.D.G.MAG.BR.FR.ET.HIB.REX., signed I.D.
Reverse: A royal monument flanked by Justice and Peace,
inscribed: NAT.18.MAI.1660.CORONAT.21 OCT.1714.M.12.IUN.1727., signed I.D.

r. GEORGE II.

Obverse: Bust of George II in profile to left,
inscribed: GEORGIUS.II.D.G.MAG.BR.FR.ET.HIB.REX., signed I.DASSIER F.
Reverse: NUMISMATA REGUM ANGLIAE A GULIELMO PRIMO AD HAEC USQUE TEMPORA
GEORGIO II. MAGNAE BRITANNIAE FRANCIAE ET HIBERNIAE REGI SERENISSIMO ETC. DICATA
A JOANNE DASSIER GENEVENSIS REIPUB. CÆLATORE MONETALI ANNO M.DCC.XXXI.

DIMENSIONS: *38mm diameter.*

DIMENSIONS: *38mm diameter.*

DIMENSIONS: *37mm diameter.*

DIMENSIONS: *39mm diameter.*

DIMENSIONS: *39mm diameter.*

DIMENSIONS: *38mm diameter.*

DIMENSIONS: *38mm diameter.*

DIMENSIONS: *39mm diameter.*
PROVENANCE: *Museum of London.*
LITERATURE: *L. Forrer, Biographical
Dictionary of Medallists, 1904, Vol. I,
pp. 512–17.*

319 *Prospectus for a set of medals of all the Kings of England from William the Conqueror to George II*
JEAN DASSIER, 1730.

Dassier's prospectus announced his intention to produce a set of thirty-three medals of the
Kings of England, following on from his sets of French worthies in the reign of Louis IV,
and his set of the Great Reformers, which was dedicated to the Archbishop of Canterbury.

The medals would consist of a portrait of the monarch (derived from the available sources,
including busts, monuments, medals and coins) with, on the reverse, a tomb or other
symbolic device which would allude to the character of the monarch in question, and would
be inscribed with his dates and the date of his accession.

The subscriber would receive ten medals on paying half of the total cost, and the other
twenty-three would be available in early 1731. A set in bronze (*Catalogue number* 318) would
cost 6 guineas; gilt bronze, 14 guineas; silver, 15 guineas 17 shillings, and gold; 290 guineas
3 shillings.

Those who did not subscribe during 1730 would have to pay a further third on the cost of
production.

Jean Dassier (1676–1763) was chief engraver to the Republic of Geneva and visited
England in 1728. This prospectus is printed in both French and English, but a contemporary
manuscript copy, in French, in the Huguenot Library, is dated 1729.

ILLUSTRATED: *page 222.*
PROVENANCE: *British Library.*

318 k

k

l

l

m

m

n

n

o

o

p

p

q

q

r

r

320 *Abraham de Moivre*

BRONZE MEDAL, JACQUES ANTOINE DASSIER, LONDON, 1741.

Obverse: Bust of de Moivre, inscribed: ABRAHAMUS DE MOIVRE. and signed I.A.DASSIER.
Reverse: UTRIUSQUE SOCIETATIS REGALIS LOND.ET.BEROL.SODALIS. M.DCC.XLI.

DIMENSIONS: *54mm diameter.*

PROVENANCE: *Huguenot Library.*

LITERATURE: *Rococo Art and Design in Hogarth's England, Victoria and Albert Museum, 1984, p.296.*

Abraham de Moivre (1667–1754) mathematician and Fellow of the Royal Society (*Catalogue numbers* 182, 183) is known to have frequented Slaughter's Coffee House, St. Martin's Lane, which was described by George Vertue as 'the rendezvous of persons of all languages & nations Gentry artists and others'. It is possible that Dassier was amongst those who visited the coffee house.

Jacques Antoine was the son of Jean Dassier (*Catalogue numbers* 318, 319). He came to England in 1740 and published proposals for making a set of medals of distinguished living Englishmen. Vertue commented on this set in February 1740 and described the medals of Martin Folkes, Alexander Pope and Abraham de Moivre as 'done from the life and . . . free and boldly cutt but not so elaborately. nor so high finisht. as others.'

320

320

319

GUNMAKERS

The work of French gunmakers was outstanding, and during the reign of Louis XIV they set new standards in the design and finish of firearms. Two of the leading Paris makers, Pierre Monlong and Pierre Gruché, were Huguenots and took refuge in London. Both of these makers settled in Soho, in theory, beyond the control of the Worshipful Company of Gunmakers, although Pierre Monlong's premises were searched in November, 1684, and again in February, 1686, when he was fined ten shillings for possession of unproved barrels. Other leading Huguenot makers to work in London, Isaac de Seret and Landreville, who were both patronised by the 1st Duke of Devonshire, came from the French provinces. Their guns combined original mechanisms with a high standard of decoration. Second generation Huguenot gunmakers included Henry Delany, Pierre Gandon and Israel Segallas. Even in the early nineteenth century one of the leading pistol manufacturers, Isaac Riviere, was of Huguenot descent.

'Diana' detail from flintlock holster pistol by Pierre Monlong, c.1695

322

321 *Flintlock sporting gun*

PIERRE GRUCHE, PARIS, 1680–1690; INSCRIBED: GRUCHE A PARIS.

Pierre Gruché was one of the leading Paris gunmakers, but by 1699 he was recorded as working in Compton Street, Soho, on the occasion of his marriage to Marie des Champs at the French church of Hungerford Market.

This sporting gun was made in Paris, using an earlier barrel by the Italian Lazarino Cominazzo, *c.*1650, probably obtained from a specialist barrel-smith. The barrel has been damascened by the French maker to match his own more highly decorated stock and lock. The lockplate bears the maker's signature GRUCHE A PARIS beneath ornamental scrollwork and a seated figure of Fame. The stock is inlaid in silver with birds, heads of Medusa, lions and amorini.

This gun was probably presented to Charles Lennox, 1st Duke of Richmond by Louis XIV.

No piece by Gruché made in London has yet come to light.

DIMENSIONS: *overall length 1727mm.*

PROVENANCE: *Duke of Richmond and Gordon by family descent; Acquired in 1958 by H.M. Armouries, Tower of London.*

LITERATURE: *J.F. Hayward, The Huguenot Gunmakers of London, Proceedings of the Huguenot Society of London, Vol. 20 (1965), pp.655–6; 662.*

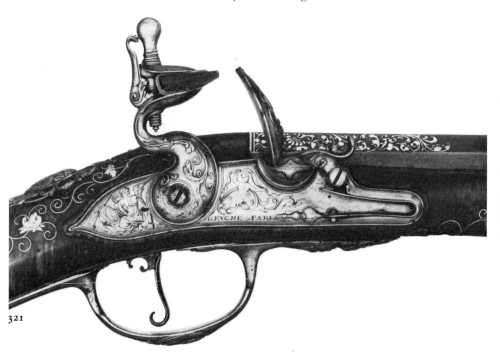

321

321

321

322 *Flintlock holster pistols, pair*

PIERRE MONLONG, LONDON, *c.*1695.

Pierre Monlong probably came from Angers, where his earliest recorded pair of pistols was made. In 1664, he was appointed 'Arquebusier de la Maison Roi'. He emigrated to London in 1684 with his wife and two children and was granted denization in 1688. By June 1689 he had been appointed Gentleman Armourer in Ordinary to William III.

Considered the finest pair of English pistols as works of art in existence, they may have been made for William III. A portrait bust chiselled on the locks certainly bears some resemblance to that monarch, and the quality of decoration is worthy of a king. The steel lock barrels and mounts are chiselled and engraved, the barrels are enriched with damascened gold set on a blued background, and the walnut stocks are inlaid with silver filigree work and cut silver sheet representing Diana flanked by hounds, on the butt; Apollo driving the Sun chariot, in front of the trigger guard and Fortitude near the fore-end. The stamped mark of the maker M under a heart in a circle is visible under the breech.

The ornament is derived from pattern books published in Paris by Claude and Jacques Simonin between 1685 and 1693, which indicates that the maker kept abreast of the latest developments in French taste even after his emigration to London.

DIMENSIONS: *overall length 533mm.*

PROVENANCE: *The Dukes of Westminster; Acquired at auction, 1974, by H.M. Armouries, Tower of London.*

EXHIBITED: *Burlington Fine Arts Club, Exhibition of Steel and Iron Work, 1900, pl.LXIII; Treasures from the Tower, 1982–3, (71).*

LITERATURE: *J. Starkie Gardner, Iron and Steel Work, 1900, pl.LXIII; J.F. Hayward, The Art of the Gunmaker, 1963, pp.66–7; J.F. Hayward, The Huguenot Gunmakers of London, op.cit., 1965, pp.651–5; 662; H.L. Blackmore, The Monlong Pistols, Proceedings of the Huguenot Society of London, Vol. 22 (1975), pp.463–4; Ibid., The Monlong Pistols, The Connoisseur, Vol.CLXXXIX, no.762, September, 1975, p.72.*

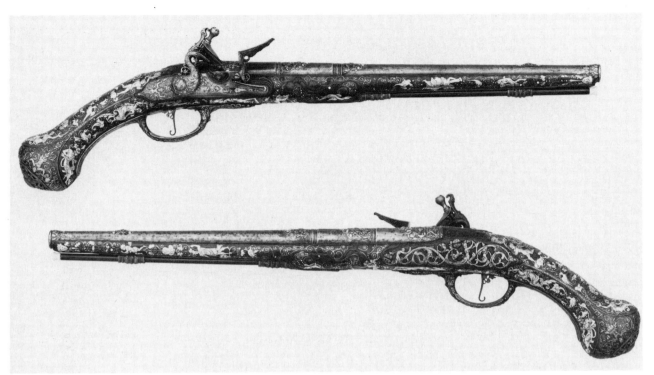

322

322

322

323 *Flintlock breech-loading sporting gun*
JACQUES GORGO, LONDON, *c.*1690.
INSCRIBED: GORGO LONDINI FECIT (ON THE BARREL).

Jacques Gorgo, of Swiss origin is recorded in London in 1686 when he married Anne de Sèvre at the French church of Les Grecs. In 1702 he is described as an 'Armourier' living in Grafton Street.

This gun reflects the high standard of design associated with the Huguenot refugee craftsmen. In order to lighten the piece, Gorgo produced the original idea of providing separate chambers linked to a single barrel by a curved connecting passage, eliminating the usual second barrel, although the gun could still fire two shots in succession before reloading.

The barrel is inlaid with gold floral scrollwork and the burr walnut stock is inlaid with silver wire. Such fine decoration was probably made by one of the immigrant goldsmiths working in Soho.

A pair of pistols and a breech-loading rifle by the same maker in London are in private collections.

DIMENSIONS: *overall length 1590mm.*

PROVENANCE: *Lord Braybrooke; purchased in 1977 by H.M. Armouries, Tower of London.*

LITERATURE: *J.F. Hayward, The Huguenot Gunmakers of London, Proceedings of the Huguenot Society of London, Vol.20 (1965), p.658–9; 662.*

324 *Flintlock fowling piece with double action*
LANDREVILLE, LONDON, *c.*1690.

Landreville was probably related to Noel de Landreville, a Grenoble gunmaker.

This piece is remarkable for its technical virtuosity, again, like the gun by Gorgo, resulting in a lightness that was welcome to the sportsman. It has two revolving chambers, each with their own pan and battery, but operated by a single lock so that the charges could be fired in quick succession. The decoration is less elaborate, the single barrel plain, although the walnut butt has steel furniture lightly engraved with scrolls.

An almost identical fowling piece is in the Glasgow Art Gallery (Scott Collection); illustrated in J.F. Hayward, 'The Huguenot Gunmakers of London', op.cit., 1965, pl.XXXIX, 1.

DIMENSIONS: *overall length 1600mm.*

PROVENANCE: *William Cavendish, 1st Duke of Devonshire; by descent to present Marquess of Hartington.*

EXHIBITED: *Treasures from Chatsworth, The Devonshire Inheritance, 1979–80, no.172.*

LITERATURE: *J.F. Hayward, The Huguenot Gunmakers of London, Proceedings of the Huguenot Society of London, Vol. 20 (1965), pp.657, 661, 662.*

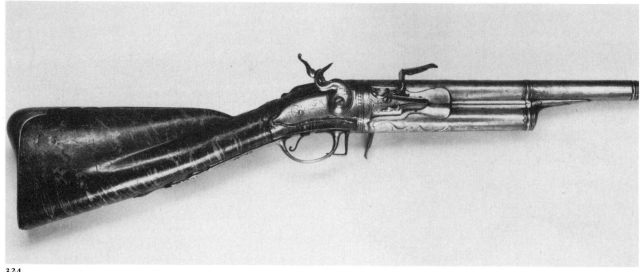

324

325 *Flintlock fowling piece*
ISAAC DE SERET, LONDON, *c.*1690.
INSCRIBED: DE SERET LONDONI (ON THE BARREL).

The de Seret family came from Crespy en Lanois (Aisne).

Isaac de Seret supplied the 1st Duke of Devonshire with two fowling pieces; that exhibited has more elaborate decoration although the other is of equally fine quality.

The high standard of decoration suggests the assistance of a goldsmith, and it is interesting to note that a Samuel de Seret, probably a relation, is described as a working goldsmith in 1712. The walnut stock is finely inlaid in silver with the figure of a classical warrior, and the steel butt plate is engraved with a figure of a sportsman.

DIMENSIONS: *overall length 1645mm.*

PROVENANCE: *William Cavendish, 1st Duke of Devonshire; by descent to present Marquess of Hartington.*

EXHIBITED: *Treasures from Chatsworth, The Devonshire Inheritance, 1979–80, no.171.*

LITERATURE: *J.F. Hayward, The Huguenot Gunmakers of London, Proceedings of the Huguenot Society of London, Vol. 20 (1965), pp.657, 661, 662.*

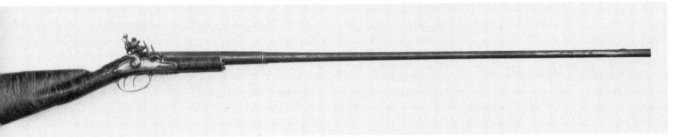

323

323

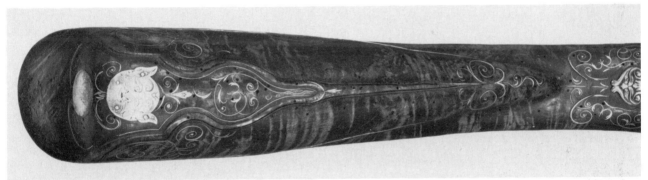

323

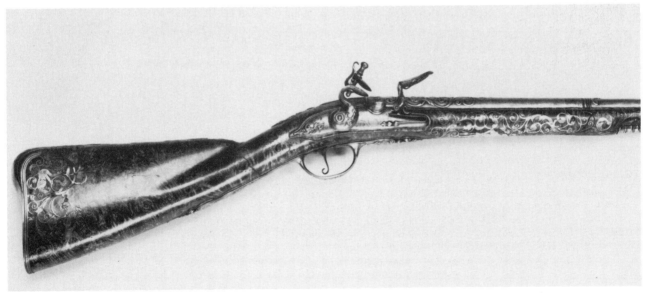

325

326 *Pair of percussion duelling pistols*

ISAAC RIVIERE, LONDON, *c.*1825–30.

In 1825, Riviere patented the enclosed lock used in the exhibited duelling pistols. Their octagonal twisted steel barrels are inscribed RIVIERE LONDON and stamped with London proof marks; the top plate is marked RIVIERE PATENT 219. The stocks have blued steel mounts which were preferred to silver as it was thought the latter might help to guide the eye of the opponent. The pistols are contained in their original mahogany case with cleaning rod, nipple key and Riviere's label with the Royal Coat of Arms.

The Riviere family came from Nérac in Gascony. Isaac Riviere (1781–1851) was the son of an armourer who worked for the East India Company. He was apprenticed to a gunmaker at Snow Hill, and by 1811 he was in business at 121 Oxford Street. Eleven years later he had two establishments, one at 315 Oxford Street, and the other at 28 Piccadilly. He specialised in silver-mounted flintlock pocket pistols.

The production of duelling pistols in which Riviere specialised ceased after 1840, but the business was taken over by his nephew? Henry Riviere who made naval officers' percussion pistols.

DIMENSIONS: *overall length 396mm.*

PROVENANCE: *Presented to H.M. Armouries, Tower of London by the Trustees of the Wellcome Museum, 1943.*

LITERATURE: *A. Merwyn Carey, English, Irish and Scottish Firearms Makers, second edition, 1968, p.84; Michael Riviere, Notes on the Huguenot family of Riviere in England, 1965, p.9; Jean Tsushima, The Riviere Family, Journal of the Honourable Artillery Company, Spring, 1980, no.417 Vol.LVII, pp.24–27.*

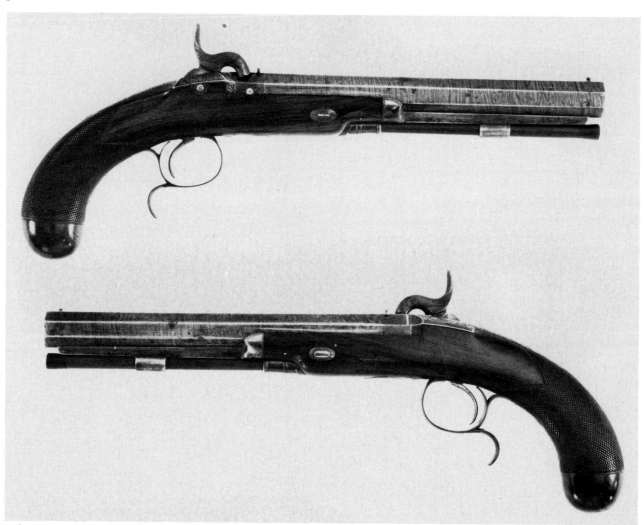

326

327 *Gunsmith's account book, 1732–1756*

Eighteenth-century gunsmiths' account books are rare. This volume, in which the pages are written in French, appears to be the work of a jobbing gunsmith, as most of the entries are for cleaning and small repairs. The clients include Colonel Dejean (1706–1764) second in command to General Wade after the 1745 Rebellion (*Catalogue number* 141) who was elected a Director of the French Hospital in 1740, and other soldiers.

The account book may be that of the Huguenot gunsmith, Pierre Cailleau (*d.* 1760) who entered the French hospital in 1746, where the volume was used as a record of stores from 1776–85.

DIMENSIONS: *440 × 330mm.*

PROVENANCE: *Huguenot Library, Ms.C 2/4.*

LITERATURE: *Irvine R. Gray, Huguenot Manuscripts: A descriptive Catalogue of the Remaining Manuscripts in the Huguenot Library, Huguenot Society Quarto Series, Vol.LVI, 1983, pp.28–9.*

GOLDSMITHS

Huguenot goldsmiths were attracted to Britain as a result of persecution, but also for economic reasons. In 1686, Louis XIV, in an attempt to finance his wars with Holland, ordered the melting down of all plate in France, and forbade the further employment of any goldsmiths. Refugee goldsmiths came from provincial towns, Lille, Le Mans, Metz and Rouen, bringing with them a mastery of the techniques required for the cast silver which was replacing the earlier embossed work. They introduced new forms; the pilgrim bottle, écuelle (a two-handled shallow bowl), soup tureen, sauceboat, and cup-shaped salt, and a vocabulary of French engraved designs. Their work, with its new purity of form and proportion and its dignity of ornament, captured the English market.

London goldsmiths objected to this unwelcome competition and presented a series of petitions against the Huguenots to the Goldsmiths' Company. Some deliberately imitated the Huguenot style or even employed Huguenot journeymen. The Huguenot goldsmiths maintained a closely knit community, standing as godparents to each other's children, and taking on their own sons as apprentices. Their skills were passed on to the next generation, and in the 1730s and 1740s, the two Huguenots Paul Crespin and Paul de Lamerie were the leading makers of Rococo silver.

Some of the finest silver in the neo-classical style made in the third quarter of the eighteenth century was the work of goldsmiths who still bore Huguenot names.

Wine cooler, silver-gilt, Paul Crespin, 1733

THE DUKE OF MARLBOROUGH

328 *Tea bowls, pair*

SILVER-GILT, PIERRE HARACHE THE ELDER, LONDON, 1688.

The bowls bear the sterling mark of Pierre Harache, and are amongst the earliest pieces of silver made by Harache in England. They are engraved with acanthus foliate scrollwork, and decorated with birds and dragons' head motifs.

Silver was not really suitable for cups designed to hold hot beverages, because of its heat-conducting qualities. Consequently, such tea cups are now relatively rare; it is probable that they were soon replaced by Chinese export porcelain cups.

Pierre Harache received denization on 26 June 1682 with his wife Anna. He was admitted to the Goldsmiths' Company by an order of the Lord Mayor and Council of Aldermen of the City of London on 21 July 1682 on payment of 46s. 8d. and presentation of a certificate which indicated that Harache, 'lately come from France for to avoid persecution and live quietly, is not only a Protestant, but by His Majesty's bounty is made a free denizen, that he may settle here freely with his family'. The certificate bore five signatures including that of the Minister of the French Church of the Savoy.

Harache is recorded as working in Suffolk Street, Charing Cross, as early as 1687 (London Gazette, no.2292, November, 1687). In December, 1691, the communion cup of the French church of St. James' Square was stolen from his premises. Harache died in 1700 and was succeeded by a goldsmith of the same name (presumably his son).

DIMENSIONS: *51mm high,* *73mm diameter.*

PROVENANCE: *Private Collection.*

LITERATURE: *Arthur Grimwade, London Goldsmiths, 1687–1837, 1982, pp.533–4.*

329 *Ewer, helmet-shaped*

SILVER-GILT, PIERRE HARACHE THE ELDER, LONDON, 1697.

INSCRIBED: (ROUND THE BASE) PRESENTED BY JOHN TANNER KAYE ESQR ONE OF THE MEMBERS TO THE COURT OF THE VINTNERS COMPANY 26TH OCTOBER 1843.

Introduced to English silver by the Huguenots, this form is based on a seventeenth-century prototype made at Rouen in tin-glazed earthenware. Pierre Harache came from Rouen, and this is one of the earliest recorded examples, although Harache made an almost identical piece in the same year for the Duke of Devonshire. (This is now, with its accompanying basin, on display in the Wilding Collection, British Museum.)

The decoration of this piece exemplifies the technical virtuosity of the Huguenot goldsmiths. The open scroll handle cast as a female term was used by Harache on the wine cooler of 1697 now in the Barber Surgeons' Company. The cut-card work (motifs cut out of sheet silver and applied with solder) which decorates the base is a feature of Huguenot silver.

The ewer has a matching basin made in 1811 by William Pitts for Augustus Frederick, Duke of Sussex, sixth son of George III. It is engraved with the coat of arms of the Duke of Sussex, John Tanner Kaye and the Vintners' Company.

DIMENSIONS: *315mm high.*

PROVENANCE: *J.T. Kaye; presented to the Duke of Sussex; Christie's June 1843 (441); bought by J.T. Kaye who presented the ewer and its accompanying basin to the Vintners' Company.*

EXHIBITED: *Catalogue of the Historic Plate of the City of London, exhibited at Goldsmiths' Hall, 1951, (182).*

LITERATURE: *J.F. Hayward, Huguenot Silver in England 1688–1727, 1959, p.44, pl.34A; A. Grimwade, London Goldsmiths, 1697–1837, 1982, p.533–4; Thomas Milbourn, The Vintners' Company, 1888, p.63; Hugh Tait, Huguenot Silver made in London, I, The Peter Wilding Bequest, Connoisseur, Vol.180, 1971, pp.267–276.*

330 *Pilgrim bottle, one of a pair*

SILVER, PIERRE HARACHE THE YOUNGER, LONDON, 1699.

The silver pilgrim bottle was introduced to this country by the Huguenot goldsmiths. Although based on a smaller medieval prototype, they were considerably enlarged and intended primarily for display on the sideboard. The joint weight of this pair is over 500 ounces.

Pierre Harache the younger entered his first mark at Goldsmiths' Hall in October 1698 giving his address as Compton Street, Soho. The very fine ornament on this pair of pilgrim bottles is worthy of the tradition inherited from this goldsmith's father. The elaborate cut-card work on the base and neck of the bottle, the female masks on the sides and the unusual trefoil-link chains are characteristic of silver made by the refugee Huguenots in London. The output of Pierre Harache the younger was considerably larger than his father's, and his patrons included the Duke of Marlborough, the Duke of Portland and Sir Paul Methuen.

It was engraved at a later date with the coat of arms of Baron Arden, c.1802, impaling those of Wilson for his wife, Margaret.

DIMENSIONS: *520mm high.*

PROVENANCE: *Lucy, Countess of Egmont; Christie's 16 April 1916(95); W.J. Farrer; bequeathed to Eton College, 1925.*

EXHIBITED: *Victoria and Albert Museum, 1957–8(29).*

LITERATURE: *E.A. Jones, Old Plate of William Francis Farrer, 1924, p.22, plates IX and XII; ibid., The Plate of Eton College, 1938, p.12–13, plate IX; Arthur Grimwade, London Goldsmiths, 1697–1837, 1982, p.534–5; J.F. Hayward, op. cit., 1959, p.38, plate 29; Charles Oman, The Eton College Plate, Part 2 (1760–1970) Connoisseur, July, 1971, p.201, pl.14; William Winter, Silver, in Treasures of Eton, edited James McConnell, 1976, p.68–9, pair illustrated pl.64.*

329

330

328

331 *Trade card of Thomas Harrache*

AT THE SIGN OF THE GOLDEN BALL & PEARL IN PALL MALL, 1751–c.1774.

Thomas Harrache was probably a grandson of Pierre Harache, the younger, by his son, also Pierre, who was born in 1697, and baptised at the French church in Leicester Fields. Thomas was bound apprentice in 1732 to a Francis Harache of St. Giles in the Fields, Snuffbox maker, an example of whose work is shown on page 233.

In April, 1748, the 'Daily Advertiser' mentions Thomas Harrache as a jeweller and goldsmith at the corner of St. Martin's Lane and Long Acre. In 1751, he moved to the sign of the Golden Ball and Pearl in Pall Mall, the address given on this trade card.

Thomas Harrache's stock varied from 'India Flower Pots' to 'A pair of Statuary Marble Vauses mounted in Ormolu', and a 'fine Antique Bronze of Laocoon' which he sold to Paul Methuen in 1774.

Thomas Harrache was a close friend of the Huguenot sculptor, L.F. Roubiliac and the sole executor of his will.

DIMENSIONS: *178 × 127mm.*

PROVENANCE: *Heal Collection: Department of Prints and Drawings, British Museum.*

LITERATURE: *Tessa Murdoch, Louis François Roubiliac and his Huguenot Connections, Proceedings of the Huguenot Society of London, Vol. 24 (1983), pp.26–45, fig.1.*

332 *Petition against admitting aliens to the freedom of the Goldsmiths' Company*

MANUSCRIPT (12 SEPTEMBER 1682).

The petition explains that 'divers Aliens and forreigners are come into this kingdome and reside in and about this City, and that some of them . . . do . . . keep houses, and shops, and exercise and practise ye said Trade and Mistery of ye Goldsmiths, by which evill example other Aliens of ye same Mistery are encouraged . . . to come and enjoy . . . the same priviledges and immunities equall with Us, which (considering the great numbers of our Natives already exercising ye said Mistery and ye deadnesse of Trade) will certainly bring us and our familyes to great Poverty and want, and put us upon ye extremity of seeking other waiyes for a Livelyhood, unlesse some speedy remedy be taken.'

The petition is signed by some of the most prominent working goldsmiths of the time including George Garthorne and Anthony Nelme. It was followed by further petitions; in 1711 complaining again of 'the admittance of the necessitous strangers, whose desperate fortunes obliged them to worke at miserable rates'. This was signed by another 53 working goldsmiths, thirteen of whom later signed yet another petition in 1715 on the same theme.

DIMENSIONS: *618 × 305mm.*

PROVENANCE: *The Worshipful Company of Goldsmiths.*

LITERATURE: *Goldsmiths' Company Court Minutes, Vol. 9, f.28.*

333 *Tea canister*

SILVER-GILT, ISAAC LIGER, LONDON, 1706

The canister is engraved with the arms of George Booth, 2nd Earl of Warrington. It has been suggested that the engraving was executed by Simon Gribelin, as he signed the engraving on the altar dish made by Liger for Warrington in 1706. The engraving is certainly after designs by Gribelin, but was probably executed by an assistant.

Liger probably came from Saumur. In 1704, he was made free of the Company of Broderers, and entered his first maker's mark at Goldsmiths' Hall later that year. He worked in Hemmings Row off St. Martin's Lane and was succeeded by John Liger, probably his son.

DIMENSIONS: *115mm high, 70mm wide.*

PROVENANCE: *Sotheby's, 20 April 1921 (74); bequeathed to the Victoria and Albert Museum by C.D. Rotch.*

LITERATURE: *Arthur Grimwade, London Goldsmiths, 1697–1837, 1982, p.582–3; J.F. Hayward, Huguenot Silver in England 1688–1727, 1959, pl.46A, pp.48, 71; Charles Oman, English Engraved Silver, 1150–1900, 1978, p.79, pl.89.*

334 *Wine fountain*

SILVER, PETER ARCHAMBO, LONDON, 1728.

INSCRIBED INSIDE THE FOOT: THIS FOUNTAIN WAS MADE FOR GEORGE BOOTH, 2ND EARL OF WARRINGTON IN 1728 BY PETER ARCHAMBO.

The silver wine fountain is a rare phenomenon, partly due to the large weight of silver required in a piece of this size. Although made for George Booth, 2nd Earl of Warrington, this piece weighing 557 ounces, was a duty dodger. The goldsmith incorporated a previously marked salver into the base of the fountain, thus avoiding a charge of 6d an ounce, which would have amounted to £14 18s. 6d. This was cut out by the Assay Office in 1929, when the piece was re-marked and is also exhibited.

The design of the fountain is close to Daniel Marot's designs for silver which were published some thirty years earlier. The ornament incorporates as handles the two boars which were supporters of Warrington's coat of arms, and the fountain is surmounted by an Earl's coronet.

The wine fountain was usually displayed on a side-board with a wine cistern on the ground beneath it. In this case, the matching wine cistern was made in 1701 by the goldsmith, Phillip Rollos the elder.

DIMENSIONS: *686mm high.*

PROVENANCE: *Foley Grey Sale, 20 April 1921(121); Presented to the Goldsmiths' Company by H.M. Parsons and L.W.B. Parsons (of Tessiers Ltd.) in 1945.*

EXHIBITED: *Treasures of London, Vancouver and Montreal, 1977, (25); Touching Gold and Silver, 500 Years of Hallmarks, Goldsmiths' Company 7–30 November 1978, (86, 87); on loan to the National Trust, Dunham Massey, 1982; The Goldsmiths and the Grape, Silver in the Service of Wine, Goldsmiths' Company, 11–28 July, 1983, (59); Heritage of Britain – Britain Salutes New York, Aspreys New York, 1983, (35), p.114.*

LITERATURE: *J.F. Hayward, The Earl of Warrington's Plate, Apollo, July, 1978, pp.32–39, pl.2.*

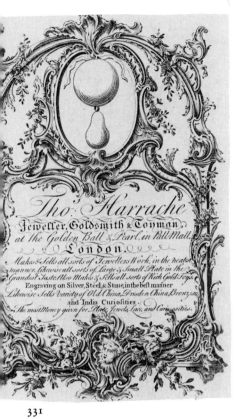

331

331

333

334

335 Bill of David Willaume, goldsmith, 1707

This bill for £31 19s. for a silver tea pot, warming-up pan and 12 forks for the 2nd Duke of Bedford is signed by the Huguenot goldsmith from Metz. The bill is in French, and no address is given, although by 1697, Willaume is recorded as working at the Golden Ball in Pall Mall.

David Willaume sold the Duke a coronet, in 1702, and issued further bills in May, 1707 and in March 1712/13. Only the last bill is in English.

David Willaume was the brother-in-law of Louis Mettayer. His daughter Anne, married the goldsmith David Tanqueray, and later became a goldsmith in her own right; and his sister-in-law, Marie Mettayer, married the engraver Simon Gribelin. Willaume was succeeded by his son, also David, when he retired from business in about 1728.

Willaume also kept running cashes (i.e. banking) at his premises in St. James' Street from 1719. With the profits of his career as a banker and goldsmith, Willaume bought the manor of Tingrith, Bedfordshire in 1730, not far from Woburn, the seat of the Dukes of Bedford. Thus through his industry, this retired refugee goldsmith acquired status as a member of the English squirearchy.

DIMENSIONS: *282 × 209mm.*

PROVENANCE: *The Marquess of Tavistock and the Trustees of the Bedford Estates.*

LITERATURE: *Gladys Scott-Thomson, The Russells in Bloomsbury, 1669–1771, 1940, pp.257–8.*

336 Tankard

SILVER-GILT, JACOB MARGAS, LONDON, 1713.
INSCRIBED: THE GIFT OF MR. HENRY PALMER, ANNO 1724.

The tankard was not a vessel that Huguenot goldsmiths would have made in France, as beer-drinking was not customary there. This exceptionally fine example exhibits the Huguenot tendency to modify the traditional English form by rounding the lower part of the body. Although the lion thumbpiece and feet are not specifially Huguenot features, they typify the sculptural quality of the cast ornament on Huguenot silver made in England.

The tankard is engraved with the Company's arms and motto 'GOD IS OUR STRENGTH'. The base is marked with the original weight 53oz 16dwt.

Jacob Margas was the elder son of Samuel Margas who was in England in 1687 when he appears in the 'Reconnaissances' of the Hugenot Church of the Savoy, described as 'de Rouen 32 ans'. Jacob is recorded in 1728 as working 'at ye corner of Cecil's Court, St. Martin's Lane' (*Catalogue number 80*).

DIMENSIONS: *230mm high.*

PROVENANCE: *Presented to the Ironmongers' Company by Henry Palmer, 1724.*

EXHIBITED: *Works of Art belonging to the Livery Companies of the City of London, Victoria and Albert Museum, 1926 (218), pl. XXX; Catalogue of the Historic Plate of the City of London, Goldsmiths' Company, 1951 (200), pl. LXII.*

LITERATURE: *J.F. Hayward, Huguenot Silver in England, 1688–1727, 1959, p.39, pl.14B; Arthur Grimwade, London Goldsmiths 1697–1837, 1982, p.590–591.*

337 Sauceboats, pair, double-lipped

SILVER, SAMUEL MARGAS, LONDON, 1726.

A pair of double-lipped sauceboats on collet feet, engraved with a coat of arms (rubbed).

Samuel Margas was the son of the goldsmith of the same name from Rouen (*Catalogue number 336*). In 1708, he was apprenticed to his brother Jacob, also a goldsmith, who was free of the Butchers' Company (*Catalogue number 80*). Samuel probably worked with his brother for some time, although he registered his first mark at Goldsmiths' Hall in 1715. In 1716 he married at St. Paul's Cathedral, Judith de la Neuve Maison, a fellow Huguenot from Spitalfields. From 1720 he was living in King Street, Covent Garden and in 1723 he became a subordinate goldsmith to George I.

Such double-lipped sauceboats were introduced to the London goldsmith's trade by the Huguenot craftsmen. Evidently popular in France, in 1700, when four sauceboats were ordered for the use of Louis XIV, they were described in the inventory as having 'deux anses et deux becs'.

DIMENSIONS: *211mm wide, 186mm broad, 111mm high.*

PROVENANCE: *Private Collection.*

LITERATURE: *Arthur Grimwade, London Goldsmiths, 1697–1837, 1982, p.590; Carl Hernmarck, The Art of the European Silversmith, 1430–1830, 1977, Vol.1, p.196.*

338 Ice pail

ONE OF A PAIR, SILVER, LOUIS METTAYER, LONDON, 1713

Ice pails, containing a single bottle of wine, were normally placed on the sideboard.

Engraved with the Royal Arms of Queen Anne and once part of the official plate of Sir Thomas Hanmer, Bart, Speaker of the House of Commons, 1714–15, they are each marked with their original weight 117ozs 19dwt.

Louis Mettayer was the son of Samuel Mettayer, minister of the church of La Patente. In 1693, he was apprenticed to his brother-in-law, David Willaume, and in 1700 entered his first mark at Goldsmiths' Hall, giving his address as 'in the Pell Mell'. He married, in 1706, Anne Hobbema who is described as living at Mr. Harache's, goldsmith in Suffolk Street.

In 1711, he stood godfather to the daughter of a fellow Huguenot goldsmith, Paul Hanet. The Mettayer family came from Picardy.

A similar pair of ice pails by the same maker, 1714, are engraved with the arms of Methuen.

DIMENSIONS: *239mm high.*

PROVENANCE: *W.J. Farrer; presented to Eton College, 1925.*

LITERATURE: *E.A. Jones, Old Plate of William Francis Farrer, 1924, p.46, pl.XXIV; E.A. Jones, The Plate of Eton College, 1938, p.15, pl. XI; J.F. Hayward, Huguenot Silver in England, 1959, p.37 (as Ashmolean Museum); Charles Oman, The Eton College Plate, Part 2 (1760–1970) Connoisseur, July, 1971, p.202, pl.15; William Winter, Silver, in Treasures of Eton, edited James McConnell, 1976, p.69, both illustrated pl.65.*

336

338

337

339 Chamber pot

SILVER, SIMON PANTIN, LONDON, 1716.

Silver chamber pots were used from the second half of the seventeenth century in the dining room.

Like Pierre Harache, to whom he was apprenticed, Pantin came from Rouen. He registered his first mark at Goldsmiths' Hall in 1701, and until 1717 worked in St. Martin's Lane. In that year he moved to Castle Street, near Leicester Fields and took on as apprentice his son, also Simon, who eventually succeeded him at Castle Street. Simon Pantin the younger was in turn succeeded by his son Lewis, from 1734, and the fourth generation was represented in the trade by Lewis Pantin the younger.

DIMENSIONS: *198mm diameter.*

PROVENANCE: *Hoare's Bank.*

EXHIBITED: *Catalogue of the Historic Plate of the City of London, Goldsmiths' Hall, 1951 (205); Pomp, Royal Scottish Museum, 1969, (93).*

LITERATURE: *Arthur Grimwade, London Goldsmiths 1697–1937, 1982, p.613.*

340 Écuelle

ONE OF A PAIR, SILVER, ISAAC LIGER, LONDON, 1726.

The écuelle, a flat covered bowl with two lobed handles, was of continental origin and when filled with sweetmeats was the usual present given to a wife in childbed. Not many examples made by the Huguenot goldsmiths in England have survived, but the écuelle is another instance of the new forms which the Huguenot goldsmiths introduced to this country.

Isaac Liger's most important patron was probably the 2nd Earl of Warrington (*Catalogue number 333*).

DIMENSIONS: *270 × 102mm.*

PROVENANCE: *Carter Collection; Ashmolean Museum.*

341 Salts

PAIR, SILVER-GILT, ANNE TANQUERAY, LONDON, 1726.

The circular cup-shaped salt, more graceful than the typical English trencher salt, was introduced by the Huguenot goldsmiths. They were frequently gilded inside to protect the silver from the chemical reaction caused by salt.

Anne Tanqueray was the daughter of the goldsmith David Willaume and married in 1717 another Huguenot goldsmith, David Tanqueray. She carried on her husband's business after his death.

DIMENSIONS: *87mm wide, 37mm high.*

PROVENANCE: *Mrs. A.J. Carter; acquired by the Victoria and Albert Museum, 1927.*

LITERATURE: *J.F. Hayward, Huguenot Silver 1688–1727, 1959, p.52, pl.67B; Arthur Grimwade, London Goldsmiths 1697–1837, 1982, pp.676–677.*

342 Trade card of Pezé Pilleau

AT THE SIGN OF THE GOLDEN CUP IN SHANDOIS STREET, 1719–1755.

The Pilleau family came from Le Mans. Pezé Pilleau senior was a goldsmith in St. Martin's Lane. His son, also Pezé, was apprenticed in 1710 to the Huguenot goldsmith John Chartier.

By 1719, Pilleau junior had set up shop 'over against Slaughter's Coffee House, at the upper end of St. Martin's Lane'. In the same year he moved to the sign of the Golden Cup in Chandos Street, the address given on this trade card.

As the card claims, Pilleau junior succeeded his father in the 'Art of Making and Setting Artificial Teeth . . . No ways discernable from Natural ones'. The rows of dentures at the top of the card advertise this fact.

'The Postman', for February, 1696, reported that 'Mr Pilleau a French goldsmith does give Notice that by an Experience of 18 Years he has found out a way to make and set Artificial Teeth in so firm a manner that one may chew with them'. In January, 1719, the same publication reported that Mr. Pileau (sic) (junior) 'continueth to make and set Artificial Teeth and whole Jaws or Rows with the utmost nicety'.

There is no other record of goldsmiths in eighteenth century England making artificial teeth.

DIMENSIONS: *155 × 109mm.*

PROVENANCE: *Heal Collection, Department of Prints and Drawings, British Museum.*

LITERATURE: *Lindsay Lillian, A Short History of Dentistry, London, 1933, p.47; Notes and Queries, August 5th, 1939, p.101.*

343 Set of tea canisters and sugar bowl

SILVER-GILT, PEZE PILLEAU, LONDON, 1738.

Apart from his dental activities, Pilleau appears to have specialised in the production of vessels and containers associated with serving tea, coffee or chocolate. His relatively modest surviving output is characterised by a very high standard of design and finishing, no doubt inherited from his Huguenot master, the goldsmith John Chartier.

DIMENSIONS: *sugar vase 100mm high, 108mm wide at lid, 64mm wide at base; canister 100mm high, 80mm wide, 61mm wide at base.*

PROVENANCE: *Private Collection.*

LITERATURE: *Sir Charles Clay, Notes on the Ancestors and Descendants of Pezé Pilleau, the London Goldsmith, Proceedings of the Huguenot Society of London, Vol.16 (1940), pp.338–368; Arthur Grimwade, in Huguenot Society Quarto Series, Vol. XLVII, 1961, The Register of the Reformed Church at Le Mans, Appendix, pp.21–23.*

343

340

P. Pilleau Goldsmith,
at the Golden Cup,
in Shandois Street
Makes, & Sells, Gold, & Silver Plate,
He Likewise Succeeds his Father
Lately Deceas'd.
Who liv'd at ye corner of Newport
Street, & St. Martins Lane,
in ye Art of Making and Setting
Artificial Teeth
No ways discernable from Natural ones

342

339

344 Paul Crespin (1694–1770)

PORTRAIT, OIL ON CANVAS, ATTRIBUTED TO PIERRE SUBLEYRAS, c.1726.

The Crespin family appear to have been well established in England before the Revocation. A Paul Crespin, perhaps the goldsmith's grandfather, was married at the Threadneedle Street French church in December, 1654. Paul was born in 1694, the son of Daniel Crespin of the parish of St. Giles in the Fields, Westminster. He was apprenticed to the Huguenot Jean Pons in 1713, and had registered his first mark by December, 1721, when he was described as free of the Longbowstring Makers' Company.

In 1724 Crespin made for the King of Portugal a curious silver vessel for bathing, which weighed about 6030 ounces. In 1726, Crespin combined with other Huguenot goldsmiths to provide a large set of plate for the Empress Catherine of Russia. Some of this silver can still be seen in the Hermitage today. Crespin appears to have specialised in the production of small luxury items in the 1740s, and he probably collaborated with Nicholas Sprimont on the lavish centrepiece for Frederick, Prince of Wales. Of all the second generation goldsmiths he appears to have been most closely in touch with the latest developments in French taste. He eventually died in Southampton in January, 1770.

Crespin's elder daughter, Magdalene, married the Huguenot clockmaker, Francis-Gabriel Barraud (see *Catalogue numbers* 369, 370), and this portrait has descended in the family to its present owners in New Zealand. Enigmatically known as 'The Ancestor', it shows the goldsmith holding a silver vase of apparently late seventeenth-century design.

COLOUR PLATE: *page 15*.

DIMENSIONS: *1140 × 990mm*.

PROVENANCE: *Private Collection*.

LITERATURE: E.M. Barraud, *The Story of a Family*, The Research Publishing Company, 1967, pp.59–60, pl.VIII; Arthur Grimwade, *London Goldsmiths, 1697–1837*, 1982, pp.478–479; Christopher Lever, *Goldsmiths and Silversmiths of England*, 1975, p.192.

345 Chocolate pot

SILVER, PAUL CRESPIN, 1738; INSCRIBED: THIS CHOCOLATE POT WAS GIVEN BY LIONEL, EARL OF DYSART TO THE HONBLE MRS. TOLLEMACHE, APRIL 29TH, 1791.

This chocolate pot with its rounded body, flat lid, and baluster handle is of the type associated with French silver and the work of the Huguenot goldsmiths. It has the customary small aperture in the lid through which the separate swizzle-stick or molinet, as exhibited, was inserted to stir the beverage.

The chocolate pot is engraved with the arms of Lionel Tollemache, 4th Earl of Dysart and his wife Grace Carteret, daughter of John Earl of Granville. It is marked with the original weight 38ozs 1dwt.

Paul Crespin supplied the Tollemache family with considerable quantities of plate in the 1730s and 1740s, including a large dinner service. He supplied this chocolate pot on 17 June, 1738 at a cost of £14 4s. 1d. (Information kindly supplied by Mrs. Philippa Glanville.)

DIMENSIONS: *240mm high*.

PROVENANCE: *Farrer Collection; Ashmolean Museum*.

LITERATURE: E.A. Jones, *Old Plate of William Francis Farrer*, 1924, p.144, pl.LXXVII; *Rococo Art and Design in Hogarth's England*, Victoria and Albert Museum, 1984, pp.104,324.

346 Rectangular dish

SILVER, PAUL CRESPIN, LONDON, 1729.

A plain oblong tray with a raised edge border on moulded feet, and engraved with contemporary armorials.

DIMENSIONS: *180 × 245 × 32mm*.

PROVENANCE: *Private Collection*.

346

347 Cup and cover

SILVER, PAUL DE LAMERIE, LONDON, 1730.

A two handled cup and cover with moulded ribs on a circular foot. The lower section of the cup is decorated with applied strapwork, and the cup is engraved with additional shell motifs and bands of ornament. It is engraved with the coat of arms and crest of the Huguenot Chardin family.

It was probably made for Sir John Chardin (2nd Baronet). On his death it passed to his sister Julia, who married in 1711 Sir Christopher Musgrave of Edenhall. Their father, also Sir John Chardin, was Court Jeweller to Charles II.

The cup is marked with the original weight 31ozs 16dwt.

Paul de Lamerie was born in 1688 in the Netherlands of Huguenot parents. His mother came from Rouen and his father was an officer in the army of William III. In 1689 the family moved to London, where their son was apprenticed to the Huguenot goldsmith Pierre Platel (from Lille) in 1703. De Lamerie registered his first mark in 1712.

DIMENSIONS: *185mm high, 108mm diameter*.

PROVENANCE: *By family descent to Sir Richard Musgrave; Farrer Collection; Ashmolean Museum*.

LITERATURE: E.A. Jones, *Old Plate of William Francis Farrer*, 1924, pp.96–7, pl.L.

344

345

347

348 *Tea equipage*

SILVER, PAUL DE LAMERIE, LONDON, 1735.

This tea equipage, the earliest complete English tea set preserved, was made as a wedding present for the Huguenots Jean Daniel Boissier and Suzanne Judith Berchère who were married at St. Peter le Poor, London, in April, 1735, and later purchased Lime Grove, Putney. The bride's father, Jaques Louis Berchère, from Paris, a jeweller and banker in Broad Street and an officer of the French church, Threadneedle Street, was probably responsible for the commission. Jean Daniel was the son of Guillaume Boissier, admitted as a Burgess of Geneva in 1695.

The three canisters and cream jug bear the London hallmarks for 1735–6, and were specially made for the set. The other items were not hallmarked.

The canisters are engraved with initials G., B. and S. for Green tea, Bohea tea and sugar respectively. With the exception of the strainer spoon and sugar nippers, every piece, including the silver mounts on the original velvet-lined mahogany case, is engraved with the arms of Boissier impaling Berchère. The intertwined handles of the 12 teaspoons, the elaborate scroll handle of the cream boat, and the chased, cast and engraved ornament on the canisters are early examples of the Rococo style in English silver, of which Paul de Lamerie was the leading exponent. The knives (used to cut the cane-sugar) and the sugar nippers were supplied by a specialist John Allen, who registered his mark as a smallworker at Goldsmiths' Hall in May, 1733.

DIMENSIONS: *canister 118mm high; teaspoon 122mm long.*

PROVENANCE: *Boissier Family; Sotheby's 8.4.1954 (51); Christie's 21.6.1967 (88); bt. Partridge; Christie's 26.6.1974 (111); bt. Shrubsole; Purchased by the Leeds City Art Galleries, 1975.*

EXHIBITED: *Rococo Art and Design in Hogarth's England, Victoria and Albert Museum, 1984 (G.1), p.107.*

LITERATURE: *Anthony Wells-Cole, Two Rococo Masterpieces, Leeds Art Calendar, no.79, 1976, pp.13–24.*

349 *Oval soup tureen*

SILVER, PAUL DE LAMERIE, LONDON, 1741.

The soup tureen is also said to have been a Huguenot introduction. This handsome example is distinguished by fine lions' head masks and claw and ball feet.

The tureen bears de Lamerie's third mark registered at Goldsmiths' Hall in 1739, when his address was given as Gerrard Street, Soho. In 1743, de Lamerie became Fourth Warden of the Goldsmiths' Company, and by 1747, Second Warden. He died in 1751 and was buried at St. Ann's, Soho.

Paul de Lamerie was also a Lieutenant Colonel in the Westminster Militia.

A more elaborately decorated tureen, but of the same form, 1738, is illustrated by P.A.S. Phillips, Paul de Lamerie, 1935, pl.cxx. It shows that the goldsmith continued to work in a more sober style, whilst producing more elaborate Rococo pieces on demand.

DIMENSIONS: *444mm wide, 275mm high.*

PROVENANCE: *Rev. William Hetherington, presented to Eton College, 1772.*

LITERATURE: *Charles Oman, The Eton College Plate, Part 2 (1760–1970) July 1971, fig.3; E.A. Jones, The Plate of Eton College, 1938, p.21; William Winter, Silver, in Treasurers of Eton, edited James McConnell, 1976, pp.74–5; illustrated pl.69.*

349

348

350 *Tea urn*

SILVER, FRANCIS BUTTY AND NICHOLAS DUMEE, LONDON, 1766.

Francis Butty (listed as a Huguenot by Joan Evans in Huguenot Goldsmiths in England and Ireland, Proceedings of the Huguenot Society of London, Vol. 14 (1931–2), pp.496–594) entered his first mark in partnership with Lewis Herne in 1757. His second mark entered in partnership with Nicholas Dumée (Joan Evans, *op.cit.*) was used until 1773 when the 'Gentleman's Magazine' records their bankruptcy.

This tea urn, with its almost effeminate delicacy, is engraved with an unidentified coat of arms in a floral cartouche. (Quarterly or and sable, in the first, an escallop sable, in the fourth an escallop, or, with in pretence, a pale goutté de poix, or.)

Butty and Dumée supplied Durham Cathedral in 1766 with an altar service consisting of pairs of flagons, chalices, large and small patens, two handled cups, pricket candlesticks and an almsdish.

DIMENSIONS: *510mm high.*

PROVENANCE: *G.R. Brigstocke; presented to Eton College, 1957.*

LITERATURE: *Charles Oman, The Eton College Plate, Part 2 (1760–1970) July 1971, p.203, pl.18; William Winter, Silver, in Treasures of Eton, edited James McConnell, 1976, p.81.*

350

CLOCK & WATCHMAKERS

During the Reformation many French clockmakers became Protestants. The provincial towns of Blois and La Rochelle became centres of both Protestantism and watchmaking as the earlier watches by Gribelin and Fonnereau illustrate. The clockmakers employed by Henry VIII at Nonsuch were Huguenot immigrants, as was Nicholas Urseau, Clockmaker to Elizabeth I. By 1627, the Free Clockmakers of London complained of being 'exceedingly oppressed by the intrusion of French clockmakers'.

After 1680, over ninety names of watchmakers are recorded in the registers of the Huguenot churches. They include the De Baufre family from Paris, responsible for developing Nicolas Facio's invention of the jewelled movement in watches, for which they took out a patent in 1704.

The development of London's horological industry owed much to the immigration of French craftsmen. By the early eighteenth century, the French authorities had to invite an English clockmaker to revitalise the French clockmaking industry at Versailles.

Trade card of Daniel &
Thomas Grignion

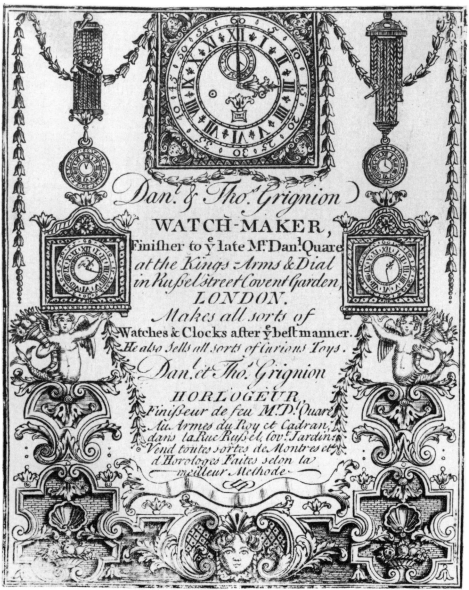

366

351 *Oval watch with compass and sundial*
SILVER AND GILT METAL, ABRAHAM GRIBELIN, BLOIS, 1ST QUARTER
OF THE SEVENTEENTH CENTURY.
INSCRIBED ON THE BACK OF THE MOVEMENT: GRIBELIN A BLOYS.

An oval watch in a silvered case with gilt mounts. The steel watch face is engraved with rural and sporting scenes and has steel hands within an applied gilt hour band. The case is chased with foliate scrollwork and grotesque ornament on the base, with an oval classical scene (much rubbed) possibly representing Venus and Mars. The cover bears the initials CPK and a coat of arms. The watch has a verge escapement fusee and gut. The under cover contains a folding sundial and compass.

Abraham Gribelin was the son of Simon Gribelin, a clock and watchmaker in Blois from *c.*1588 to 1633. Abraham is mentioned in the registers of Louis XIII's household as 'horloger du Roi' in 1631 and from 1632–7. He died in 1671 aged 82. He was the grandfather of Simon Gribelin, the engraver, who took refuge in London in 1681.

The Ashmolean Museum has an astronomical striking clock by the same maker, and a fine shell-shaped watch is in the British Museum.

DIMENSIONS: *50mm diameter.*

PROVENANCE: *Presented by W.E. Miller to the London Museum, 1934; Museum of London.*

LITERATURE: *E. Develle, Les Horlogers Blésois au XVIe et au XVIIe siècle, 1931, pp. 81,86.*

352 *Octagonal watch*
GILT METAL, FONNEREAU, LA ROCHELLE, *c.*1640.
INSCRIBED ON THE BACK OF THE MOVEMENT: FONNEREAU A LA ROCHELLE.

An octagonal watch with a gilt dial engraved with a rustic scene. The centre of the gilt hand is formed as a sunflower. The balance cock is pierced with a floral design. The case is of faceted crystal on a gilt framework.

Members of the Fonnereau family settled in Ipswich, where the house they occupied from 1735 to 1892, Christ Church Mansion, is open to the public.

DIMENSIONS: *28mm wide; 40mm long.*

PROVENANCE: *Given to the London Museum by W.E. Miller, 1934; Museum of London.*

LITERATURE: *Bourriau, R.P., Notes pour servir à l'histoire des horlogers à La Rochelle du XVIe siècle au debut du XVIIIe siècle, Besançon, 1934.*

353 *Pair-case watch*
GOLD, SIMON DE CHARMES, LONDON, *c.*1700.
INSCRIBED: S. DECHARMES, LONDON.

A gold pair-case watch, with blued steel hands and the maker's name De Charmes engraved on the chased cartouche in the centre. The inner gold case bears the incuse maker's mark PR and contains on the exterior a revolving disk to cover the keyhole when not in use. The outer gold case is engraved with a central landscape encircled by bands of grotesque foliate scrollwork featuring masks and birds.

Simon De Charmes was admitted to the Clockmakers' Company in 1691. His marriage to Eliene Dieu in December 1696 is recorded in the Registers of the Huguenot church of Berwick Street.

On November 16th, 1705, The Daily Courant announced, 'Lost, between Convent Garden and Leicester Fields, on Wednesday, Nov. 14th, a silver watch with a silver chain. Whoever brings the said watch to Mr. S. de Charmes, Watchmaker, at his house, the Sign of the Clock, the corner of Warwick St., Charing Cross shall have 2 guineas Reward'.

A fine gold pair-case watch by the same maker formerly belonging to the Duke of Bridgewater is in the Clockmakers' Company Collection.

In 1730, Simon De Charmes built Grove Hall, Hammersmith, where he retired.

DIMENSIONS: *43mm; 47mm; 55mm diameters.*

PROVENANCE: *Museum of London.*

LITERATURE: *F.J. Britten, Old Clocks and Watches and Their Makers, 2nd edition, 1904, p. 592, 9th edition, 1982, p. 421.*

354 *Pair-case watch and fob chain*
SILVER, DAVID LESTOURGEON, LONDON, 1702.

A silver pair-case watch with a silver dial with an opening to show the mock pendulum movement, and steel hands. The back plate supports a parcel-gilt plaque chased with a medallion portrait of William III, surrounded by military trophies; engraved with a skull and cross bones with the initial 'W' and inscribed 'Died March 8, 1702'. The pierced outer case is engraved with a floral pattern and an armorial shield surmounted by a helmet, and is attached to a silver chain of oblong links with the winding key at its end.

David Lestourgeon probably came from Rouen. He was made free of the Clockmakers' Company in 1698.

A watchmaker of this name is recorded in Lothbury, City of London, 1693–1701, and a goldsmith of the same name was living in Church Lane, St. Martin in the Fields, 1700–1709.

Similar watches with repoussé busts of William III are in the Clockmakers' Company Collection and the Metropolitan Museum of Art. David Lestourgeon appears to have specialised in the production of commemorative watches. The British Museum have another example adorned with a bust of Queen Anne on the back of the movement.

DIMENSIONS: *44mm; 46mm; 58mm diameters.*

PROVENANCE: *Given by W.B. Anderson to the London Museum, 1920; Museum of London.*

LITERATURE: *George Baillie, Watchmakers and Clockmakers of the World, 1947, Vol. I, p.196; W.D. Bushell, The Two Charles Lesturgeons, Surgeons of Cambridge, Their Huguenot Ancestors and their Descendants, 1936, p. 29; F.J. Britten, Old Clocks and watches and their Makers, 1904, p. 647; Cecil Clutton and George Daniels, Clocks and Watches in the Collection of the Worshipful Company of Clockmakers, 1975, nos. 112,87.*

352   351   351   351

353   353   353

354

354

355 *Copy of Petition from Nicolas Facio, Peter and Jacob Debaufre*

COPY, LONDON, 1704.

This petition 'praying for the continuance to them for a longer term of the sole use of their invention for jewelling and clock and watches' was presented to the House of Commons on 6 December 1704. It refers to the patent granted to the signatories on 1 May, 1704, for 'An Art of Working Pretious or more Common Stones (whether Naturall or Artificial), Christal, or Glass, and certain other Matters different from Metals, so that they may be employed and made use of in Clockwork and Watchwork and many other Engines not for Ornament only, but as an Internal and Usefull Part of the Work or Engins itselfe, in such Manners as have not heretofore been used'.

Jacob was the son of Peter Debaufre; both watchmakers received naturalisation in February 1703/4 when it was stated that Jacob was born in Paris. James (*Catalogue number* 356) appears to have been Jacob's younger brother, born in London in 1691. Their father Peter entered the Clockmakers' Company in 1689. He is recorded as living in Leicester Fields in 1695.

Nicolas Facio de Duillier (1664–1753) was a Swiss geometrician, and was apparently responsible for the idea of using jewels in watchmaking. This patent was opposed by the Clockmakers' Company who claimed that other members had jewelled pivots before 1704 and that the watch Facio had submitted actually had a fake jewel.

PROVENANCE: *Library of the Clockmakers' Company, deposited in the Guildhall Library, Ms. 3940.*

LITERATURE: *John Bromley, Catalogue of the Clockmakers' Library, 1977, 933, no. 3, p. 80; P.A.S. Phillips, Paul de Lamerie, His Life and Work, 1935, pp 55–59, Appendix II.*

356 *Silver Pair-case watch*

DEBAUFRE, *c*.1740.
INSCRIBED ON THE BACK OF THE MOVEMENT: DEBAUFRE LONDON.

A silver pair-case watch with champleve dial and ivory minute band, enclosing an hour band I–XII, inscribed in the centre Debaufre London. It is probable that this watch is a contemporary fake of continental manufacture. However, the use of the name 'Debaufre', indicates the respect with which the work of this watchmaking family was held. It is probably intended to refer to James Debaufre, the son of Peter Debaufre, a Huguenot emigré from Paris. The inner case bears the incuse maker's mark LKG beneath a crown. The outer case is embossed with a scene of the Judgement of Solomon, surrounded by a border of trophies and foliage. The case is signed Mauris Fecit.

James Debaufre was admitted to the Clockmakers' Company in 1712, when his address was given as Church Street, Soho. Other watches by this maker are in the Victoria and Albert Museum, the British Museum and the Clockmakers' Company Collection.

James Debaufre's only son, Joseph, married in 1750, Susannah de Lamerie, second daughter of the goldsmith, Paul de Lamerie.

DIMENSIONS: *46mm; 52mm; 60mm diameter.*

PROVENANCE: *Presented to the London Museum by W.E. Miller, 1934; Museum of London.*

LITERATURE: *George Baillie, Watchmakers and Clockmakers of the World, 1976, p. 78; J.F. Hayward, English Watches, Victoria and Albert Museum, 1969, pl. 33; R. Noel Hill, Huguenot Clock and Watchmakers Connoisseur, Vol. 121, March 1948, pp. 26–30, p. 27.*

357 *Pair-case watch*

GOLD, HENRY MASSY, LONDON, *c*.1700.
INSCRIBED ON THE BACK OF THE MOVEMENT: HENRY MASSY, LONDON.

A gold pair-case watch signed Massy, London in the centre of the dial. The inner case is decorated with foliate scrollwork interspersed with roundels containing two landscape vignettes, and with putti supporting a vase of flowers, in the manner of Simon Gribelin. The outer case is similarly engraved.

Henry was the son of Nicholas Massy, a watchmaker from Blois who settled in England, and entered the Clockmakers' Company in 1682. In 1692 Henry also became free of the Company.

DIMENSIONS: *45mm diameter.*

PROVENANCE: *British Museum, Department of Medieval and Later Antiquities.*

LITERATURE: *George Baillie, Watchmakers and Clockmakers of the World, 1976, p. 213; F.J. Britten, Old Clocks and Watches and their Makers, 9th edition, 1982, p. 536.*

358 *Watch movement*

JACOB MASSY, LONDON.
INSCRIBED: ON THE BACK, JACOB MASSY, LEICESTERFIELDS, LONDON, AND THE MOVEMENT NUMBER 1037, *c*.1715.

Jacob was the brother of Henry Massy (*Catalogue number* 357). He became free of the Clockmakers' Company in 1715.

DIMENSIONS: *40mm diameter.*

PROVENANCE: *British Museum, Department of Medieval and Later Antiquities.*

LITERATURE: *George Baillie, Watchmakers and Clockmakers of the World, 1976, p. 213; F.J. Britten, Old Clocks and Watches and their Makers, 9th edition, 1982, p. 536.*

356

356

To the Hon.ble the Comons of England in Parliam.t Assembled.

The humble Petition of Nicholas Facio Gent. and Peter Debaufree and Jacob Debaufree Watchmakers

Sheweth

That her most Gracious Maj.ty was pleased by Letters Patents dated 1.o May in the 3.d year of her Reign to Grant to your Pet.rs the sole use and exercise within the Kingdoms of England & Ireland & Dominions thereunto belonging of a certain new Art or Invention or working & Figuring precious or more comon stones & certain other matters different from Mettalls So that they may be Imployed and made use of in Clockwork or watchwork and many other Engines, not for ornament only, but as internall and usefull part of the Work or Engine it self, in such manner as have not heretofore been used, and very much conducing to the greater perfection of Watches and Clocks together with the advantages arising thereby for the space of fourteen yeares from the date of the said Letters Patents.

That your Pet.rs by their great pains & expences both before and since the Granting the said Letters Patents have greatly Improved the said Inventions which are likely to be of great use and advantage to the Publick, but the same will require a far greater expence, whereby your Pet.rs may deserve a better encouragem.t by having a longer term of years allowed, than by the s.d Letters Patents is granted them, otherwise they will not be able to prosecute the same effectually.

Y.r Pet.rs therefore humbly pray your Hon.rs to give them leave to bring in a Bill for granting them such further term of for the sole use of their said Inventions, after the expiration of the said Letters Patents as to your Hon.rs in y.r great wisdom shall seem meet.

And y.r Pet.rs shall ever pray &c.

Nicolas Facio, Peter debaufre Jacob debaufre.

355

356

359 *Pair-case watch*
GOLD, PAUL BEAUVAIS, LONDON, 1708.

A gold pair-case watch, signed P. Beauvais, London, 1708. The dial face is decorated with a small painted miniature. The outer case bears the incuse maker's mark AR; the inner case, the mark IW and the number 693.

Paul Beauvais married Anne Convers at the Huguenot Church of the Savoy in November 1696. Two daughters, Susanne and Françoise were baptised there in 1703 and 1705. His address was given as the Crowned Cadran (Dial) in Castle Street.

DIMENSIONS: *45mm diameter.*

PROVENANCE: *British Museum, Department of Medieval and Later Antiquities.*

LITERATURE: *F.J. Britten, Old Clocks and Watches and their Makers, 9th edition, 1982, p. 366; R. Noel Hill, Huguenot Clock and Watchmakers, Connoisseur, Vol. CXXI, 1948, pp. 26–30,62.*

360 *Pair-case watch*
SILVER, DAVID COMPIGNE, WINCHESTER, 1718.
INSCRIBED ON THE BACK OF MOVEMENT: DAVID COMPIGNE, WINTON.

A silver pair-case watch, inscribed on the dial 'Compigné Winton'. David Compigné (1669–1757) came from Caen in France and settled in Winchester, where he made the town clock.

His second son, Michael, was apprenticed to a silversmith, Peter Pare, in London, a relative of his mother's. Michael set up his own business at St. Andrew's Square, Seven Dials.

DIMENSIONS: *42mm diameter.*

PROVENANCE: *Ilbert Collection; Department of Medieval and Later Antiquities, British Museum.*

LITERATURE: *History of the Compigny Family, typescript in the Huguenot Library compiled by James Compigné (1751–1837) Clerk in the Customs House.*

361 *Tavern Clock*
ABRAHAM PERINOT, LONDON, c.1735.
INSCRIBED: AT THE BASE OF THE DIAL, ABRAHAM PERINOT LONDON.

This tavern clock has a break arch topped door with large side ear pieces and a cushion-shaped base. The dial has a minute band enclosing an hour band with Roman numerals. The brass hands are probably replacements.

The movement, consisting of a fine wheel train, four pillars and unusually shaped plates, is driven by its original tapered weight.

Abraham Perinot was born in London in 1689, the son of Jean Perinot, a master cabinet maker from La Capelle in Picardy, who is recorded as working in Long Acre (Register of the Huguenot Church of the Savoy). Abraham was baptised at the church of La Patente in Soho.

In the 1750s he is recorded as living in the parish of St. Marylebone. In February, 1782 he entered the French Hospital where he died the same month.

DIMENSIONS: *1537 × 750mm.*

PROVENANCE: *Private Collection.*

LITERATURE: *F.J. Britten, Old Clocks and Watches and their Makers, 2nd edition, 1904, p. 373; Ronald Rose, English Dial Clocks, 1978, pl. 24.*

362 *Pair-case repeating watch*
PAUL DANIEL CHENEVIX, c.1735.

This repeating watch is contained in a transversely hinged gold case, set with panels of lapiz lazuli in chased, pierced and enamelled cagework. The watch has diamond push pieces, gold hands and its original dust cover. It is inscribed with the movement number 851.

Paul Daniel Chenevix is recorded as a goldsmith and toyman at the Golden Door in Suffolk Street from 1731 (*Catalogue number* 381). The movement was probably supplied by one of the working watchmakers, whose names, as Campbell noted in 'The London Tradesman', 1747, rarely appeared on their watches. The strong French character of this case (close to designs by Juste Aurèle Meissonier) indicates that he may well have supplied the French market.

DIMENSIONS: *50mm diameter.*

PROVENANCE: *Duke of Newcastle, Christie's 1937; Mallett Collection; Ashmolean Museum.*

363 *Pair-case watch*
SILVER, PETER CHAPEAU, LONDON, 1748.
INSCRIBED ON THE BACK OF THE MOVEMENT: PETR CHAPEAU LONDON 1211.

A silver pair-case watch, in an earlier outer case inlaid with tortoiseshell and decorated with silver piqué flowers, birds and rabbits. The inner silver case bears the maker's mark IH and the hallmark for 1748. The watch has a champlévé silver dial inscribed 'Chapeau London', with a minute band 5–60 enclosing an hour band I–XII. Only one steel 'beetle' hand survives. The cock at the back of the movement is pierced with a grotesque mask at the foot.

It has not been possible to trace this maker in the Huguenot records. A Marie Chappeau is described as the wife of Elie Bernard, watchmaker from Le Mans, and it is probable that Peter Chapeau was connected to this family.

DIMENSIONS: *36mm; 41mm; 53mm diameters.*

PROVENANCE: *Presented by Henry Miller to the London Museum, 1934; Museum of London.*

LITERATURE: *F.J Britten, Old Clocks and Watches and Their Makers, 2nd edition, 1904, p. 578; 9th edition, 1982, p. 398.*

362

362

362

361

363

363

363

364 Triple-case repeating watch

GOLD, ISAAC DUHAMEL, LONDON, c.1750.
INSCRIBED AT THE BACK OF THE MOVEMENT: ISAAC DUHAMEL LONDON, 167.

The middle case of embossed gold in high relief probably represents Esther and Ahasuerus; the outer case of two bezels is of gold studded tortoiseshell; the inner case bears the mark of the Huguenot watch case maker, Stephen Goujon, who was master of the Clockmakers' Company 1760–1.

The white enamel dial has no minute figures, and both the dial and the hands have been replaced. The movement has a silver dust cap and a diamond endstone.

In 1707, an Isaac Duhamel was described as a goldsmith working in Castle Street, St. Martin's in the Fields. It is probable that the goldsmith was in some way connected to this watchmaker.

There is a clock by Isaac Duhamel in the Royal Collection.

DIMENSIONS: 40mm; 48mm; 56mm diameters.

PROVENANCE: Purchased by the Clockmakers' Company, 1895.

LITERATURE: Cecil Clutton and George Daniels, Clocks and Watches in the Collection of the Worshipful Company of Clockmakers, 1975, no.172, p.29.

365 Thomas Grignion (1721–1784), watchmaker

PORTRAIT DRAWING, BLACK CHALK AND STUMP HEIGHTENED WITH WHITE ON BLUE PAPER, CHARLES GRIGNION, LONDON, 1737.
INSCRIBED ON THE VERSO: THOS GRIGNION OF GREAT RUSSELL STREET, COVENT (GARDEN) DRAWN BY CHAS GRIGNION SENR IN 1737 ON THOMAS'S RETURN FROM PARIS. AGED 24 YEARS.

Thomas Grignion is shown whole length, standing towards the front, looking right, with his head nearly in profile, wearing a hat and a sword, with his right hand thrust in his pocket.

Thomas Grignion made a turret clock for St. Paul's Covent Garden in 1740, which was unfortunately burnt in 1795. It was acclaimed as the first long pendulum clock in Europe. After the fire, it was replaced with a new mechanism by Thomas Grignion the younger. His father was also a member of the Royal Society of Arts, and in 1759 presented a regulator, which can still be seen on the premises today.

Charles Grignion was Thomas's elder brother. He studied drawing under Le Bas in Paris and then under Gravelot at his drawing school in Covent Garden, where Thomas Gainsborough was a fellow pupil (Catalogue number 284). Grignion later made his name as an engraver, working for William Hogarth and engraving Thomas Bentley's illustrations to the poems of Thomas Gray. From 1750 to 1772 he lived at 28 James Street, Covent Garden. His obituary in the 'Monthly Magazine', 1808, described him as the 'Father of engraving in this Country'.

DIMENSIONS: 330 × 185mm.

PROVENANCE: Purchased May 1890 at the Percy sale; British Museum, Department of Prints and Drawings.

LITERATURE: Laurence Binyon, Catalogue of Drawings by British Artists of Foreign Origin working in Great Britain, Department of Prints and Drawings, British Museum, 1900, Vol. II, p.252; F.J. Britten, Old Clocks and Watches and Their Makers, 9th edition, 1982, p.466.

366 Trade card of Daniel & Thomas Grignion

AT THE KING'S ARMS AND DIAL, RUSSEL(L) STREET, COVENT GARDEN, c.1730–c.1763.

Daniel Grignon (1684–1763) arrived in London as a refugee from Poitou in 1688. The name was later anglicised to Grignion.

As the trade card indicates, the Grignions, father and son, were finishers to the late Mr. Daniel Quare (who died in 1724). They are described as watchmakers although they also sold 'all sorts of Curious Toys'. They appear to have been connected by marriage with the Harrache family, and may have supplied toys made by Thomas Harrache. They also specialised in arranging the production of fine chased watch cases. One surviving bill dated December 1750 for £31.10.0 was for 'a gold watch going upon jewels No. 1118 chased by Moser (George Michael) with the Judgement of Hercules'.

Their shop in Russell Street, Covent Garden, was on the Bedford Estate, and papers relating to the family are to be found with the Bedford Estate Papers deposited in the Greater London Record Office. Thomas Grignion also cleaned and mended watches for the Russell family in the 4th Duke's time.

Thomas Grignion was succeeded by a watchmaker of the same name who worked on the same premises till 1821.

ILLUSTRATED: page 243.

DIMENSIONS: 154 × 129mm.

PROVENANCE: Heal Collection, Department of Prints and Drawings, British Museum.

367 Pair-case repeating watch

GOLD, THOMAS GRIGNION, LONDON, 1766.
INSCRIBED ON THE BACK OF THE MOVEMENT: THOS GRIGNION LONDON 1464.

Both cases are pierced and engraved. The watch has a stirrup pendant, white enamel dial, steel beetle hands and a ruby endstone. The back of the movement is protected by a silver dust cap.

There is a silver pair-case watch and a watch movement by this maker in the same collection, and another watch movement by Daniel and Thomas Grignion in the British Museum. In 1756, Thomas Grignion charged £63 for a similar gold chased repeating watch.

DIMENSIONS: 43mm; 48mm diameters.

PROVENANCE: Presented by John W. Carter, 1912; Clockmakers' Company Collection.

LITERATURE: Cecil Clutton and George Daniels, Clocks and Watches in the Collection of the Worshipful Company of Clockmakers, 1975, no.327, p.45.

364

364

365

367

367

367

368 Pair-case repeating watch

GOLD, PERIGAL, LONDON, c.1755.
INSCRIBED ON THE BACK OF THE MOVEMENT: 'PERIGAL' (AND THE MOVEMENT
NUMBER) 1465.

The dust cap bears the name of John Perigal, who was recorded as free of the Clockmakers'
Company. He was a member of a Huguenot family whose ancestor, Jean Perigal, an ivory
turner, left Dieppe for Dover in 1688.

The pierced inner case is engraved with a spray of flowers and bears the maker's mark DA.
The outer case is embossed in high relief with a scene representing the Triumph of the
Mordecai, and is signed by the chaser McGowan.

A Francis Perigal became Master of the Clockmakers' Company in 1756. He worked near
the French church in Threadneedle Street.

In 1786, a Francis Perigal, described himself as 'Watchmaker to the King'.

DIMENSIONS: *41mm diameter.*
PROVENANCE: *Ashmolean Museum,
Oxford.*
LITERATURE: *Frederick Perigal,
The Story of John Perigal of Dieppe,
Proceedings of the Huguenot Society of
London, Vol. 2 (1888), pp.14–42;
F.J. Britten, Old Clocks and Watches
and Their Makers, 9th edition,
1982, p. 565.*

369 Pair-case watch

SILVER-GILT, FRANCIS GABRIEL BARRAUD, LONDON, 1756.
INSCRIBED ON THE BACK OF THE MOVEMENT: BARRAUD.

This watch has an enamel dial, although the beetle hands are nineteenth-century replacements.
The signature on the back of the movement is similar to that on the watchmaker's trade card
(*Catalogue number* 370). The outer case is pierced and engraved with a floral design. Both cases
bear the maker's mark HG and the London hallmark for 1756.

The Barraud family came from Angoulême. Francis Gabriel's father was naturalised in
April, 1704. His elder brother Philip was an engraver and published 'A New Book of Single
Cyphers' in 1782. Francis Gabriel married the daughter of Paul Crespin, the goldsmith. In his
mother-in-law's will, 1775, he is described as a watchmaker of the parish of St. Giles,
London, living in St. Andrew Street. By 1781, the family had moved to Wine Office Court,
Fleet Street.

This is the earliest recorded watch by Francis Gabriel Barraud.

Miss Barraud also presented the Clockmakers' Company with a musical table clock, c. 1767
by Barraud. The clock has a verge escapement with hanging balance, strikes the hours, and
also plays four tunes on seven bells.

DIMENSIONS: *35mm; 40mm diameters.*
PROVENANCE: *Bequeathed by
Miss E.M. Barraud; Clockmakers'
Company Collection.*
LITERATURE: *Cecil Clutton and
George Daniels, Clocks and Watches in
the Collection of the Worshipful
Company of Clockmakers, 1975,
no.191, p. 31; Cedric Jagger,
P.P. Barraud, 1968, pp.102,140, pl. X.*

370 Trade card of Francis Gabriel Barraud, Watch & Clock-Maker

8 WINE OFFICE COURT, FLEET STREET, c.1781.

Francis Gabriel Barraud moved to Wine Office Court, Fleet Street, from St. Andrew Street,
Seven Dials in about 1781. He was succeeded by his son Paul Philip in 1796.

DIMENSIONS: *58 × 58mm.*
PROVENANCE: *Banks Collection,
Department of Prints and Drawings,
British Museum.*
LITERATURE: *Cedric Jagger,
P.P. Barraud, 1968.*

371 Watch

GOLD, JAMES TREGENT, LONDON, 1767.

A gold watch with white enamelled dial and pierced hands. The case bears the London
hallmark for 1769–70, and is enamelled and decorated in the centre back with a dark blue
vase (some enamelling is missing).

James Tregent is first recorded in 1759. He became a member of the Clockmakers'
Company in 1781 and later watchmaker to the Prince of Wales.

A fine enamelled watch by the same maker is in the Victoria and Albert Museum, and is
attached to a gold chatelaine. Another example in the Clockmakers' Company collection is
signed 'Jas. Tregent Leicester Square London 825'.

DIMENSIONS: *137; 147mm diameters.*
PROVENANCE: *Given to the London
Museum, 1915, by J.G. Joicey; Museum
of London.*
LITERATURE: *George Baillie,
Clockmakers and Watchmakers of the
World, 1976, Vol. I, p. 317;
F.J. Britten, Old Clocks and Watches
and their Makers, 2nd edition, 1904,
p. 707; J.F. Hayward, English
Watches, Victoria and Albert Museum,
1969, pl. 43.*

372 Trade card of James Tregent, Watch & Clock Maker

IN CRANBOURN STREET, LEICESTER SQUARE, 1757.

James Tregent worked in Cranbourn Street, Leicester Square, London. His card is surmounted
by the Prince of Wales' Feathers and the date, presumably of his appointment as watchmaker
to the Prince (later George III) in 1757 and states that he is 'Watch and Clock Maker to their
Royal Highnesses The Prince of Wales and Duke of Kent'.

DIMENSIONS: *92 × 64mm.*
PROVENANCE: *Banks Collection,
Department of Prints and Drawings,
British Museum.*
LITERATURE: *F.J. Britten, Old Clocks
and Watches and their Makers,
9th edition, 1982, pp.626–7.*

369

368

368

369

370

371

371

372

373 *Pair-case watch*

SILVER, ROBERT CHASSEREAU, LONDON, 1813.
INSCRIBED ON THE BACK OF THE MOVEMENT: ROBERT CHASSEREAU LONDON N 2026.

A silver pair-case watch with a white enamelled dial and copper hands.

The outer case is overlaid with tortoiseshell, and painted with a landscape scene enclosed in a floral border. It bears the incuse mark WH and the London hallmark for 1813–14.

This maker is recorded as working at 4 Beach Street, Barbican, 1804–8. By 1813 Chassereau was working from 34 Coppice Row, Clerkenwell.

The Chassereau family came from Niort in Poitou. This watchmaker's great grandfather, Jacob, was naturalised in 1709. His grandfather, Peter, was a surveyor and architect, who advertised from the Golden Head, the upper end of Berwick Street, near Soho Square in the Gentleman's Magazine, 1741. Robert Chassereau's father, also Robert, was a carver and gilder.

DIMENSIONS: *150; 152; 163mm diameter.*

PROVENANCE: *Given to the London Museum by J.G. Joicey, 1912; Museum of London.*

LITERATURE: *Pedigree of the Chassereau family, Huguenot Library.*

373   373   373

374 *Watch movement by Henry Lepine*

INSCRIBED: LEPINE HIGH STREET CANTERBURY, NO. 3755, *c.*1845.

A contemporary watch paper records Henry Lepine as a 'Watch & Clock Maker, Silversmith and Jeweller in the High Street, Canterbury'. Owing to failure of health and 'misfortunes in trade', he entered the French Hospital in 1850, where he remained until his death twenty-five years later.

Henry Lepine was the son of William Lepine (d. 1837) of St. Peter's Street, Canterbury. His ancestors had come to England at the time of the Revocation of the Edict of Nantes and settled in Canterbury as master silkweavers.

DIMENSIONS: *46mm diameter.*

PROVENANCE: *City of Canterbury Museum.*

LITERATURE: *Charles Marmoy, The French Protestant Hospital; Extracts from the Archives of 'La Providence' relating to the inmates and Applicants for Admission, 1718–1957, Huguenot Society Quarto Series, Vol. LIII, 1977, under Lepine.*

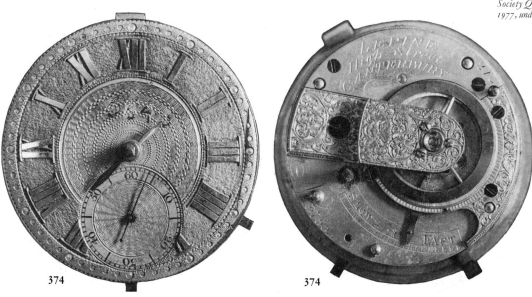

374   374

JEWELLERS

Apart from the refugee goldsmiths and watchmakers, London gained a group of specialist craftsmen who worked as jewellers, watchcase makers, snuff-box makers or even as engravers producing designs for luxury items in metalwork. Thus Simon Gribelin's pattern books, published in London in the 1680s and 1690s, were used by both jewellers and watchmakers.

John Obrisset produced a range of boxes in horn and tortoiseshell between 1705 and 1728, designed to contain tobacco. Second generation refugees, Paul Daniel Chenevix and Thomas Harrache, ran shops which supplied a wide range of luxury items, from silver and jewellery to Dresden porcelain and bronze statuettes.

Trade card of Paul Daniel Chenevix

The firm of Tessier's was founded in the eighteenth century by the grandson of a Huguenot refugee, Lewis de Tessier.

381

375 *Queen Anne*

PORTRAIT PLAQUE, SILVER, MOUNTED ON A TORTOISESHELL BOX, JOHN OBRISSET, LONDON, 1705

For biographical information on this maker *Catalogue number* 301.

This is one of only two recorded silver portrait plaques actually struck with Obrisset's initials OB and dated 1705. The other example in the Museum of London is also mounted on a tortoiseshell box. (See Catalogue no.302 for a similar portrait plaque of Queen Anne in tortoiseshell.)

DIMENSIONS: *61 × 46 × 38mm.*

PROVENANCE: *British Museum, Department of Medieval and Later Antiquities.*

LITERATURE: *P.A.S. Phillips, John Obrisset, 1931, no.44, p.64.*

376 *Prince George of Denmark*

PORTRAIT PLAQUE, TORTOISESHELL MOUNTED ON HINGED SILVER-FRAMED BOX, JOHN OBRISSET, LONDON, 1708

The portrait plaque of Prince George bears the unique signature I. OB.F 1708.

The reverse of the box contains a portrait plaque in tortoiseshell of Queen Anne, facing to the left. This is also signed 'OB' and dated 1705.

DIMENSIONS: *65 × 50 × 15mm.*

PROVENANCE: *A.W. Forbes; given to the British Museum, Department of Medieval and Later Antiquities, 1889.*

LITERATURE: *P.A.S. Phillips, John Obrisset, 1931, no.55, p.65; C.H. Read, English Work in impressed Horn, in Some Minor Arts as practised in England, 1894, illustrated pl.7. (Information kindly given by Tim Wilson.)*

377 *The conversion of St Paul*

PLAQUE, PRESSED HORN MOUNTED IN OVAL HORN BOX, JOHN OBRISSET, LONDON, c.1710. INSCRIBED: ACTES.YE.IX, AND O B (WITH THE LATER INSCRIPTION) THEOPHILUS CARTER OBT 19 MAY 1780 AET 7?2.

The design of this plaque is derived from the bas-relief on the West Front of St. Paul's Cathedral which was carved by Francis Bird. It is probable that Obrisset based this design on one of the contemporary engravings of the Cathedral such as that published by Gribelin in 1702. P.A.S. Phillips suggested that this box, which is one of several examples, was probably produced to commemorate the opening of St. Paul's Cathedral for service in 1710.

DIMENSIONS: *102 × 82 × 28mm.*

PROVENANCE: *British Museum, Department of Medieval and Later Antiquities.*

EXHIBITED: *The Horner's Craft, Worthing Museum and Art Gallery, 5th May – 29th September, 1973 (39).*

LITERATURE: *Robin Fedden, John Obrisset, a notable Huguenot craftsman, Connoisseur, Vol.180, 1972, pp.13–17, fig.1; P.A.S. Phillips, John Obrisset, 1931, no.77, p.70.*

378 *Engraved Designs for Jewellery and Watchcases*

VOLUME, SIMON GRIBELIN, LONDON, 1722.

The title page is lettered by hand 'Livre de Petite Estampes Gravée Sur Plusieurs Ouvrage par Sim. Gribelin fait Relié a Londre 1722'.

The eighty-nine leaves of this volume contain pulls from many of the smaller objects which Gribelin engraved (*Catalogue number* 379) as well as selections from his pattern books published in 1682 and 1687 and vignettes cut from larger engravings that he evidently felt could be used as sources for decorating smaller objects.

DIMENSIONS: *Quarto.*

PROVENANCE: *Horace Walpole; purchased at the Strawberry Hill Sale, 1842, by Hugh Hume Campbell; St. Mary's College, Strawberry Hill.*

EXHIBITED: *Horace Walpole and Strawberry Hill, Orleans House Gallery, Twickenham, 20 September – 7 December 1980 (97).*

LITERATURE: *Horace Walpole, A Catalogue of Engravers, 1763, p.118.*

379 *Comfit box*

SILVER-GILT, NO MAKER'S MARK, c.1690.

Simon Gribelin specialised in engraving designs for watchcases and jewellery; it is probable that he also engraved watchcases and snuffboxes himself although this is the only identified example that has yet come to light.

The pull from this comfit box is included in the larger volume of engravings selected by Gribelin from his own work in the British Museum (f61) and also in the smaller volume which formerly belonged to Horace Walpole (*Catalogue number* 378, f32).

DIMENSIONS: *92mm wide; 13mm high.*

PROVENANCE: *C.D. Rotch bequest; acquired by the Victoria and Albert Museum, 1962.*

LITERATURE: *Charles Oman, English Engraved Silver, 1150–1900, 1978, p.73, pl.84.*

380 *Trade card of Peter Parquot, Jeweller & Goldsmith*

AT THE SIGN OF THE EAGLE & PEARL, IN KING STREET, SOHO, c.1744.

Peter Parquot is recorded as a jeweller in 1744. It is probable that his father was the watchmaker Pierre Parquot, whose son, also Pierre, was baptised at the Huguenot church of Rider Court in 1709. F.J. Britten records a watch by Parquot dated 1706.

DIMENSIONS: *164 × 121.*

PROVENANCE: *Heal Collection, Department of Prints and Drawings, British Museum.*

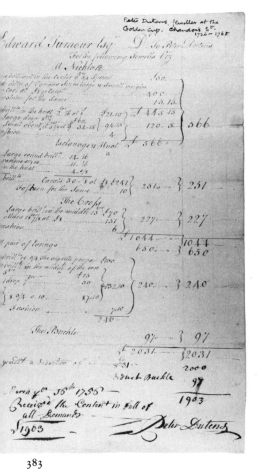

383

378

380

379

381 _Trade card of Paul Daniel Chenevix_

AT THE SIGN OF THE GOLDEN DOOR, SUFFOLK STREET, 1731–1742.

Paul Daniel Chenevix was the grandson of Philip Chenevix who received letters of naturalisation in 1682. The family came from Picardy. His father, also Philip, a Major in the 2nd Carabineers, was killed at Blenheim, 1704.

Paul Daniel Chenevix is first recorded at the sign of the Golden Door, Suffolk Street in 1731 when he sold a pair of silver buckles (bill in Halliwell-Phillipps Collection, Library of Congress). In 1729 he had premises in Pall Mall, for in May of that year Benjamin Mildmay, Earl Fitzwalter paid £6 11s for 'a long gold head for a cane, with my coronet upon it'. The shop was run by his wife after his death in the 1740s (_Catalogue number_ 382) Mrs. Chenevix married secondly Peter Russel, toyman. The latter eventually took over the business on her death in 1755.

ILLUSTRATED: _page 255._

DIMENSIONS: _190 × 220mm._

PROVENANCE: _Banks Collection, Department of Prints and Drawings, British Museum._

LITERATURE: _A.C. Edwards, The Account Books of Benjamin Mildmay, Earl Fitzwalter, 1977, p.78, 132._

382 _Satirical Print of the Chenevix Toyshop_

LONDON, 1750.

The publication of this print was announced in the 'General Advertiser', 18 January 1751. 'Price 6d A Humourous Print: Occasioned by a Lady's Coach standing cross the Footway, at a Toyshop, at the bottom of the Haymarket, Charing Cross'. The toyshop in question, situated at the corner of Cockspur Street and Warwick House Street, is that opened by Paul Daniel Chenevix, goldsmith by 1731. On his death, the toyshop was carried on by his wife, who earned for herself the reputation of 'toy-woman à la mode'. In 1747, Horace Walpole purchased from Mrs. Chenevix the lease of Strawberry Hill, Twickenham.

DIMENSIONS: _274 × 178mm._

PROVENANCE: _Department of Prints and Drawings, British Museum._

LITERATURE: _R.A. Austen Leigh, The Family of Chenevix, Proceedings of the Huguenot Society of London, Vol.17 (1944–5), pp.311–336; Ambrose Heal, The London Goldsmiths, 1200–1800, 1972, pl.XIV, p.125; Hugh Phillips, Mid-Georgian London, 1964, p.95; Frederick George Stephens and Edward Hawkins, Catalogue of Political and Personal Satires in the British Museum, 1877, Vol.III, Part 1 (2) 1734–1750, no.3085, pp.781–2._

383 _Bill of Peter Dutens, Jeweller_

LONDON, 1756.

Peter Dutens is recorded at the Golden Cup, Chandos Street, 1726–1765; a copy of his trade card is in the Victoria and Albert Museum.

This bill to Edward Turnour Esq., for a total of £1903 covers the cost of a brilliant necklace £566; an esclavage and knot set with brilliants £227; a pair of earrings £650, and a buckle for £97.

ILLUSTRATED: _page 257._

DIMENSIONS: _311 × 201mm._

PROVENANCE: _Heal Collection, Department of Prints and Drawings, British Museum._

384 _Trade Card of Marie Anne Viet and Thomas Mitchell_

AT THE SIGN OF THE DIAL AND KING'S ARMS, CORNHILL, ENGRAVED BY JAMES SARTOR, LONDON, 1742.

Marie Anne Viet appears to have been the daughter of Claude Viet, clockmaker, who is recorded as working in Sweeting Alley, in the City in 1700.

In 1715, she was apprenticed to her father, allegedly the first female apprentice to be bound in the London Clockmakers' Company. As this trade card indicates, Marie Viet went into partnership with Thomas Mitchell, who was probably a relative by marriage, and they worked at the sign of the Dial and Kings Arms, Cornhill from at least 1742. The trade card, inscribed in both English and French, advertises all 'sorts of Curiosities in Gold, Silver, Mother of Pearl, Tortoiseshell, Agat, Amber, Ivory', many of which are shown round the borders of this elaborate card.

The verso is inscribed in pen with lines from a poem and musical notation for a song.

James Sartor worked as an engraver at Mr. Drakes, jeweller over against the Crown Tavern near Earl's Court in Drury Lane. Sartor's trade card is also in the Heal Collection.

DIMENSIONS: _298 × 188mm._

PROVENANCE: _Heal Collection, British Museum, Department of Prints and Drawings._

LITERATURE: _Ambrose Heal, The London Goldsmiths, 1200–1800, 1972, pl.LXXIV, p.261; Philip J. Shears, Huguenot Connections with the Clockmaking Trade in England, Proceedings of the Huguenot Society of London, Vol. 20 (1958–64), pp.167–8._

385 _Walk Book for Warning Carriers_

MANUSCRIPT, 32FF., LONDON, 1744.

This contains the names and addresses of bankers, refiners, goldsmiths, jewellers, watchmakers, toymen and pawnbrokers to whom warnings for lost bank notes or silver were delivered by the carrier from Goldsmiths' Hall.

Three different walks are listed. John Holtom's walk from St. Martin's Le Grand took him via Fleet Street, Strand, Long Acre, Charing Cross and Whitehall to Westminster. Mr. Weatherhead's walk was from Goswell Street, through Hatton Garden to St. Giles', Soho. Many of the names listed in these walks are of Huguenot origin.

DIMENSIONS: _165 × 200mm._

PROVENANCE: _The Worshipful Company of Goldsmiths._

EXHIBITED: _London Silver 1680 to 1780, Museum of London Exhibition Catalogue, 1982, p.40, no.2._

STAND COACHMAN, OR THE HAUGHTY LADY WELL FITTED.

At a Toy Shop hard by Charing Cross t'other Day, | But being that Favour most rudely denied, | The Mobb seeing this, they all laugh'd at the Whim, | The Lady much ruffled, soon alter'd her Tone,
A Lady's Coach stood quite across the Foot Way: | By John on the Box, and his Lady beside; | And swore 'twas as free for the rest, as for him: | And call'd to her Coachman in haste to move on:
A Person did civily th'Coachman intreat | The Gentleman, finding that Words wou'd not do, | So hoisting each other, just like a Ship's Crew | 'Tis hop'd the fair Ladies from hence will beware,
To pull up, and let him pass over the Street: | He op'd the Coach Doors, and genteely went thro' | Bespatter'd and dirty, began to march thro': | How they stop a Free Passage with such haughty Air.

Taken from Fact, and Publish'd according to Act of Parliament, for J. Wakelin in Flower de Luce Court, Fleet Street. Price 6.d 1750.

382

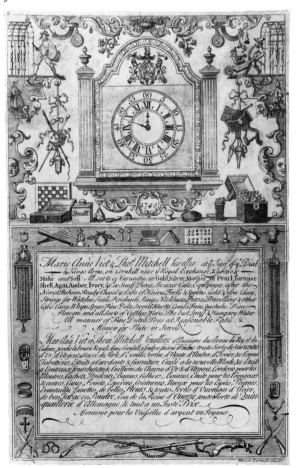

Marie Anne Viet & Tho: Mitchell Jeweller at ∫ Sign of ∫ Dial & Kings Arms, on Cornhill near ∫ Royal Exchange LONDON

384

JEWELLERS
ACCOUNTS
MADE EASY:
Consisting of 175 TABLES,

FOR THE USE

Of all Merchant JEWELLERS,
DIAMOND-CUTTERS, GOLD
and SILVER-SMITHS;

By which any Weight of Diamonds
may be calculated at View.

By J. H. DESAGULIERS,
Book-Keeper.

LONDON:
Printed for the AUTHOR; and Sold by CHARLES
HOGUEL, Bookseller, near Somerset-House, in the
Strand; and by JOSEPH DUKE and BARTHO-
LOMEW MAY, Booksellers, at Virgil's Head, behind
the Royal-Exchange. M DCC XXXIV.

[Price Two Shillings.]

386

386 *Jewellers Accounts made Easy*
J.H. DESAGULIERS, LONDON, 1734.

J. H. Desaguliers was probably a relative of Dr. J.T. Desaguliers, natural philosopher and divine.

ILLUSTRATED: *page 259.*
PROVENANCE: *British Library.*

The volume contains 175 tables for the use of 'all Merchant Jewellers, Diamond-Cutters, Gold and Silver-smiths'; by which any weight of diamonds may be calculated. Its publication was prompted by the expansion of the diamond trade in London, as a result of the discovery of new diamond mines in Brazil.

Tessiers Limited

The firm was founded by Lewis de Tessier (*d.*1811) of Old Broad Street, whose grandfather settled in England in 1712. The family originally came from Languedoc.

387 *Hair bracelet in gold mounts with miniature attached to clasp*
H. & E. TESSIER, LONDON, 1860.

This hair bracelet belonged to a Miss Slade, the miniature mounted in the clasp represents the owner, aged 5, and is engraved on the reverse 'July 1860'. Miss Slade later became Mrs. Higson and died in 1938 aged 83.

DIMENSIONS: *175 × 360mm.*
PROVENANCE: *Tessiers Ltd.*

This bracelet is contained in its original case. In 1860 the Tessier family had premises at 32 South Audley Street and 26 New Bond Street.

388 *Heart-shaped pendant*
CRYSTAL IN GOLD RIBBON MOUNT SET WITH TURQUOISES AND SURMOUNTED WITH A GILT CYPHER AH SET WITH CORAL. HENRY TESSIER, LONDON, *c.*1870.

The pendant is contained in its original case. Henry Tessier, Court Jeweller, worked at 32, South Audley Street, Grosvenor Square.

DIMENSIONS: *50 × 35mm.*
PROVENANCE: *Tessiers Ltd.*

389 *Crystal cross*
WITH ENAMELLED MOUNT ENTWINED WITH A SCROLL. INSCRIBED: DIEU VOUS PROTEGE, *c.*1870.

The cross, in its original case, was supplied by Henry Tessier, who described himself as 'Manufacturing Jeweller to the Queen, and their Royal Highnesses the Prince and Princess of Wales'.

DIMENSIONS: *77mm long.*
PROVENANCE: *Tessiers Ltd.*

390 *Set of eight garnet buttons, in gold snake mounts*
TESSIER & SONS, LONDON, *c.*1860.

The buttons are in their original case.

DIMENSIONS: *15mm diameter.*
PROVENANCE: *Tessiers Ltd.*

391 *Bill from Tessier & Sons to Lady Ward, 1851*

The heading describes the jewellers as 'Artists in Hair' (*Catalogue number* 387).

PROVENANCE: *Tessiers Ltd.*

392 *Photograph of Louis Edward Tessier (1841–1895) as a young man*
FROM A DAGUERREOTYPE, *c.*1860.

The great grandson of Lewis de Tessier, Louis Edward also became a master jeweller and carried on the family business. His second son, Henry Alexander, sold the four businesses in Mayfair and retired to Devon.

PROVENANCE: *Tessiers Ltd.*

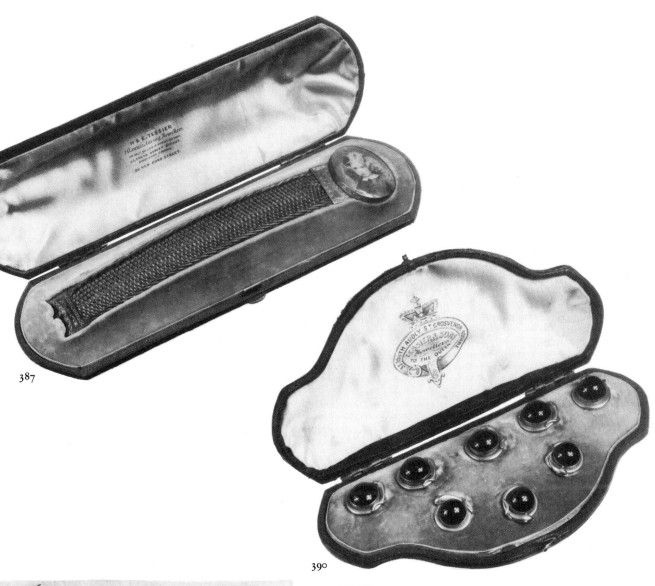

387

390

391

392

MINIATURES

393 *An Unknown Lady*
MINIATURE ON VELLUM, ISAAC OLIVER, c.1595–1600.
INSCRIBED: INFELIX SPECTATOR.

The lady is shown three quarters to the left, wearing a black dress with a white ruff, against a blue background. The miniature is mounted in a chased metal gilt frame.

Isaac Oliver (d.1617) came to London as a child in 1568, with his father Pierre Oliver, a Huguenot goldsmith. A pupil of Nicholas Hilliard (1547–1619), the greatest limner of his day, Oliver nevertheless was influenced by art movements abroad, both in Flanders and in Italy. Under James I, he was appointed limner to Anne of Denmark. His miniatures reflect the courtly elegance and classical allusion which were cultivated in the late Renaissance world of masques and revels.

DIMENSIONS: *55 × 45mm.*

PROVENANCE: *The Duke of Buccleuch and Queensberry, KT.*

EXHIBITED: *Nicholas Hilliard and Isaac Oliver, An Exhibition to commemorate the 400th Anniversary of the Birth of Nicholas Hilliard, Victoria and Albert Museum, 1947 (156); Roy Strong, Artists of the Tudor Court, The Portrait Miniature Rediscovered 1520–1620, Victoria and Albert Museum, 1983 (157).*

LITERATURE: *Erna Auerbach, Nicholas Hilliard, 1961, p.244, pl.210; 329 (245); Burlington Magazine, LXXII, 1938, p.223. H.A. Kennedy, Early English Portrait Miniatures in the Collection of the Duke of Buccleuch, ed. C. Holmes, The Studio, 1917, pl.XXII.*

394 *Louis XIV, Philipe Duc d'Orleans, Maria Theresa, Queen of Louis XIV, Princess Henrietta, 1st wife of Duc d'Orleans, and a lady said to be the Princess Palatine*
MINIATURES ON ENAMEL, THE FIRST THREE BY JEAN PETITOT AND THE LAST TWO BY W. ESSEX, AFTER PETITOT, LONDON, 1836, SIGNED ON THE REVERSE, INSET IN THE LID OF A CIRCULAR CHASED GOLD SNUFF BOX.

Jean Petitot (1607–91) evolved the technique developed by Jean Toutin, a French goldsmith, for painting on enamel. Born in Geneva, the son of a Huguenot sculptor, he is thought to have worked in Paris under Toutin before obtaining employment at Charles I's court around 1637 and introducing the art of painting enamel miniature portraits to England. After his return to France in the 1640s, he was employed by Louis XIV to paint portraits of the royal family and nobility at Court.

DIMENSIONS: *95mm diameter, each oval approximately 25mm.*

PROVENANCE: *The Duke of Buccleuch and Queensberry, KT.*

395 *Madame de Maintenon (1635–1719)*
MINIATURE ON VELLUM, JAMES BORDIER.

The sitter is shown seated, wearing a red dress and a blue cloak and holding a book, against a curtain and landscape background.

James Bordier (1616–1684) worked closely with Petitot in Geneva, Paris and London. He remained in England after Petitot had left but in 1668 he was back in France operating as a secret agent for the Genevese government at Versailles.

DIMENSIONS: *89 × 65mm.*

PROVENANCE: *The Duke of Buccleuch and Queensberry, KT.*

396 *Prince Eugene of Savoy (1663–1738)*
MINIATURE ON VELLUM, BENJAMIN ARLAUD.

The sitter is shown three quarters to the right, wearing a full length wig and armour with a white lace cravat and the Chain of the Golden Fleece. The miniature is mounted with a filigree frame with a ribbon tie surmount.

Little is known about Benjamin Arlaud (fl.1701–31) other than the fact that he was the younger brother of the miniaturist Jacques Antoine Arlaud (1668–1746) and that he is thought to have arrived in England from Geneva around 1700–05. Working exclusively in watercolour and bodycolour on vellum, he captured a sitter's individual character with great directness without losing the required air of dignified nobility. From his signed works, it would appear that he was particularly well patronised by the Duke of Portland, the Earl of Oxford and after Blenheim by the Duke of Marlborough, Prince Eugene of Savoy and their principal English Officers.

DIMENSIONS: *oval 67mm.*

PROVENANCE: *The Duke of Buccleuch and Queensberry, KT.*

LITERATURE: *H.A. Kennedy, Early English Portrait Miniatures in the Collection of the Duke of Buccleuch, ed. C. Holmes, The Studio, 1917, pl.LXIII.*

394

393

395

MADAME DE MAINTENON

396

PRINCE EUGENE

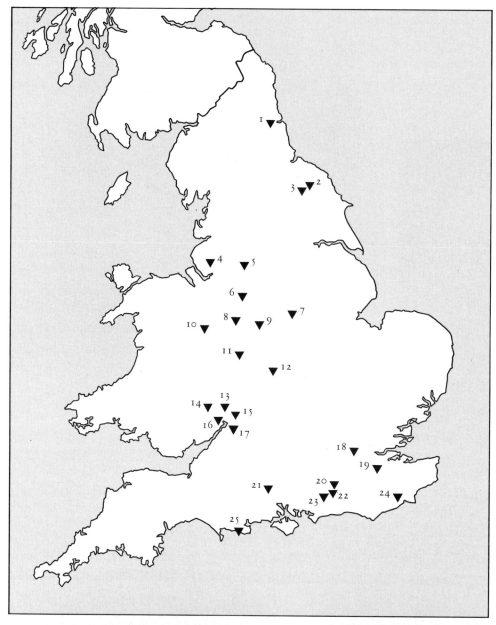

There was glassmaking throughout this period in the traditional glassmaking area in the Surrey-Sussex Weald, which was near to the main ports of entry, London, Southampton and Rye. From the 1580s, there was a gradual westward migration. Furnaces were set up in other forest areas for the duration of the fuel supply. The glassmakers then moved on, or back to the Weald. Later many Huguenots worked for Mansell and became involved in the development of the new coal-fired furnaces.

1 NEWCASTLE-UPON-TYNE
(1617–) COAL

2 ROSEDALE

3 HUTTON COMMON

4 BICKERSTAFFE

5 HAUGHTON GREEN,
DENTON
(–1653) COAL

6 BIDDULPH
NEAR CONGLETON

7 WOLLATON
(1612–1617) COAL

8 BISHOPS WOOD,
ECCLESHALL

9 BAGOTS PARK

10 RUYTON-XI-TOWNS

11 KINGSWINFORD,
NEAR STOURBRIDGE
(1612–) COAL

12 ASHOW, KENILWORTH

13 NEWENT

14 ST WEONARDS

15 GLOUCESTER
(–1696–) COAL

16 NEWNHAM-ON-SEVERN
(–1696–) COAL

17 WOODCHESTER

18 SOUTHWARK
(1615–) COAL

19 KNOLE

20 ALFOLD

21 BUCKHOLT

22 WISBOROUGH GREEN

23 PETWORTH

24 NORTHIAM

25 KIMMERIDGE
(1615–1623)
SHALE COAL

SCIENCE MUSEUM

*Making broad glass in
the eighteenth century*

GLASS

The contribution of sixteenth-century Protestants from the Spanish Netherlands, Normandy and Lorraine to the development of glassmaking in Britain is important historically, fundamental technically but extremely difficult to find today.

The immigrants came from the specialised glassmaking areas which supplied the English market at a time when local religious upheaval threatened this trade and society itself. They arrived when the small English glass industry, mainly utilitarian, itinerant, intermittant and forest-based (and lacking the powerful protection of a town-based guild system or of the continental concept of the 'gentilhomme verrier', which carried practical aristocratic privileges including tax exemptions) was unable to fulfil a growing demand for good domestic glazing and glassware for the table.

Normandy and Lorraine were renowned for window glass. In Normandy, four privileged families, the de Caqueray, de Brossard, de Bongard and le Vaillant families made 'crowns' – large round discs – by blowing and spinning, while the Lorrainer families of de Bisval, de Hennezal, Thiétry and Thysac produced 'broad glass' by blowing long cylinders of glass which were cut open and flattened. 'Menu verre' (tableware and other small items) were blown by the du Houx, Massey, Bigault, Bonny and Finance families and by Flemish glassmakers like the Vinions.

Jean Carré, Arras-born merchant from the glass-making centre of Antwerp (which included Italians making fine crystal glass *a la façon de Venise*) 'cam hither for religion' in 1567 and immediately obtained licences to build a Venetian furnace for crystal glass in London and two window glass furnaces at Fernfold in the Surrey-Sussex Weald. The crown glass house run by the Bongars continued into the seventeenth century, but the broad glass enterprise was soon replaced by a group producing vessels from good quality ordinary green glass. By his death in 1572, Carré had introduced the full range of contemporary glassmaking techniques, skilled workers to practise them and the necessary capital.

The immigrants of the 1570s and 1580s were no longer protected by patents and moved to wherever they could find wood for their furnaces and a market for their glass. Traces of Huguenot-run small furnaces for window and green vessel glass can be found in many parts of Britain.

The number of glassmakers, the lack of any privileged protection, and the growing opposition to the use of English forests for fuel and the consequent use of more economic coal brought changes in the organisation of glass manufacturing. The new system of industrial monopolies granted to courtier entrepreneurs was vigorously opposed by the children of the 'gentilhommes verriers' who had pushed the British glass industry into a new phase of development. Gradually, most of them came under the control of Sir Robert Mansell.

However, the Tyzacks and the Henzeys are still remembered for having established the glass industry in Stourbridge and Newcastle upon Tyne in the seventeenth century and descendants of Huguenot glassmakers could be found in the British glass industry until comparatively recently.

397 *Goblet*

CRISTALLO GLASS, ENGRAVED BY ANTHONY DE LYSLE, ATTRIBUTED TO THE GLASSHOUSE OF
JACOB VERZELINI, *c*.1586.
INSCRIBED: RP MP 1586 GOD.SAVE.QUYNE.ELISABETH.

The pointed oviform bowl was blown into a ribbed mould and further decorated with a fine
applied trail. The inscription is engraved on the narrow band around the top of the goblet
above a running plant scroll edged with hatching separating three cartouches, one containing
the initials, 'RP' united by a love knot, another similarly the initials 'MP', and the third the
date 1586. The stem consists of a wide depressed hollow ribbed knop between two small
knops and the engraved foot has a narrow folded edge. The initials are thought to stand for
Roger and Maud Puleston of Emral, Flint (Clwyd) who celebrated their thirtieth wedding
anniversary in 1586. The loyal sentiment may have been inspired by the foiling of the
Babington Plot against the Queen in the same year.

DIMENSIONS: *165mm high.*

PROVENANCE: *Lt.-Col. C.P. Prescot;
Victoria and Albert Museum.*

LITERATURE: *Wilfred Buckley,
Diamond Engraved Glasses of the
Sixteenth Century, 1929;
R.J. Charleston, English Glass and the
Glass used in England, circa 400–1940,
1984, pp. 53–9; W.A. Thorpe, An
Historic Verzelini Glass, Burlington
Magazine, Vol. LXVII, 1935,
pp.150–157; ibid., The Lisley Group
of Elizabethan Glasses, The Connoisseur,
Vol. CXXII, December 1948,
pp.110–117; W.A. Thorpe, English
Glass, 1961, pp. 94–113.*

398 *Bowl*

BLACK OPAQUE GLASS, EARLY SEVENTEENTH CENTURY, FROM THE HAUGHTON GREEN
GLASSHOUSE, DENTON, NEAR MANCHESTER, *c*.1605–53.

The bowl and wide thick foot are blown in one piece with a rounded kick at the base. The
shape and small size might suggest its use as a salt container for the table.

Black opaque glass was produced by a combination of iron, manganese and sulphur oxide
(from coal) in the reducing atmosphere of the furnace. This piece was excavated from the site
of the Haughton Green Glasshouse near Manchester which was worked by the du Houx
family, makers of 'menu verre', from Lorraine whose names occur in the local parish
registers as well as in Southampton, Buckholt, Gloucestershire, Cheswardine, Bishop's Wood
and Stourbridge.

The glasshouse site at Haughton Green, Denton was excavated by Ruth Hurst Vose for
the Pilkington Glass Museum in 1969–1970.

DIMENSIONS: *70mm wide, 32mm high.*

PROVENANCE: *Pilkington Glass
Museum.*

LITERATURE: *R.J. Charleston,
English Glass and the Glass used in
England, circa 400–1940, 1984;
Eleanor S. Godfrey, The development of
English Glassmaking 1560–1640, 1975;
Ruth Hurst Vose, Bickerstaffe and
Haughton Green Excavations, in
Annales du 5e Congrès de l'Association
Internationale pour l'Histoire du Verre,
1970, pp. 137–144; ibid., Glass, 1975,
p. 62, pl. VII; ibid., Glass, 1980,
pp.109,146,156.*

398

397

CERAMICS

The work of Bernard Palissy (1510–1590) potter of Saintes, North of Bordeaux, attracted royal patronage in France, achieved popularity in seventeenth century England, and underwent a revival of interest in the nineteenth century. In the late seventeenth century, Daniel Marot's designs were used by Adrianus Kocks who produced blue and white tin-glazed earthenware from his manufactory at Delft.

In England, second generation Huguenot refugees played a crucial part in the foundation of the porcelain manufactories at Derby and at Chelsea, where Nicholas Sprimont drew on other Huguenot craftsmen for models and clock movements. In the early 1750s, Stephen Theodore Janssen and a Mr. Delamain opened an enamelling business at York House, Battersea. Independent enamellers working in London included Jean Mussard, trained in Geneva, and Anthony Tregent. Some of these craftsmen were trained as jewellers initially. James Giles, apprenticed to a jeweller, became, like his father, an independent decorator of porcelain, for which he achieved considerable recognition in his own lifetime.

Display of ceramics designed by Daniel Marot, c.1702

399 *Circular dish*

EARTHENWARE, COLOURED AND GLAZED, BERNARD PALISSY OR HIS SCHOOL, FRANCE, LATE SIXTEENTH CENTURY.

The dish is moulded directly from a cast taken from a pewter dish by François Briot. The raised boss in the centre is decorated with a seated female figure representing Temperance, the bed of the dish is decorated with four cartouches representing the four elements separated by terminal figures. On the rim, oval cartouches contain representations of the seven Liberal Arts and Minerva. The dish is coloured in brown, yellow, green and blue, with mottling on the sides and on the reverse. The letter F is incised on the back of the boss.

Bernard Palissy (1510–1590) worked as a glass painter and land surveyor before experimenting with tin-glazed pottery. By 1548, he was sufficiently successful to attract the patronage of the Constable of France, Anne de Montmorency, for whom he produced a grotto for the Château at Ecouen. His appointment at Court protected him in the 1560s from the persecution of the Protestants in France.

Only the surviving fragments of a grotto made for Catherine de Medici at the Tuileries can be attributed to Palissy with any certainty. A large quantity of pottery made in this manner and based on metalwork designs has been attributed to Palissy, but much of this was probably made by his followers.

Palissy ware enjoyed a certain popularity in seventeenth-century England, as copies were made in London in the 1640s and 1650s. In the nineteenth century, this interest was revived, bringing with it an increase in the influence of Palissy ware on contemporary pottery. This revival was partly inspired by a fascination with Palissy the man as writer, craftsman and Huguenot.

Other impressions of the Briot mold are in the Wallace Collection (with matching ewer), in the Louvre and in the collection of Edouard de Rothschild.

COLOUR PLATE: *page 14.*

DIMENSIONS: *425mm diameter.*

PROVENANCE: *Bequeathed by George Salting to the Victoria and Albert Museum, 1910.*

LITERATURE: *Hans Demiani, François Briot, Casper Enderlen und das Edelzinn, Leipzig, 1897, pl. 1; A.V.B. Norman, Wallace Collection, Catalogue of Ceramics, I, 1976, pp. 31–4, 333–335.*

400 *Milk pan*

TIN-GLAZED EARTHENWARE, PAINTED IN BLUE, DELFT, ADRIANUS KOCKS, *c.* 1690–4.

The pan has spreading convex sides with an outcurved rim which forms a pouring lip at one point. The rim is decorated with gadrooning and plant motives reserved in blue. The centre of the dish is painted with a rosette surrounded by four radiating palmettes. The sides are decorated with four landscapes showing farm buildings, cattle and rustic figures, and are separated by lambrequin motifs with diaper work. The back of the dish is painted with gadroons alternating with plant sprays and is marked with the A.K. monogram in blue.

This milk pan is part of a set of dishes and tiles designed by Daniel Marot for the dairy adjoining Queen Mary II's lodgings in the Old Water Gallery at Hampton Court. Another milk pan and one of the tiles are also in the Victoria and Albert Museum. Other tulip vases and cream pans still survive at Hampton Court, and some of the wall tiles are now in the Rijksmuseum.

DIMENSIONS: *483mm diameter, 120mm high.*

PROVENANCE: *Sotheby's 6.2.1948(76); Victoria and Albert Museum.*

LITERATURE: *Arthur Lane, Daniel Marot; Designer of Delft Vases and of Gardens at Hampton Court, Connoisseur, CXXIII, 1949, illustrated IX, p. 21.*

401 *Tulip vase*

TIN-GLAZED EARTHENWARE, PAINTED IN BLUE, DELFT, ADRIANUS KOCKS, *c.* 1694.

The tulip vase was a European contribution to the range of blue and white vessels made in China which were collected for display at the end of the seventeenth century. They were probably inspired by vases for bulb-growing which were made in Persia during the seventeenth century.

These vases were usually made in sections, like a pagoda, and could be dismantled. This vase is in two parts; the lower part has a hollow circular pedestal foot with a knopped stem, supporting an inverted bell-shaped bowl. The upper part, of domed shape, supports six vertical straps each with a small compartment designed to hold a bulb, with an opening at the base, through which the roots could pass to reach the water inside the vase. The painted decoration consists of gadroons, rosettes, reserved trefoils and trellis work, and is typical of the designs of Daniel Marot. This vase was almost certainly made for Queen Mary's Water Gallery at Hampton Court (*Catalogue number* 400). Two similar examples were with the auctioneers, Puttick and Simpsons, in April, 1949 (illustrated Connoisseur, September, 1949).

It is probable that the bill due to Adrianus 'Koex' of Delft for 'Dutch or China Ware sent to her late Majty the sume of Thirteen Hundred and Fifty Gilders 3 Styvers' (£122. 14s. 9d.) covered the cost of the tiles, tableware and tulip vases that were specially commissioned for Hampton Court to the designs of Daniel Marot.

DIMENSIONS: *305mm high.*

PROVENANCE: *Given by Mr. R.J. Charleston, 1954; Victoria and Albert Museum.*

LITERATURE: *Michael Archer, Pyramids and Pagodas for Flowers, Country Life, 22 January 1976, pp. 166–9; Arthur Lane, Daniel Marot; Designer of Delft vases and of gardens at Hampton Court, Connoisseur, Vol. CXXIII, 1949, p.19.*

399

400

401

402 Sauceboat

SILVER-GILT, ONE (OF A SET OF FOUR), NICHOLAS SPRIMONT, LONDON, 1743.

This sauceboat is part of a marine service made for Frederick, Prince of Wales by Nicholas Sprimont and Paul Crespin. The service consists of an elaborate centrepiece, four sauceboats, four salts and four Rococo dishes. In contrast to the centrepiece, the sauceboats are distinguished by an economy of ornament; the shell-boat is supported by two dolphins and the very finely modelled human figure may have been inspired by a bronze prototype.

Nicholas Sprimont came from a family of silversmiths in Liège, which was in the southern Netherlands, and had a culture with a strong French bias. Sprimont identified with the Huguenot community in London, collaborating with the goldsmith Paul Crespin, marrying Anne Protin at the Knightsbridge Chapel in November, 1742, and standing godfather to Roubiliac's daughter Sophie at the Huguenot Chapel in Spring Gardens in 1744.

DIMENSIONS: 230mm high.

PROVENANCE: Her Majesty the Queen.

EXHIBITED: Rococo Art and Design in Hogarth's England, the Victoria and Albert Museum, 1984, G.17.

LITERATURE: Arthur Grimwade, Rococo Silver, 1727–1751, 1974, pp.16,31,44, pl. 32A; The Royal Collection, Garrard Inventory, privately printed, 1911, 228; E.A. Jones, The Gold and Silver of Windsor Castle, 1911, p.100, pl. LI; Charles Oman, Royal Plate from Buckingham Palace and Windsor Castle, Victoria and Albert Museum Picture Book, 1954, fig.11.

403 Salt cellar

SOFT-PASTE PORCELAIN, CHELSEA, 1746; INCISED ON THE BASE WITH A TRIANGLE AND THE DATE 1746.

This piece is probably made from a model by Nicholas Sprimont as the shape, a stylised shell supported on two dolphins, relates closely to the set of silver-gilt sauceboats in the Royal Collection two of which bear Nicholas Sprimont's hallmark for 1743 (Catalogue number 402).

Although from his arrival in London, c. 1742, Sprimont worked as a goldsmith, and was tenant of a house on the north side of Compton Street, Soho, by 1747 he was also paying rates for the site of the Chelsea Porcelain Factory. This is probably one of the earliest productions of that new enterprise.

DIMENSIONS: 97mm high.

PROVENANCE: Hilton Price Collection; Sotheby's 1911, London Museum; Museum of London.

EXHIBITED: Rococo Art and Design in Hogarth's England, Victoria and Albert Museum, 1984, O4.

LITERATURE: John Mallet, 'Chelsea' in R.J. Charleston, English Porcelain 1745–1850, 1965, p. 29, pl. 1c.

404 Trump

SOFT-PASTE PORCELAIN, CHELSEA, c. 1747–50.

This reclining figure of a pug dog has been identified as a companion to the bust of its owner, the artist William Hogarth. Trump also appears in the painter's self portrait of 1745 (Tate Gallery). As a result of his friendship with the manager of the Chelsea Porcelain Factory, Nicholas Sprimont, Roubiliac's name has been previously associated with a number of Chelsea models, but this is the only model known to have come from his hand. Two other porcelain versions of this model are recorded. It was also reproduced by Josiah Wedgwood in black basalt.

DIMENSIONS: 265mm long.

PROVENANCE: Christie's 24.10.1966(2), Victoria and Albert Museum.

EXHIBITED: Rococo Art and Design in Hogarth's England, Victoria and Albert Museum, 1984, E.4.

LITERATURE: K.A. Esdaile, The Life and Work of L.F. Roubiliac, 1928, pp. 3,50–1,178; Bevis Hillier 'Hogarth's Trump', The Times, 20 April 1968; J.V.G. Mallet, Hogarth's Pug in Porcelain, Victoria and Albert Museum Bulletin, Vol. III, no. 2, April 1967 (reprinted 1971); ibid, Wedgwood and the Rococo, Apollo, May 1974, pp. 320–329.

404

405 Clock with soft paste porcelain surround

CHELSEA AND STEPHEN RIMBAULT, LONDON, c. 1760–69.

INSCRIBED: (ON THE BACK OF THE MOVEMENT) F.F.J. PARSONS LONDON FECIT, 1755.

The enamelled face of the clock is inscribed with the name of a well-known Huguenot clockmaker who specialised in musical clocks, Stephen Rimbault of Great St. Andrew's Street.

The porcelain surround is decorated in underglaze Mazarine blue with gilt flowers. It supports at each upper corner a music-making putto, and on a raised dome in the centre, a female figure with a boy playing a horn. The figure holds a sheet of music which is inscribed 'Sung by Miss Young Ranelagh' a reference to Cecilia Young who married Thomas Arne, the composer, or to her sister Isabella, who is known to have performed at Ranelagh.

Three other Chelsea gold anchor clocks are recorded. One, also with a movement by Rimbault, is in the collection of the Duke of Northumberland at Alnwick.

This is another instance of the happy collaboration of two Huguenot craftsmen trained in different disciplines. Even if Rimbault only put his name to the clock, it was probably assembled in his workshop. Nicholas Sprimont remained in charge of the Chelsea Manufactory until 1769.

DIMENSIONS: 521mm high.

PROVENANCE: The Wernher Collection, Luton Hoo.

EXHIBITED: Rococo Art and Design in Hogarth's England, Victoria and Albert Museum, 1984, O.40.

LITERATURE: Dr. Bellamy Gardner, Chelsea Porcelain Clocks, Connoisseur, December, 1935.

402

403

405

406 *Figures representing the Four Seasons*
PORCELAIN, DERBY, *c.* 1753–5.

Spring is represented by a naked girl seated on a rock, her hands on a basket of flowers, some of which have fallen. Summer is another girl seated on a sheaf of corn, supporting part of that sheaf over her right arm. Autumn is a boy entwined in garlands of vine, who holds a bunch of grapes in his right hand over his mouth, and a cup in his left hand. Winter, another boy, shelters beneath a large cloak, reclining against a tree stump, whilst he warms his hands over the fire.

The modeller for the Derby factory from its beginnings in 1750 to 1756 was Andrew Planché, son of Paul Planché and Marie Anne Fournier, who was apprenticed to a London jeweller and goldsmith, Edward Montenay. The early products of the Derby factory were mostly figures derived from earlier sculptural prototypes.

Andrew Planché's younger brother, Jacques, was a watchmaker who trained in Geneva, and later became an assistant to Vulliamy. The latter also combined with Derby to make porcelain clocks.

DIMENSIONS: *Winter 105mm high; Autumn 127mm high; Spring 120mm high; Summer 115mm high.*

PROVENANCE: *Spring and Summer, given by Major Kenneth Dingwall, 1917; Autumn and Winter by J.H. Fitzhenry, 1909; Victoria and Albert Museum.*

LITERATURE: *W.B. Honey, English Pottery and Porcelain, 1947, p.159; John Twitchett, Derby Porcelain, 1980, pl.17.*

407 *Group representing Taste*
PORCELAIN, DERBY, ATTRIBUTED TO ANDREW PLANCHE, *c.* 1750–55.

The figure of a chinaman stands to the left holding a glass and bottle, while at his feet are two further flasks. He wears a white coat, red sash, yellow jacket with a pink collar and sleeves, a crimson flowered underskirt, and a black pointed hat. His companion, a small boy, leans over a basket containing bottles. He wears a yellow jacket with a red sash.

There seems to have been a particular interest in chinoiserie at Derby. The two obvious sources for exotic figures at this time were De Ferriol's 'Recueil de cent estampes representant differentes Nations du Levant', with engravings by G. Scotin, which was published in Paris in 1714, and engravings after Boucher by Ravenet.

COLOUR PLATE: *page 14.*

DIMENSIONS: *223mm high.*

PROVENANCE: *Bequeathed to the Victoria and Albert Museum by Mr. Wallace Elliot.*

LITERATURE: *J.L. Dixon, English Porcelain of the eighteenth century, 1952, p.16, pl.35.*

408 *Enamel box*
BATTERSEA, *c.* 1755.

The box is formed of five plaques of aventurine glass held together by a metal mount. The cover is of enamel on copper painted in brown with the subject 'Paris presenting the apple to Hibernia', probably based on an engraving by S.F. Ravenet after J. Gwyn. On the inside, the cover is painted with a portrait of Maria Gunning, Countess of Coventry (1733–60).

The enamelling business at York House, Battersea, first traded under the names of Janssen, Delamain and Brooks. Stephen Theodore Janssen, of Huguenot descent, was a prominent merchant stationer, and in a good position to obtain the fine paper used for transfer printing, the method used to decorate their products. John Brooks, the manager, probably invented this process, but the identity of Delamain remains uncertain. He may be connected to Henry Delamain, potter (who was responsible for introducing coal firing in his Dublin kilns), who died in 1757, but is more likely to be linked with a Huguenot goldsmith of that name recorded in Soho in 1742, and if so, he probably took care of the mounts for the Battersea products. In 1753, the venture got into financial difficulties, and John Brooks was forced to borrow money from Peter Gandon, a gunsmith of Westminster, probably a son of the Huguenot refugee gunmaker of the same name. However by May, 1754, Peter Gandon was bankrupt, and by 1756, Janssen had suffered the same fate.

DIMENSIONS: *98 × 67mm.*

PROVENANCE: *Given to the Victoria and Albert Museum in memory of the Hon. Mrs. N. Ionides, 1963.*

LITERATURE: *Aubrey J. Toppin, Battersea; Ceramic and Kindred Associations; 2, York House and its Artists, Transactions of the English Ceramic Circle, 2, no. 9 (1946), pp. 170ff and pl. LXIII,b.*

409 *Plaque*
COPPER, PAINTED IN ENAMEL. JEAN MUSSARD, LONDON, 1760.
INSCRIBED: JEAN MUSSARD A LONDRES 1760.

The plaque is painted with a scene of an oriental lady at her toilet. She is seated on a crimson cushion with gold trimming and tassels, and she is dressed in an ermine-trimmed blue coat over loose white draperies. Behind her stands a negro hair-dresser in a scarlet robe; to the right, a kneeling woman is drying her left foot. The subject is taken from a J. Daulle engraving 'La Grecque sortant du Bain'.

Jean Antoine Mussard was born in Geneva, *c.*1707. This is his earliest recorded signed work in England. He exhibited at the Society of Artists in 1763, 1766 and 1768.

DIMENSIONS: *48mm high, 38mm wide.*

PROVENANCE: *Given to the Victoria and Albert Museum in memory of the Hon. Mrs. N. Ionides, 1963.*

LITERATURE: *H. Clouzot, Dictionnaire des Miniaturistes sur Email, 1924, pp.145–6; Therle and Bernard Hughes, English Painted Enamels, 1951, p. 76, pl. 22; M. Jourdain, Subjects in English 18th Century Enamels, Connoisseur, LXX, 1924, p.132–3.*

406

408

409

407

410 *Coffee cup and saucer*

PORCELAIN, DECORATED BY JAMES GILES, c.1770.

The cup and saucer are decorated with bouquets of flowers in natural colours, and below the rim with a thin stem of foliage turned about a brown band, in imitation of Japanese Imari porcelain. The bases are marked with crossed swords in imitation of the mark of the Meissen factory and a '9' in blue.

James Giles was the son of a china painter of the same name, and the grandson of Abraham Giles, cabinet maker and refugee from France. He was apprenticed to a jeweller in 1733 and later worked in Worcester, decorating porcelain for the manufactory there. By 1756, he had returned to London living initially in Kentish Town, but moving to 82 Berwick Street, Soho, in 1763, where he remained for thirteen years. In 1771, he insured his utensils and stock in trade with the Sun Insurance Company for £2,000, an indication that his business as a china painter was substantial.

DIMENSIONS: *Cup, 76mm high; saucer, 130mm wide.*

PROVENANCE: *Bequeathed to the Victoria and Albert Museum by Herbert Allen, 1935.*

LITERATURE: *Gerald Coke, In Search of James Giles (1718–1780), 1983.*

410

411

411 *Coffee cup and saucer*

CHINESE EXPORT PORCELAIN, CHIEN LUNG, c.1745.

A coffee cup and saucer decorated with the coat of arms of the Motteux family, impaling those of Babthorpe.

Peter Motteux (1660–1718) was born at Rouen and came to England in 1685. From 1691 he edited 'The Gentleman's Journal', which contained news of the month and miscellaneous prose and poetry. One of the earliest periodicals of its type to be published in London, it preceded 'The Tatler' and 'The Spectator' by almost twenty years. His English translation of 'Don Quixote' was published in 1712.

During Queen Anne's reign, Motteux had a shop at the sign of the Two Fans, near the Old India House, where he sold 'China and Japan Wares, Tea and Fans'. Richard Steele in 'The Tatler', 3 December, 1712, described Motteux's warehouses 'filled and adorned with Tea, China, and Indian Ware. In one place were exposed to view Silks of various Shades and Colours, rich Brocades, and the wealthiest Products of foreign Looms.'

For the funeral card of another member of the family see *Catalogue number* 164.

DIMENSIONS: *Cup, 62mm high, saucer, 118mm diameter.*

PROVENANCE: *Heirloom and Howard Ltd.; purchased by the Museum of London, 1983.*

LITERATURE: *Aubrey J. Toppin, The China Trade and some London Chinamen, Transactions of the English Ceramic Circle, no.3, 1935, p.48; Sir George Birdwood, The East India Company, Journal of Indian Art, Vol. 3, July 1890; Sir Paul Harvey, The Oxford Companion to English Literature, 1932, under Motteux.*

CITY COMMERCE

The 1690s were a revolutionary decade in terms of economics and international trade, introducing a new world of banks, of stocks and shares, of new credit instruments and a public debt.

A large proportion of the most wealthy Huguenot refugees were merchants and members of the consistory of the French Church, Threadneedle Street. They included, between 1698 and 1700, Etienne Seignoret, a silk merchant of Lombard Street (worth about £90,000), David Bosanquet, whose assets amounted to £100,000 on his death in 1732, and some twenty other members with assets of over £5000.

Huguenot merchants made substantial subscriptions to the new Bank of England in the 1690s, which helped to finance the war against France. Seven of the original 24 Founder-Directors of the Bank of England were of Huguenot or Walloon descent. They included Sir John Houblon, who subscribed £10,000 and became Governor (1694–1697), and his brothers James and Abraham.

Huguenots were actively engaged in insurance. During the eighteenth century, successive generations of the Bosanquet family were Directors of the Royal Exchange Assurance and several Minets of the London Assurance Company.

In 1697, the broker John Castaing, began publishing his 'Course of the Exchange' which continues today as 'The Stock Exchange Daily Official List', the third oldest continually published newspaper in the world. In the late eighteenth century, members of the Cazenove family left Geneva for London. In 1823, Philip Cazenove founded the firm of Cazenove & Co., which in 1984 received a grant of arms, the first City stockbrokers ever to achieve this honour.

Detail from John Rocque's 'Map of London', 1746, showing the location of the French Church, Threadneedle Street

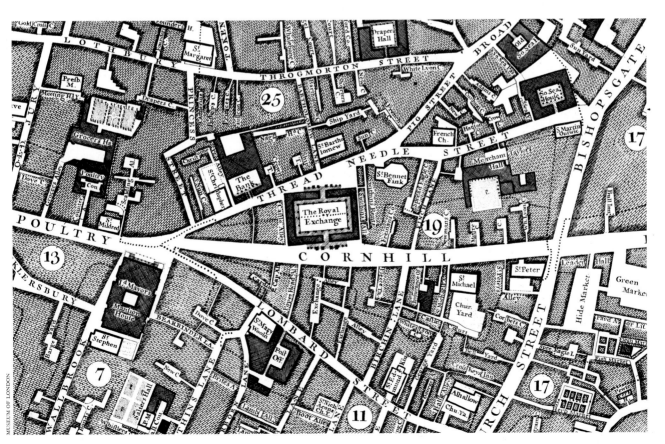

412 *Sir John Houblon (1632–1711)*
PORTRAIT, OIL ON CANVAS. ISAAC WHOOD, c.1695–6.

Sir John Houblon, the first Governor of the Bank of England, is shown three-quarter length, seated in an armchair, in his Mayoral robes, with the sword and mace to the right.

The Houblons were a remarkable merchant family, a father and five sons, who were noted for their success, liberality and mutual affection. They traded with France, Portugal, Spain and the Mediterranean. Their father, James (1592–1682), was the son of a Huguenot refugee from Lille. He lived in Bearbinder Lane in a house which he rebuilt after the Fire. One of his sons, also James, was a particular friend of Samuel Pepys.

Sir John, the third eldest son, knighted in 1689, was Lord Mayor 1695–6, and the first Governor of the Bank of England (1694–7). He was also an Admiralty Commissioner (1694–9) and Master of the Grocers' Company in 1696.

The painter, Isaac Whood, who was also of Huguenot descent, was born in London in 1688, and died in 1752. Several of his paintings, executed for the Duke of Bedford, remain at Woburn Abbey.

DIMENSIONS: *990 × 1250mm.*

PROVENANCE: *Bank of England.*

LITERATURE: *An Historical Catalogue of Engravings, Drawings and Paintings in the Bank of England, 1928, no. 248; W. Marston Acres, Huguenot Directors of the Bank of England, Proceedings of the Huguenot Society of London, Vol.15 (1934–37), p.238.*

413 *The Triumphs of London*
ELKANAH SETTLE, 1695.

This is the printed account of the Mayoralty pageant of Sir John Houblon, of the Grocers' Company, 1695.

Elkanah Settle (1648–1724), pet poet of the Court of Charles II, and successful rival, as far as contemporary judgement was concerned, of John Dryden, succeeded to the post of City Laureate in 1691. He contributed yearly pageants until 1708, when the printed descriptions cease, and gave the title 'The Triumphs of London' to the series.

A butt for caricature as a voluminous and reckless dunce, Settle gained a place in Pope's 'Dunciad'. After enduring much poverty, and in his old age roaring as a dragon in a droll at Bartholomew Fair for a living, much to the discredit of the City, he ultimately obtained admission to Charterhouse, where he died in 1724.

PROVENANCE: *Guildhall Library.*

LITERATURE: *Nichols's Lord Mayors' Pageants, 1831; F.W. Fairholt, History of Lord Mayors' Pageants, 1843, Vol. 1, pp.109,121–2.*

414 *Cash book of the Bank of England*
LONDON, 1694.

The first page of this the first cash book of the Bank of England shows the contemporary pious opening 'Laus Deo' and a first credit of £300,000 received from the Commissioners appointed to take the subscription. Several well-known Huguenot names are included.

The Bank of England Act, 1694, states that it is 'An Act for granting to their Majesties Several Rates and Duties upon Tunnage of Ships and Vessels, and upon Beer, Ale and other Liquors: for securing certain Recompenses and Advantages, in the Said Act mentioned, to such persons as shall voluntarily advance the Sum of £1,500,000 towards carrying on the War against France'.

Of the £1,200,000 subscribed to the Bank in 1694, one hundred and twenty-three newly arrived Hukuenots provided at least £104,000. By 1697, around £330,000 or 15 per cent of the total Bank Stock of £2,200,000 was held by investors of Huguenot extraction. It is significant that the officers of the French church of London felt confident enough to invest surplus charitable funds in the Bank even as early as 1695.

PROVENANCE: *Bank of England.*

LITERATURE: *John Giuseppi, The Bank of England, A History from its foundation in 1694, 1966, pp.11–12; Robin Gwynn, Huguenot Heritage, 1985, pp.155–6.*

415 *Minute book of the Bank of England*
LONDON, 1694.

The minutes of the first Court of Directors, which record the sealing of the Bank's Charter 27 July 1694.

Those Directors who had not attended at the sealing took their oaths before the Governor, Sir John Houblon, and the Deputy Governor.

The meeting then proceeded to decide how the banking business was to be conducted. Those who deposited money should have the choice of three methods. They might receive 'Running Cash Notes', payable on demand, either in whole or in part, the amounts of part-payments being endorsed on the notes; they might keep a 'book or paper' in which amounts received or paid on their account would be entered up at the Bank; or they themselves might draw 'notes' on the Bank to the extent of their deposits, which the Bank would 'accept'. All these were existing methods practised by the goldsmith-bankers, the three instruments of business utilised being, in embryo, the bank-note, the passbook and the cheque respectively.

PROVENANCE: *Bank of England.*

LITERATURE: *John Giuseppi, The Bank of England, A History from its foundation in 1694, 1966, pp.18–19.*

DETAIL

412

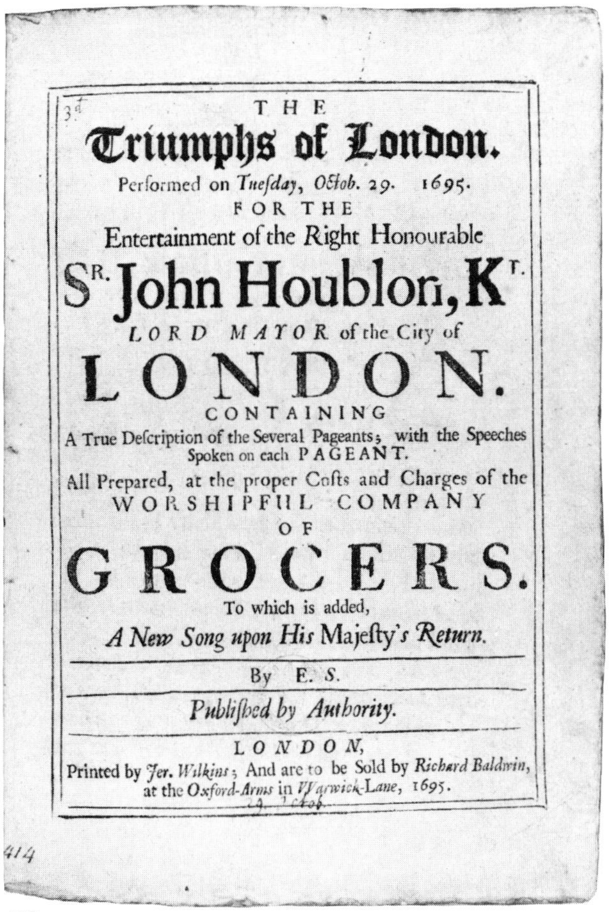
3d

THE

Triumphs of London.

Performed on *Tuesday, Octob.* 29. 1695.

FOR THE

Entertainment of the Right Honourable

Sr. John Houblon, Kt.

LORD MAYOR of the City of

LONDON.

CONTAINING

A True Description of the Several Pageants; with the Speeches Spoken on each PAGEANT.

All Prepared, at the proper Costs and Charges of the WORSHIPFUL COMPANY OF

GROCERS.

To which is added,

A New Song upon His Majesty's Return.

By E. S.

Published by Authority.

LONDON,

Printed by *Jer. Wilkins*; And are to be Sold by *Richard Baldwin*, at the *Oxford-Arms* in *Warwick-Lane*, 1695.

414

413

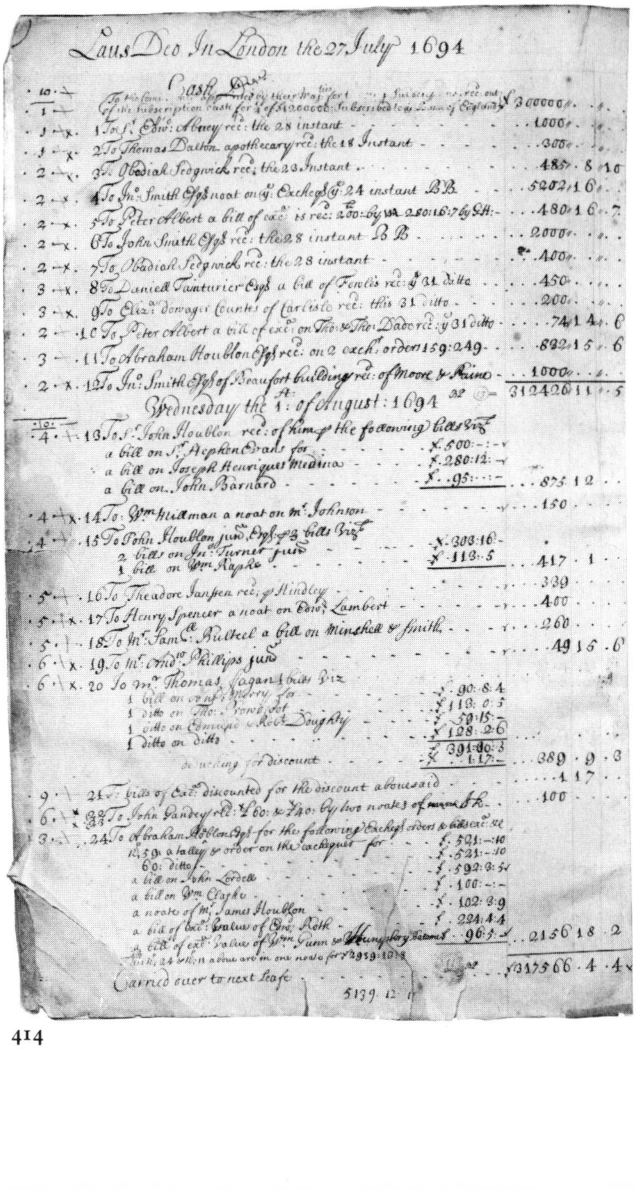
Laus Deo In London the 27 July 1694

Cash Debtor

10 / 1	To the Comm... appointed by their Maj.ties for t... Subscrip... rec. out of the subscription cash for ¼ of £1200000 Subscribed to ye Bank of England	£ 30000	
1 x	1 To Sr Edw: Abney rec: the 28 instant	1000	
1 x	2 To Thomas Dalton apothecary rec: the 18 Instant	300	
2 x	3 To Obadiah Sedgwick rec: the 23 Instant	485	8 10
2 x	4 To Jno Smith Esqr noat on ye Excheq^r d^o 24 instant BB	5202	16
2 x	5 To Peter Albert a bill of exc^a is rec: 200: by ... 280:16:7 by GH	480	16 7
2 x	6 To John Smith Esqr rec: the 28 instant BB	2000	
2 x	7 To Obadiah Sedgwick rec: the 28 instant	400	
3 x	8 To Daniell Tanturier Esqr a bill of Fowlis rec: ye 31 ditto	450	
3 x	9 To Eliz^a dowager Countes of Carlisle rec: this 31 ditto	200	
2	10 To Peter Albert a bill of exc^a on Tho: & Tho: Dadoe rec: ye 31 ditto	74	14 6
3	11 To Abraham Houblon Esqr rec: on 2 exch^r orders 159: 249	832	15 6
2 x	12 To Jno Smith Esqr of Beaufort building rec: of Moore & Raine	1000	
		31242	11 5

Wednesday the 1st of August: 1694

10 / 4	13 To Sr John Houblon rec: of him p the following bills Viz^t			
	a bill on Sr Stephen Evans for	£ 500: –: –		
	a bill on Joseph Henriques Medina	£ 280:12: –		
	a bill on John Barnard	£ 95: –: –	875	12
4 x	14 To Wm Hillman a noat on Mr Johnson		150	
4	15 To John Houblon jun^r Esqr p 3 bills Viz^t			
	2 bills on Jno Turner jun^r	£ 303:16: –		
	1 bill on Wm Raphe	£ 113: 5	417	1
			339	
5	16 To Theadore Janssen rec: p Hindley		400	
5 x	17 To Henry Spencer a noat on Edw: Lambert		260	
5	18 To Mr Sam^el Bulteel a bill on Minshell & Smith		49	15 6
6 x	19 To Mr And^w Phillips jun^r			
6 x	20 To Mr Thomas Fagan 4 bills Viz			
	1 bill on ... Merry for	£ 90: 8: 4		
	1 ditto on Tho: Crowfoot	£ 113: 0: 5		
	1 ditto on Edmund & Robt Doughty	£ 59:15: –		
	1 ditto on ditto	£ 128: 2: 6		
		£ 391:06:3		
	deducting for discount	£ 1:17: –	389	9 3
			1	17
9	21 To bills of Exc^a discounted for the discount abovesaid			
6 x	22/23 To John Gandey rec: £60: & £40: by two noates of ...		100	
3	24 To Abraham Houblon Esqr for the following Excheq^r orders & bills exc^a Viz			
	N° 59 a talley & order on the exchequer for	£ 521: –:10		
	60: ditto	£ 521: –:10		
	a bill on John Lordell	£ 592: 3: 5		
	a bill on Wm Clarke	£ 100: –: –		
	a noate of Mr James Houblon	£ 102: 3: 9		
	a bill of exc^a value of Edw: Roth	£ 224: 4: 4		
	a bill of exc^a value of Wm Gunn & Humphrey Batemen	96: 5: –	2156	18 2
	N° 24 ... above are in one noate for £2959:10:8			
	Carried over to next leafe		£ 37566	4 4
	5139 12 1			

414

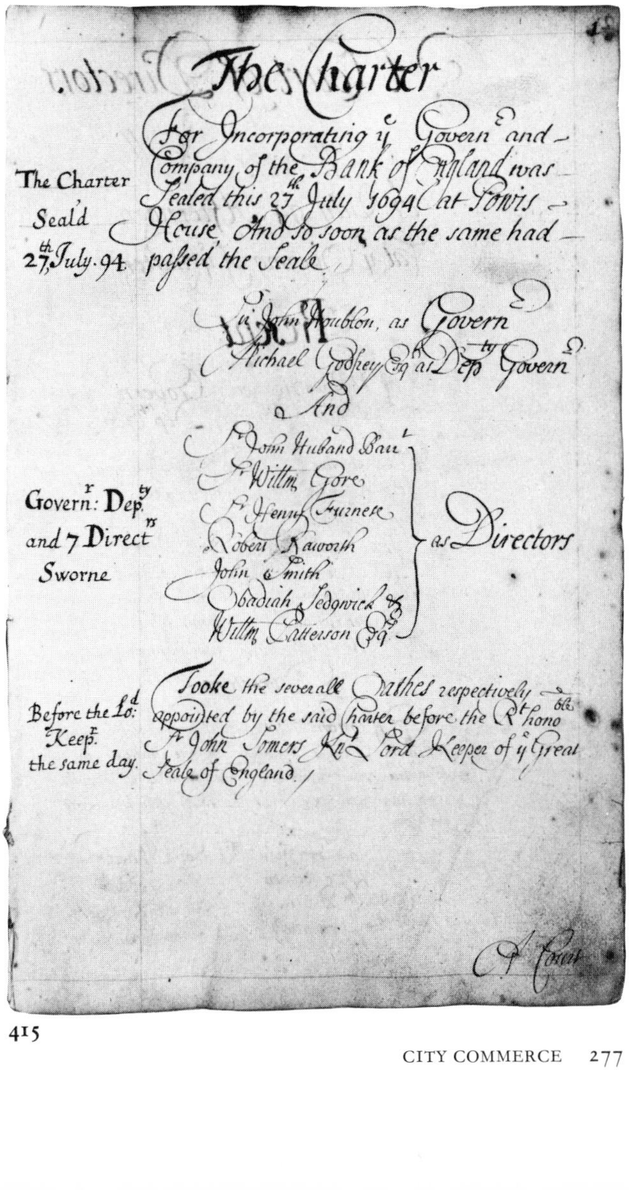
The Charter

For Incorporating y^e Govern^r and Company of the Bank of England was Sealed this 27th July 1694 at Powis House And so soon as the same had passed the Seale,

The Charter Seal'd 27th July. 94

Sr John Houblon, as Govern^r
Michael Godfrey Esqr as Dep^ty Govern^r
And
Sr John Huband Bar^t
Sr Willm Gore
Sr Henry Furnese
Robert Raworth
John Smith
Obadiah Sedgwick &
Willm Patterson Esq^rs
as Directors

Govern^r: Dep^ty and 7 Direct^rs Sworne

Tooke the severall Oathes respectively appointed by the said Charter before the R^t hono^ble Sr John Somers Kn^t Lord Keeper of ye Great Seale of England,

Before the Lo^d Keep^r the same day.

415

416 *Proposall about the Coyn*

TRANSCRIPT, SIR JOHN HOUBLON, 1695.

The Recoinage Act of 21 January 1696 aimed at the restoration of the silver coinage to its former standard; devaluation was considered inadvisable. It had been preceded by a Royal Proclamation on 19 December that as from 1 January 1696, no clipped crowns or half-crowns were to be accepted, except in payment of taxes or as contributions to Government loans, and then only until 22 February: shillings were given until 2nd March and sixpences until 2 April. After the dates given clipped coins were to have no currency, except by weight. This policy, too drastic and too hurried, had to be revised in 1696.

In its corporate capacity, the Bank was not consulted as to policy, but the views of the Governor, Sir John Houblon, had been taken by the Lords Justice. Houblon was in favour of recoinage because he believed that bad silver money was the root cause of high prices and unfavourable exchanges; he was for restoration as against devaluation. In his 'Proposall', Sir John said that clipping and counterfeiting the coinage resulted in both obstruction to our inland trade, and prejudice to foreign trade. He advocated a general calling-in of plate in exchange for good payments.

By March 1697, the cash shortage was greatly eased and the problems set by the recoinage were virtually over.

In token of their appreciation of his efforts, the Directors, in 1697, presented Sir John with a silver tankard (*Catalogue number* 417).

PROVENANCE: *Goldsmiths' Library, University of London.*

LITERATURE: *Catalogue of the Goldsmiths' Library of Economic Literature, 1982, Vol. II, 134, no. 187 (viii) from a collection of late seventeenth-century transcripts (1695–1696) of proposals relating to the recoinage; Sir John Clapham, The Bank of England, 1694–1797, 1944, pp. 34–5.*

417 *The Houblon Tankard*

SILVER, ATTRIBUTED TO WILLIAM GAMBLE, LONDON, 1695; INSCRIBED (ON THE FRONT): THE GIFT OF THE DIRECTORS OF THE BANK OF ENGLAND TO SIR JOHN HOUBLON GOVERNOR, LORD MAYOR OF LONDON, IN TOKEN OF HIS GREAT ABILITY, INDUSTRY AND STRICT UPRIGHTNESS AT A TIME OF EXTREME DIFFICULTY. 1696; (AND ON THE LID): THE GIFT OF THE LOAN COMMITTEE OF 1893 OF THE NEW YORK CLEARING HOUSE ASSOCIATION TO FREDERICK D. TAPPEN, CHAIRMAN IN TOKEN OF HIS GREAT ABILITY, INDUSTRY AND STRICT UPRIGHTNESS AT A TIME OF EXTREME DIFFICULTY. 1873, 1884, 1890, 1893. NEW YORK, NOVEMBER, 1893. (ON THE BOTTOM): PRESENTED TO THE BANK OF ENGLAND BY THE NEW YORK CLEARING HOUSE ASSOCIATION SEPTEMBER 5, 1924, (AND ON THE HANDLE). D/PD.

The difficulty alludes to the fact that in 1696, as a result of the first serious run on the bank, due to shortage of cash occasioned by the Recoinage Act, there was no dividend for the Bank proprietors, and the price of Bank stock fell. The position gradually improved, and by 1697, the Bank had recovered its prestige and position. Sir John Houblon, the first Governor, relinquished that post in 1697, although he remained a Director until 1711.

DIMENSIONS: *152mm high.*

PROVENANCE: *Sir John Houblon: purchased in London by an American silversmith; New York Clearing House Association by 1893; Frederick D. Tappin; returned to former owner; presented by them to the Bank of England, 1924.*

EXHIBITED: *Historic Plate of the City of London, Goldsmiths' Hall, 1951 (177).*

LITERATURE: *John Giuseppi, The Bank of England, A History from its foundation in 1694, 1966, p 31; Lady Archer Houblon, The Houblon Family its story and times, 1907; Charles Oman, A Catalogue of the Plate belonging to the Bank of England, 1967, no. 51.*

418 *Sir John Houblon's house*

WATERCOLOUR, T.C. DIBDIN, NINETEENTH CENTURY.

John, the third son of James Houblon and Mary, daughter of Jean du Quesne, was originally in business with his father. By 1677, he had leased land in Threadneedle Street and built a house for his merchant business. The first Bank was built on the site of his house in 1734, having existed for the first few months of its life in the Mercers' Company Hall in Cheapside, then moving to Grocers' Hall in Poultry. It was to remain there for nearly forty years.

DIMENSIONS: *220 × 145mm.*

PROVENANCE: *Bank of England.*

LITERATURE: *An Historical Catalogue of Engravings, Drawings and Paintings in the Bank of England, 1928, no. 3; John R. Woodhead, The Rulers of London, 1660–1689, London and Middlesex Archaeological Society, 1965.*

419 *Bank of England Porter*

PHOTOGRAPH.

The uniform worn on Court days is based on the livery worn by the servants of Sir John Houblon.

PROVENANCE: *Bank of England.*

The Gift of the Directors of
to Sir John Houblon Gover
of London in token of his
and strict uprightness at a ti
1696

417

Houblon House

418

420 *Agreement between Portals and the Bank of England*
27 NOVEMBER 1724.

Henry Portal agreed to make better paper than the Bank had been using previously, at a cost of 8 shillings a ream.

Henry Portal left Poitiers during the persecution as a child and settled with his family at Southampton. He learnt his trade at South Stoneham, at one of the papermills run by the White Papermakers Company (*Catalogue number 256*). Many of the refugees who settled in Southampton worked at the paper mills in the locality. At South Stoneham, Portal gained the patronage and friendship of William Heathcote of Horsley. In 1711, aged twenty-one, Portal went to Winchester where he was naturalised as an English subject at the Castle, at the Court of Quarter Sessions, on 26 July. He was afterwards described as Henry Portal of South Stoneham, Gentleman.

In 1712, he took a lease of Bere mill on the Test near Whitchurch, of which Mr. Heathcote had a title rent-charge, and having engaged the services of some of the French workmen from South Stoneham, he commenced paper-making on his own account. His business prospered and in 1719, he acquired and rebuilt a neighbouring mill at Laverstoke. In 1723, Mr. Heathcote's uncle became Governor of the Bank of England, which was in need of protective paper for their bank-notes. Henry Portal obtained the privilege of manufacturing the bank-note paper, which has continued through generations of the Portal family, in direct descent to the present day.

PROVENANCE: *Bank of England.*

LITERATURE: *Sir Francis Portal, Portals: the Church, the State and the People, leading to 250 years of papermaking, 1962.*

421 *Twenty pound note on Portal's paper, 1759*

In 1724, new paper for the Bank of England note came into use. This harder, better textured paper, invented by Henry Portal, possessed a definition and clarity hitherto unobtainable. This technical improvement, which greatly reduced the risk of forgery, enabled the Bank to print notes for fixed sums. In 1725, £20, £30, £40, £50, and £100 notes were printed. In 1743, the £ sign was added. By 1759, £10 and £15 printed notes were issued to meet an urgent demand. In 1765, a note for £25 was issued for the first time.

DIMENSIONS: *118 × 205mm.*

PROVENANCE: *Bank of England.*

LITERATURE: *John Giuseppi, The Bank of England, 1966, pp. 56–7.*

422 *Inkstand*
SILVER, PAUL DE LAMERIE, LONDON, 1733.

This inkstand of impressive proportions was probably made for Sir Robert Walpole. The double-hinged lid bears in the upper centre the cypher RW and two collars of the Order of the Garter with the interlaced initials P.B. The latter stand for Peter Burrell, of Langley Park, Beckenham, Kent, a sub-governor of the South Sea Company, whose brother, Sir Merrick Burrell, was Governor of the Bank of England from 1758 to 1760. The lower lid bears the Burrell arms, vert, on each of three escutcheons argent a bordure engrailed or, and the motto PERFLUCTUS AD ORAM.

One half of the inkstand forms a pen tray; the other is divided into five compartments with a pounce-box at each end. The inkstand, supported on four scroll feet, is chased with Rococo decoration of shells and foliated scrolls.

DIMENSIONS: *380 × 185mm.*

PROVENANCE: *Sir Robert Walpole; according to Burrell family tradition presented to Peter Burrell, by descent to Sir Edward Durand; Christie's 5 May 1937(108); Bank of England.*

LITERATURE: *E.A. Jones, An Historic Silver Inkstand made by Paul de Lamerie, Connoisseur, XCVIII, 1936, pp. 140–1; Charles Oman, A Catalogue of the Plate belonging to the Bank of England, 1967, no. 176, pl. XXXVI; R.A. Woods, The Bank of England, An illustrated Visit, 1975, no. 96.*

423 *Sir Edward des Bouveries, 1621–1694*
PORTRAIT, OIL ON CANVAS BY FRIEDRICH KERSEBOOM.

Edward des Bouveries was the only son of Edward des Bouveries and Mary, daughter of Jasper Fournestraux. He married Anne, daughter of Jacob de la Forterie. He became an eminent merchant in the Levant Company of ample fortune who was knighted by James II in 1684–5. He died at his seat in Cheshunt, Hertfordshire.

His grandfather, Laurens de Bouveries (1536–1610) was a master silk weaver of Sainghen, near Lille, and came to England with his wife in 1568, settling first in Sandwich, then at Canterbury. Laurens appears to have fled from his prosperous aristocratic Catholic family in Flanders, who lived at Château Bouverie.

Sir Edward's father settled in London and carried on his business as a merchant in Broad Street; Sir Edward's eldest son, William, was a Director of the Bank of England.

The Earls of Radnor, descendants of the Huguenot Bouverie family, have been almost continuously Governors of the French Hospital.

DIMENSIONS: *995 × 870mm.*

PROVENANCE: *Earl of Radnor, Longford Castle.*

LITERATURE: *Helen Mathilda Radnor, Catalogue of the Collection of Pictures at Longford Castle, 1927, Vol. 2, 1909, no. IV, pp. 14–17.*

424 *Purse of Edward des Bouveries*
SILVER AND GOLD THREAD ON LEATHER, 1690;
INSCRIBED: EDWARD DES BOUVERIE CONSTANTINOPLE, 1700.

Possibly given to Sir Edward des Bouveries (1688–1731) by his father Sir William des Bouveries (1656–1717).

This Sir Edward entered into a partnership with the Hon. Nathaniel Harley, brother of the 1st Earl of Oxford, Aleppo merchant in July 1712.

DIMENSIONS: *153 × 76mm.*

PROVENANCE: *Earl of Radnor, Longford Castle.*

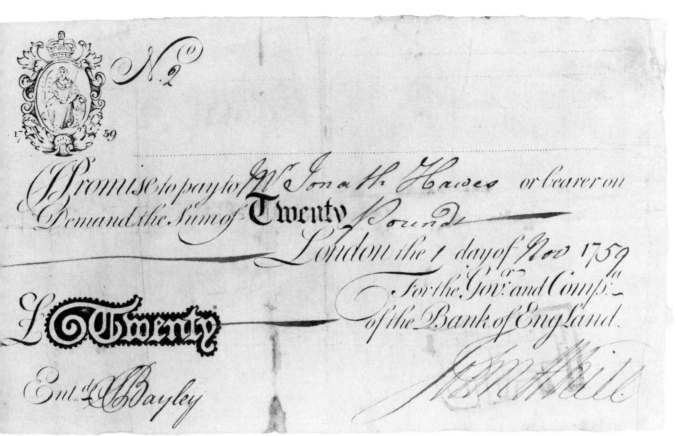

421

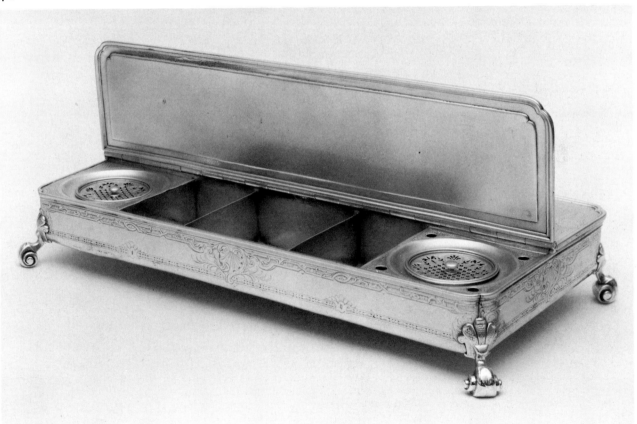

422

425 *Act for changing the name of des Bouveries to Bouverie*
MANUSCRIPT, 1736.

This private act enabled Sir Jacob Des Bouveries, 1st Viscount Folkestone, and other members of his family, to change their surname to Bouverie.

PROVENANCE: *Wiltshire County Record Office.*

426 *The Course of the Exchange*
JOHN CASTAING, 1698.

John Castaing was a Huguenot refugee, who was working as a broker in London by the early 1690s. In 1697 he began publishing this twice weekly newspaper, a list of market prices in government loans, which continues to appear today as 'The Stock Exchange Daily Official List'. It is the third oldest continuously published newspaper in the world and was of considerable importance in the development of the English stock market and the eighteenth-century English economy generally.

In a 1743 court case concerning the South Sea Bubble, one witness produced the 1720 volume of the 'Course of the Exchange'; it still bears inscriptions showing that it was introduced as evidence.

PROVENANCE: *Guildhall Library.*

LITERATURE: *John J. McCusker, Money and Exchange in Europe and America, 1978.*

427 *Phillip Cazenove (1798–1880)*

a. PORTRAIT LITHOGRAPH, 1851.

Phillip Cazenove, who founded Cazenove & Co. was educated at Charterhouse. He was admitted to the Stock Exchange in 1823, and carried on business in partnership with his Huguenot brother-in-law, John Francis Menet, under the style of Menet and Cazenove. The latter years of his life were devoted to numerous charitable works in the fields of church, medicine and education, and his obituary in 'The Times' described him as a businessman of great capacity and a philanthropist of large sympathies.

b. FOUNDER'S MEDAL, SILVER, CAZENOVE & CO, COPY STRUCK BY SPINK & SONS, 1984. INSCRIBED ON THE REVERSE: PHILLIP CAZENOVE.

The medal shows on the obverse, the Royal Coat of Arms, and on the reverse, the arms and motto of the City of London.

This is a copy of the original broker's medal, which was struck in 1823 for Phillip Cazenove, from a pattern by John Milten, Royal Engraver to the Mint, in 1801. The medal entitled Cazenove to practise as a stockbroker in the City of London.

DIMENSIONS: *780 × 630mm.*

PROVENANCE: *Cazenove & Co.*

DIMENSIONS: *38mm diameter.*

428 *Cazenove & Co*

a. ACCOUNT WITH THE BANK OF ENGLAND, 10TH JANUARY 1855.

The address is given as 39, Lothbury, and the names of the partners are Philip Cazenove, Henry Cazenove junior, and Edward Cazenove. The account shows the business connections of Cazenove in the 1850s.

PROVENANCE: *Cazenove & Co.*

b. A LIST OF STOCK AND A LIST OF CLOSING PRICES AT 4 O'CLOCK FOR 30TH DECEMBER 1859, AND TWO LETTERS, P. CAZENOVE & CO, 1859, REPRODUCTION.

One of the letters is dated 30 December 1859 and reads;

'Dear Sir,
We beg to inclose the part inclosed of a new Canada Government 5pC.ʳ Loan at par with interest from 1st Jan 1860 – Discount will be allowed as payments in full, reducing the price to about 97½. The existing Canada 5pC.ʳ have lately stood at from 4 to 5 pC.ʳ higher, and with the remarkable demand on the part of investors for this class of security there can be no doubt the present issue will at once be absorbed.

By the authority of the London Agents we are forming a Subscription List for the above Loan, and will be glad to include your name if you think proper to apply for an allotment.
Yours faithfully
P. Cazenove & Co.'

The second two-page letter to Messrs. John Foster and Sons, Black Dike Mills, Bradford, encloses a menu of the separate units paid by the client for the Indian Rupee and Rupian Stocks, and reads, '23rd Decr. 1859. . . If you decide on taking any San Paolo shares please send us a telegraph to that effect tomorrow as the subscription List will be finally closed tomorrow afternoon – Applications have already been received for considerably more than the entire Capital. . . . Cazenove & Co.'

DETAIL

429

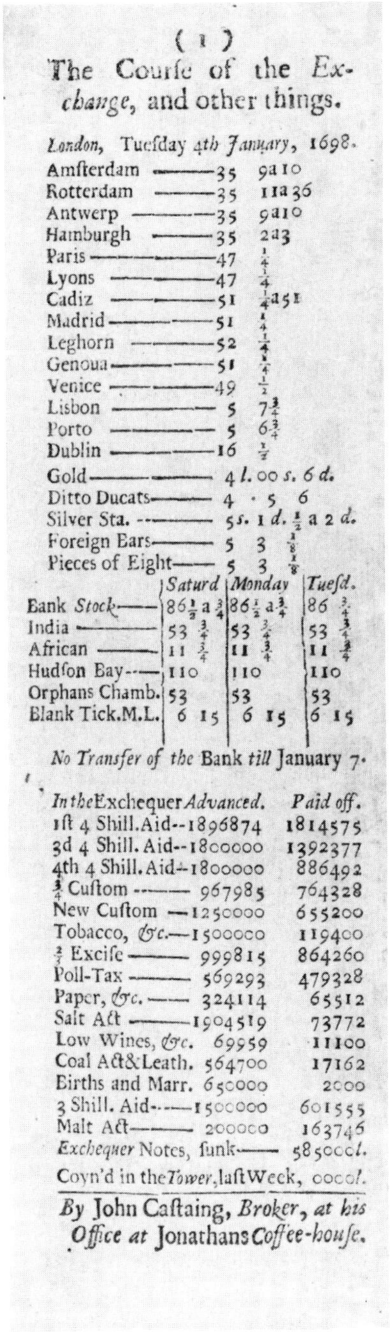

(1)

The Course of the *Exchange*, and other things.

London, Tuesday *4th January*, 1698.

Amsterdam	35	9a10
Rotterdam	35	11a36
Antwerp	35	9a10
Hamburgh	35	2a3
Paris	47	$\frac{1}{4}$
Lyons	47	$\frac{1}{4}$
Cadiz	51	$\frac{1}{4}$a51
Madrid	51	$\frac{1}{4}$
Leghorn	52	$\frac{1}{4}$
Genoua	51	$\frac{1}{4}$
Venice	49	$\frac{1}{2}$
Lisbon	5	$7\frac{3}{4}$
Porto	5	$6\frac{3}{4}$
Dublin	16	$\frac{1}{2}$
Gold	4 *l.* 00 *s.* 6 *d.*	
Ditto Ducats	4 · 5 6	
Silver Sta.	5*s.* 1 *d.* $\frac{1}{2}$ a 2 *d.*	
Foreign Bars	5 3 $\frac{1}{8}$	
Pieces of Eight	5 3 $\frac{1}{8}$	

	Saturd	*Monday*	*Tuesd.*
Bank *Stock*	$86\frac{1}{2}$ a $\frac{3}{4}$	$86\frac{1}{2}$ a $\frac{3}{4}$	86 $\frac{3}{4}$
India	53 $\frac{3}{4}$	53 $\frac{3}{4}$	53 $\frac{3}{4}$
African	11 $\frac{3}{4}$	11 $\frac{3}{4}$	11 $\frac{3}{4}$
Hudson Bay	110	110	110
Orphans Chamb.	53	53	53
Blank Tick.M.L.	6 15	6 15	6 15

No Transfer of the Bank *till* January 7.

In the Exchequer *Advanced.*		*Paid off.*
1st 4 Shill. Aid	1896874	1814575
3d 4 Shill. Aid	1800000	1392377
4th 4 Shill. Aid	1800000	886492
$\frac{3}{4}$ Custom	967985	764328
New Custom	1250000	655200
Tobacco, *&c.*	1500000	119400
$\frac{2}{3}$ Excise	999815	864260
Poll-Tax	569293	479328
Paper, *&c.*	324114	65512
Salt Act	1904519	73772
Low Wines, *&c.*	69959	11100
Coal Act&Leath.	564700	17162
Births and Marr.	650000	2000
3 Shill. Aid	1500000	601555
Malt Act	200000	163746
Exchequer Notes, sunk		585000*l.*

Coyn'd in the *Tower*, last Week, 00000*l.*

By John Castaing, *Broker, at his Office at* Jonathans *Coffee-house.*

426

427*a*

DOMINE DIRIGE NOS

427*b*

DIEU ET MON DROIT

b

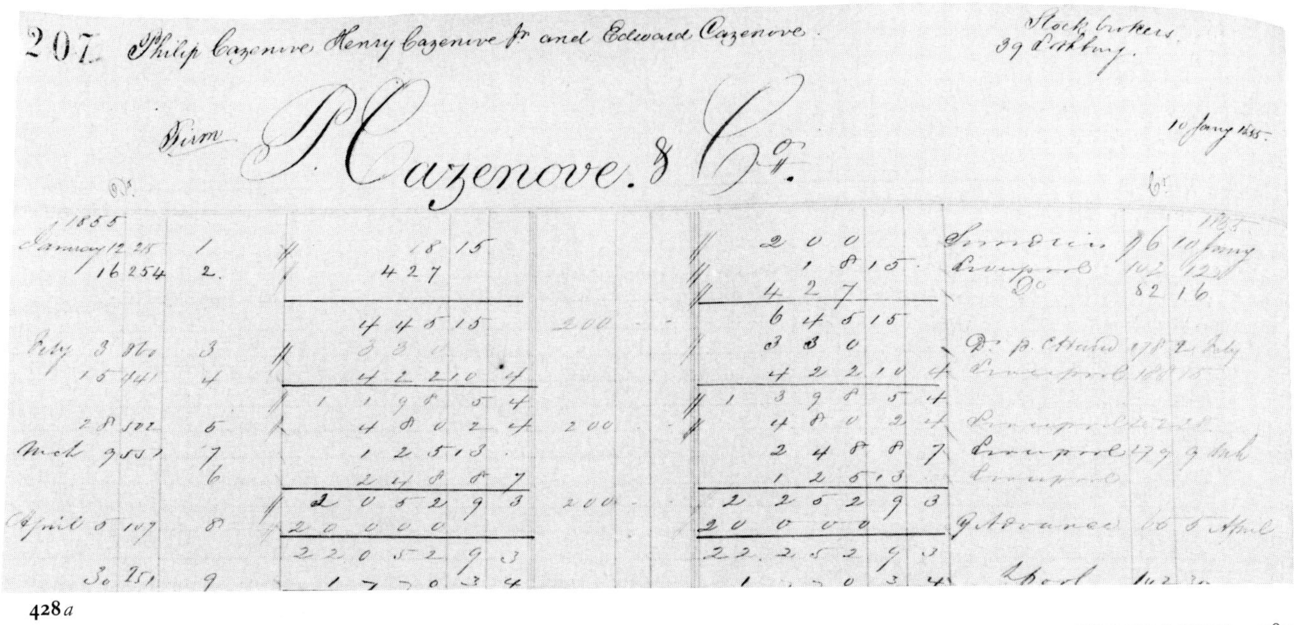
207 Philip Cazenove Henry Cazenove Jr and Edward Cazenove
Stock brokers
Firm P. Cazenove & Co.
10 Jany 1855

428*a*

429 *Grant of Arms to Cazenove & Co, 1984*
PHOTOGRAPH.

The firm's business today is transacted in the new issue and money markets, as well as in the more usual field of stockbroking and investment advice, both in this country and overseas.

ILLUSTRATED: *page 282.*

PROVENANCE: *Cazenove & Co.*

430 *A Treatise concerning the East India Trade*
BEING A MOST PROFITABLE TRADE TO THE KINGDOM, AND BEST SECURED AND IMPROVED IN A COMPANY AND A JOINT STOCK. THOMAS PAPILLON, 1680.

Papillon, a merchant of Huguenot origin from Tours and Dijon, was born at Putney 6 September, 1623.

Implicated in the riotous proceedings of 26 July, 1647, when the mob broke into St. Stephen's and forced Parliament to rescind the recent ordinance by which the City of London was deprived of the control of its militia, he escaped to France to avoid arrest, and was later imprisoned in Newgate, then released. Apart from defending the autonomy of the French Church, of which he was a deacon, against the Privy Council in 1657, Papillon was not active in public affairs until the Restoration, when he gave evidence to the Lords' committee to consider the decay of trade, and to encourage foreigners to settle in England.

In 1681, Papillon served on the 'English Committee', supervising the distribution of charitable funds to the French Refugees; in 1705, the Committee was joined by Sir John Houblon.

Papillon became Deputy Governor of the East India Company in 1680–2, and a leading City Whig. He was M.P. for Dover 1674, and again 1689–1695. He censured the pass system depriving English ships of protection on the high seas unless they were provided with Government licences. In 1679, he was prominent in the hostile examination of Pepys.

He represented the City of London in Parliament from 1695 to 1701, and became an Alderman in 1689. He joined the new East India Company, having terminated his connection with the old Company when the scheme for its reconstitution was defeated in 1681.

Papillon was Victualling Commissioner for the Navy 1689–1701, an onerous duty. He died in London on 5 May 1702, and was buried in the parish church of his Kent manor, Acrise.

PROVENANCE: *Guildhall Library.*

LITERATURE: *A.F.W. Papillon, Memoirs of Thomas Papillon of London, Merchant, 1887; Irene Scouloudi, Thomas Papillon, Merchant and Whig, 1623–1702, Proceedings of the Huguenot Society of London, Vol. 18 (1947–52), pp. 49–72; John Evelyn's Diary, ed. E.S. De Beer, 1951, Vol. III, pp. 172, John R. Woodhead, The Rulers of London, 1660–1689, London and Middlesex Archaeological Society, 1965.*

431 *Richard Ducane (1681–1744)*
a. PORTRAIT, OIL ON CANVAS, MME HOADLY, 1713;
INSCRIBED ON REVERSE OF CANVAS: RICHARD DU QUESNE, SON OF PETER DU QUESNE AND JANE BOOTH, BORN 13TH OCTOBER 1681. DRAWN BY MME HOADLY, 1713.

Richard Ducane was a descendant of the refugee Jean Du Quesne, who had fled from Flanders to avoid Alva's persecution (*see Catalogue number 74*).

He was a Director of the Bank of England, 1720, Governor of Christ's Hospital, a member of the Grand Committee of St. Thomas's Hospital and the Committee of Guy's Hospital.

The Ducane family had been associated with the Bank of England since its establishment, but Richard was the first member of the family to become a Director. He was a merchant in the parish of St. Pancras, Soper Lane.

He died in 1744 and was buried at his Essex seat, Great Braxted, which he had acquired through his marriage to Anne, the daughter of Nehemiah Lyde in 1710. He represented Colchester in Parliament from 1715 to 1722.

DIMENSIONS: *760 × 635mm.*

PROVENANCE: *Private Collection.*

LITERATURE: *E.F. Ducane, Some Account of the Family of Du Quesne, 1876, p. 21.*

b. TOBACCO BOX, SILVER, MAKER'S MARK RUBBED, LONDON, 1706.
INSCRIBED ON THE COVER: THE RICHARD VENTO & VELIS (AND ON INSIDE BASE),
EAST INDIA 1724 MR: RICHARD DU CANE IN PANCRAS LANE NEAR BUCKLERSBURY, IF LOST A REWARD, LONDON 3.0 MAR 1706.

The lid of the tobacco box is engraved with a vessel representing 'The Richard.'

DIMENSIONS: *97 × 80mm.*

PROVENANCE: *Private Collection.*

432 *Partnership articles of Minet and Fector*
PARCHMENT, 15 FEBRUARY 1783.

Isaac Minet was born in Calais 15 September 1660. His ancestry can be traced back to one Ambrose Minet, who was born at Cormont in the Boulonnais in 1613. After severe persecution as a heretic, Isaac escaped to England by rowing across the Channel in 1686 (*Catalogue number 48*).

He established his business in Dover in 1690, and he also owned the packet boat plying from Dover to Calais. His business and bank became well known under the name of Minet and Fector. A London house of business was also established in Austin Friars, and merged under Isaac's son William.

In 1842, the business merged into the Dover branch of the National and Provincial Bank.

PROVENANCE: *Huguenot Library, Ms.F Mt. 206.*

LITERATURE: *Irvine R. Gray, Huguenot Manuscripts: A Descriptive Catalogue of the Remaining Manuscripts in the Huguenot Library, Huguenot Society Quarto Series, Vol. LVI, 1983, pp. 149–156; William Minet, The Huguenot Family of Minet, 1892; Ibid., Isaac Minet's Narrative, Proceedings of the Huguenot Society of London, Vol. 2 (1887–8), pp. 428–445.*

431 *a*

THE

Eaſt-India-Trade

A MOST

Profitable Trade

TO THE

KINGDOM,

AND

Beſt Secured and Improved

IN A

COMPANY,

AND A

JOINT-STOCK.

REPRESENTED

In a Letter written upon the Occaſion of
two Letters lately publiſhed, inſinuating
the Contrary.

LONDON, Printed in the Year, 1680.

430

431 *b*

433 *Daniel Minet (1729–1790)*

OIL ON CANVAS, ATTRIBUTED TO THOMAS GAINSBOROUGH, *c*.1779.

The son of Daniel Minet and grandson of the refugee Isaac Minet (*Catalogue numbers* 48, 432), Daniel was orphaned at 14 years of age and adopted by his uncle William Minet, who continued his father's business.

Daniel does not appear to have been connected with the family business, but rather developed tastes of a literary and scientific kind. On 7 May, 1759 he was entered as a student-at-law at the Inner Temple, and later, in 1767, became both a Fellow of the Royal Society and of the Society of Antiquaries.

He was never called to the Bar, perhaps because of his appointment to the post of Surveyor of Customs; this he obtained through his uncle's influence with Lord Chancellor Hardwicke. (Hardwicke was a Dover man, and known to the Minet family there.)

In the testimonials presented for his election to the Society of Antiquaries, Daniel is described as 'a gentleman well versed in the history and antiquities of this Kingdom'. One of the signatories is the antiquarian, André C. Ducarel, Lambeth Palace Librarian (*Catalogue number* 228).

Daniel Minet FRS, FSA, lived in Grosvenor Street and at Bengeo, Hertfordshire. He is commemorated by a plaque on the north wall of Bengeo parish church.

DIMENSIONS: *875 × 760mm.*

PROVENANCE: *Society of Antiquaries.*

LITERATURE: *William Minet, The Huguenot Family of Minet, Proceedings of the Huguenot Society of London, Vol. 2 (1887–8), pp. 109–110.*

434 *Sir Samuel Romilly (1757–1818)*

PORTRAIT, OIL ON CANVAS, SIR THOMAS LAWRENCE, *c*.1810.

Sir Samuel Romilly was a law reformer who became Solicitor General.

He was a member of a refugee family from Montpellier, and the youngest son of Peter Romilly, a jeweller of Frith Street, Soho. Romilly was connected by marriage with the Roget family (*Catalogue numbers* 218, 219). He was elected a Director of the French Hospital in 1786.

By 1802, Romilly was one of the recognised leaders of the Chancery Bar; in 1806, he was sworn in as Solicitor General and knighted. In the same year, he was elected M.P. for Queenborough.

As a law reformer, Romilly ranks very highly. A man of mercy, reason and eloquence, he tackled with vigour the tendency of contemporary English criminal law to resort to the death penalty for trifling offences.

DIMENSIONS: *749 × 622mm.*

PROVENANCE: *Tate Gallery, on loan to the National Portrait Gallery.*

LITERATURE: *Pedigree of the Romilly family, Proceedings of the Huguenot Society of London, Vol. 8 (1905–09), pp. 310–391; 340–347; Sir Samuel Romilly, Observations on the Criminal Law of England as it relates to Capital Punishment and on the mode in which it is administered, 1810; K.K. Yung, The National Portrait Gallery, A Complete Catalogue, 1981, no. 1171.*

433

434

440

HUGUENOTS IN THE SILK INDUSTRY

From the 1670s to the 1770s the Huguenot element was a vital part of the London silk industry. Most of the refugees had been merchants, master weavers, or journeymen in various textile industries, but Protestants were forbidden entry to the 'Grande Fabrique' in Lyons, so few had experience in the manufacture of silk. They came largely from Northern France, Bas Poitou or Nîmes; only one or two had a Lyons connection, including the smuggler Seignoret and a model citizen, John Sabatier. They brought their capital and their business sense, and like many immigrants, were fiercely loyal to their new country. Some came to London via Amsterdam and some after years in Canterbury. Many came to join relatives already in London, like the Ogiers. Accepted as foreign masters by the Weavers' Company, many of the most successful were recruited for the livery in 1740, and dominated its affairs in the years of crisis in the 1760s. They entered every branch, Black, Plain, Fancy and Flowered, but the majority of weavers in each remained English. Some of the most celebrated designers were Huguenots.

The Huguenot master weavers of Spital Square, Princes Street and Church Street lived in fine houses (the weavers' lofts were nineteenth-century additions after the district was already a slum) employing both Huguenot and English journeymen from the poorer streets on outwork. Conservative in their views, they served both the French churches in the area and Christ Church, Spitalfields, and supported the poor of the district as well as their community. Ultimately, their profits went into house property and public funds. With notable exceptions, by the end of the eighteenth century, most had merged with the English professional middle classes.

*Bill of Andrew
Benjamin Guiraud, 1757*

443

435 *Act of Parliament for the further encouragement of the Manufacture of Lustrings and Alamodes within this realm and for the better Preventing the Importation of the same, 1697*

When the rules of mourning, public and private, were strict, black silks were very important. Alamodes and lustrings were light, glossy silks. The extra gloss was imparted by a secret process which involved stretching, heating, and coating the warp before weaving and/or coating the woven silk. The techniques were evolved in Lyons and lustrings were significant French exports. Brought to England in the 1680s the process was not immediately perfected.

In 1688 a patent was granted for the manufacture of lustrings and alamodes to Paul Cloudesley, William Sherrard and Peter de Cloux, a Roman Catholic Frenchman. Work was started on two looms, but the development of the patent was postponed until 1692 when the manufacture was taken up by Mr. Louis Gervais, Peter Le Keux and Hilary Reneu and incorporated in the Royal Lustring Company. After 25 March 1693, the entry of unlicensed foreign lustrings was prohibited.

The bulk of shares in the company were bought by Stephen Seignoret, although a Mr. Gervaise, Mr. Noquier and Mr. Lauze each owned a fourth part of the company. Initial success was quickly followed by a dispute with English journeymen resenting the lower paid French, which was only resolved by sacking them and increasing the wages. There were said to be 670 looms in London and 98 in Ipswich, employing 6000 people, an exaggeration unless twice the usual number were needed for lustrating silks. The Act of 1697 raised the valuation of foreign lustrings to a prohibitive level. Unfortunately for the Company, an extensive and elaborate plot to smuggle lustrings from France had been devised by Stephen Seignoret, fronted by Thomas Goudet and David Barreau. The smugglers were exposed in 1698 and heavily fined but the Company struggled through increasing difficulties until it ceased manufacturing in 1713. Nevertheless, lustrings, black, white and coloured and patterned became and remained popular products of the industry.

Stephen Seignoret was a silk merchant from Lyons, and set up in Lombard Street in partnership with René Baudouin. When he was fined £10,000 for his smuggling activities in the late 1690s, his wealth was officially estimated at between £80,000 and £100,000. In 1709 he subscribed £6,800 to the doubling of the Bank of England's capital, and he then held £14,187 East India Stock. In 1690 he helped to raise funds for the Huguenot refugees in England. He was responsible for sending money secretly to the Protestant galley slaves in France. He was a Director of the Spitalfields Maison de Charité and later one of the Founder-Directors of the French Hospital.

Seignoret, Louis Gervaise, Peter Le Keux, Etienne Noguier and Etienne Lauze all served as elders or deacons of the French Church, Threadneedle Street in the late seventeenth century.

PROVENANCE: *Huguenot Library.*

LITERATURE: *W.H Manchée, Some Huguenot Smugglers: the Impeachment of London Silk Merchants in 1698, Proceedings of the Huguenot Society of London, Vol.15 (1934–37) pp. 406–427; W.R. Scott, The Constitution and Finance of English, Scottish and Irish Joint Stock Companies to 1720, Vol. III, 1911, pp. 73–89.*

436 *Design for woven silk*

PENCIL, INK AND WATERCOLOUR ON PAPER BY JAMES LEMAN, 1718.
INSCRIBED WITH THE DATE (SE)PR 5TH 1718, THE NAME OF THE MERCER WHO COMMISSIONED IT, MR HINCHLIFFE, AND INSTRUCTIONS FOR PAINTING THE DESIGN ON POINT OR 'RULE' PAPER.

Although unsigned, this design can be identified by the handwriting.

James Leman was celebrated as a designer and manufacturer. His family emigrated first to Amsterdam and then to Canterbury before his parents moved to London. James was apprenticed to his father, Peter Leman, and his earliest surviving designs were drawn when he was still an apprentice. Some of his apprentices, like the brothers Philip and Ben Manckey, came also from Canterbury. Together with Captain Peter Lekeux, James Leman rose to be an Assistant of the Weavers' Company; they both signed the Charter of 1737.

Leman married the daughter of an English throwster, Jonathan Fuller. They lived in Steward Street, in the Old Artillery Ground, one of the older parts of Spitalfields. His will suggests that he was a man of wide interests for, as well as books, music and mathematical instruments, he had a collection of natural history specimens. His silk designs showed no special feeling for natural form because this was not required by fashion at the time.

Thomas Hinchliffe was a partner in the firm of Caleb Trenchfield and Isaac Wittington from 1711. The business was established on the north side of Ludgate Hill at the Wheatsheaf.

COLOUR PLATE: *page 16.*

DIMENSIONS: *533 × 279mm.*

PROVENANCE: *Victoria and Albert Museum.*

LITERATURE: *British Textile Designs in the Victoria and Albert Museum, ed. D. King, 1980, Vol. I, pp. xxi–xxiv and 111; Peter Thornton and Natalie Rothstein, The Importance of the Huguenots in the London Silk Industry, Proceedings of the Huguenot Society of London, Vol. 20 (1958–1964), pp. 69–73.*

437 *Communion certificate of Peter Marescoe*

1 MAY 1709, WITNESSED BY THE DESIGNER CHRISTOPHER BAUDOUIN.

Protestant weavers able to prove their apprenticeship abroad were accepted by the Weavers' Company. The process of naturalisation was more complicated and required this evidence. Peter Marescoe had been in England many years and died in 1710. (His will was proved 12 August 1710, PCC.Aug.12.London Smith fol. 188.) According to J.S. Burn, 'The figured silks which proceeded from the London Manufacturers at the end of the seventeenth century were due almost exclusively to the industry of three refugees Lanson, Mariscot and Monceaux. The artist who supplied the designs was also a refugee named Baudouin' (*Catalogue number* 438).

The claim may be exaggerated but the people were real. Marescoe and Lanson were both elders of the Threadneedle Street church in the late seventeenth century. The Marescoes came

ILLUSTRATED: *page 293.*

PROVENANCE: *Public Record Office.*

LITERATURE: *J.S. Burn, History of the French, Wallon, Dutch and other Protestant Refugees settled in England, 1846; Peter Thornton and Natalie Rothstein, The Importance of the Huguenots in the London Silk Industry, Proceedings of the Huguenot Society of London, Vol. 20 (1958–1964), pl. V, pp. 66–69; C. Weiss, History of French Protestant Refugees, 1845, p. 252.*

from Lille and Lanson from Valenciennes. Marescoe's daughter married Col. Peter Lekeux. Lekeux's nephew employed Baudouin (*Catalogue number 438*). A decree of 1681 permitted the refugees to register as 'denizens'. If they wished to bequeath property, full naturalisation was desirable and Marescoe was rich (*Catalogue numbers 132, 133*). He left real estate in and out of London as well as £50 to the poor of the French church in Threadneedle Street and £5 to the Spitalfields poor.

438 *Design for woven silk*

PENCIL, PEN, INK AND WATERCOLOUR ON PAPER BY CHRISTOPHER BAUDOUIN (*d.* BEFORE 1736); INSCRIBED ON THE BACK: FOR MR PETER LEKEUX OCTOBER THE 26 1724 FOR MR SMITH 400 CORDS NO. 8 & 11 120 DEZINES CHR: BAUD.

The design has been patched with new motifs; presumably the mercer, Smith, or the master weaver, Peter Lekeux, required changes. The pale colours probably indicated metal thread, for some details appear to be in tarnished silver.

Christopher Baudouin was probably the most celebrated designer in England of his generation. Young James Leman drew a design after one of 'Mr Budwines' when he was an apprentice. Baudouin featured in the earliest circumstantial account of the founding of the English industry as the designer supplying the weavers Lanson, Monceaux and Marescoe. Marescoe was Colonel Peter Lekeux's father-in-law (*Catalogue number 437*). Baudouin signed the petition for the 50 New Churches, as one of the principal inhabitants of Spitalfields.

He lived in Paternoster Row in Spitalfields; the exact date of his death is unknown. His style is more delicate than that of Leman or Joseph Dandridge but the 'lace' pattern with a point repeat is typical of these years.

Captain Peter Lekeux (his rank in the London Trained Bands) came from Canterbury, as did his uncle Col. Peter who was a distinguished citizen and a founder of the Royal Lustring Company. Captain Peter Lekeux (1684–1743) had an active career in the Weavers' Company, culminating in his election to the Court of Assistants in 1734, and, like his uncle, was frequently called to give evidence to Parliament and the Commissioners for Trades and Plantations. He married an English girl, Sarah Bloodworth, sister of a customer of James Leman, John Bloodworth.

Mr. Smith regularly commissioned work from Christopher Baudouin, but has not been identified.

DIMENSIONS: *610 × 253mm.*

PROVENANCE: *Victoria and Albert Museum.*

LITERATURE: *Peter Thornton and Natalie Rothstein, The Importance of the Huguenots in the London Silk Industry, Proceedings of the Huguenot Society of London, Vol. 20 (1958–1964), pp. 66–69, 78–83, pl. VI.*

439 *Design for woven silk*

PEN, INK, WATERCOLOUR ON PAPER WITH PENCILLED DEZINES (NOW RATHER FAINT) BY ANNA MARIA GARTHWAITE; INSCRIBED IN INK: MR JULIN OCTR YE 25: 1752.

The design was originally bound by Garthwaite in her book of work from that year. In the surviving index it is noted as 'a single comber brocaded lutestring pattern'.

Although eight brocaded colours appear in the design, only three are used at once. Simon Julins wove the silk of the adjacent dress (*Catalogue number 440*) as a tabby not a lutestring however.

Anna Maria Garthwaite (1690–1763) was a leading silk designer who worked freelance in Spitalfields from the mid 1720s to the mid 1750s. She came from a Lincolnshire family, but lived in Yorkshire with her elder widowed sister before coming to London to settle in a house on the corner of Princes Street and Church Street, now No. 2 Princelet Street. The names of the master weavers who bought her work and the mercers who commissioned them are inscribed on her designs and in the yearly indexes. Thirty-three of her customers, by definition in the 'Flowered' branch of the industry were probably Huguenots, and only twenty-two (including the mercers) English. Her close friends and neighbours included Peter Campart, a rich Huguenot weaver of striped and plain silks, lustring, mantua and tabby (Mortimer's 'Directory', 1763), and his wife Mary, to whom she left 2 guineas and a gold watch, respectively.

Garthwaite's Huguenot customers included Mr. Begot & Co. (Peter Bigot), Mrs. Chevet (Mary Chauvet), Mr. John Crumpler, Mr. (possibly John) Fountain, Mr. Gautier, Mr. (probably Daniel) Gobee, Mr. (probably James) Godin, Mr. William Grinsell, Mr. Roeloff Grootert, Mr. (possibly Nicholas) Hebert, Mr. Jamet, Mr. (probably Abraham) Jeudwine, Mr. Simon Julins, Mr. (probably John Luke) Landon, Mr. (possibly James) Lardant, another neighbour in Church Street, Mr. Le Count, Capn. Peter and his son Mr. Peter Lekeux, Mr. LePine, Mr. Mase and Mr. Maze, Mr. Peter Ogier of Spital Square (eventually Ogier, Vansommer & Triquet) and Mr. Peter Abraham Ogier of Princes Street, Mr. Ouvry, Mr. (probably Stephen) Paris, Mr. Phene, Mr. Pulley, Mr. John Anthony Rocher, Mr. Rondeau, Mr. John Sabatier, Mr. Sufflee, Mr. (probably Daniel) Vautier, Mr. Verbeck.

COLOUR PLATE: *page 16.*

DIMENSIONS: *438 × 302mm.*

PROVENANCE: *Victoria and Albert Museum.*

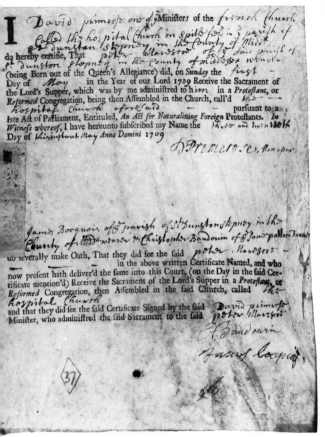

437

439

440 *Dress*

ENGLISH SILK, DESIGNED BY ANNA MARIA GARTHWAITE IN 1752 AND WOVEN BY
SIMON JULINS. ORIGINALLY MID-EIGHTEENTH CENTURY, BUT ALTERED IN THE
LATE NINETEENTH CENTURY.

The silk is a rather coarsely woven tabby, découpure 10, 2 ground to 1 brocaded weft. An
extra self-coloured flushing weft in alternate shoots.

Simon Julins (c. 1687/8–1774) was a weaver of patterned silks and bought 16 of Garthwaite's
designs between 1742–1755 for three different kinds of silk all in the middle price range. Nine
silks woven by his journeymen have come to light, in England, in Scandinavia, and in the
United States, handed down in former Colonial families.

Julins was apprenticed in 1702 and made free of the London Weavers' Company in 1710
upon the report of Margaret Hoy (his master's widow?). He became a Liveryman in 1724 and
from 1728, if not before, was living in a brick house in Booth Street, modestly insured for
£200. He was still there when he advertised as a damask weaver in 1763. An ideal immigrant,
he chiefly took English boys as his apprentices, including Richard Badcock, son of a
prosperous mercer, and he offered 22 men to fight the Young Pretender in 1745.

His career illustrates admirably Paulet's account of specialisation within the industry,
'Comme les ouvriers qui s'y donnent à un genre d'étoffes n'en fabriquent jamais d'autres, les
métiers une fois consacrés à telle ou telle étoffe ne sont jamais montés pour une autre'. Paulet,
Art du Fabricant d'Étoffes de Soie, Vols. 1–6, Nêuchatel edition, 1779, p. 21.

COLOUR PLATE: *page 16.*

ILLUSTRATED: *page 288.*

DIMENSIONS: *Width of silk 495mm
between the selvages, i.e. half ell wide,
the common width of dress silks; length
of repeat 689mm.*

PROVENANCE: *Given by the Green
family to the Victoria and Albert
Museum through Miss H.D. Green.*

LITERATURE: *British Textile Design
in the Victoria and Albert Museum,
ed. by D. King, Tokyo, 1980, Vol. II,
pl. 3; Natalie Rothstein, Nine English
Silks, Bulletin of the Needle and Bobbin
Club, Vol. 48, 1964, nos. 1 & 2,
pp. 23,24.*

441 *Firescreen*
WITH TWO PANELS OF ENGLISH BROCADED SILK, WOVEN IN SPITALFIELDS, *c.* 1745–50.
ONE PANEL ALMOST CERTAINLY DESIGNED BY JOHN VANSOMMER.

The silks in the firescreen are both dress materials which have remained in the hands of the Aubertins to the present day. The wooden frame itself probably dates from the nineteenth century. It has been used as a firescreen, hence the darkening of the panels.

John Vansommer (1706–1774) was a pupil of Joseph Dandridge (1665–1747), an important naturalist as well as a silk designer. He was credited by Malachy Postlethwayt's 'Universal Dictionary of Trade and Commerce' with being one of the three designers who introduced the 'principles of painting into the loom' in about 1732. He was, clearly, the contemporary and rival of Anna Maria Garthwaite (*Catalogue number* 439). Vansommer, like his master, was a cultivated man, and a correspondent of Voltaire. He was renowned in his own day as the only designer taken into partnership by a firm of weavers (*Catalogue number* 445). He married Ann Pain, and his sister married Louis Ferdinand Vigne, a watchmaker. One of his daughters married a merchant Peter Aubertin. John Vansommer left £20 each in his will to the French Church, Artillery Ground and the 'Soupe'. Despite his reputation, the silk on which the label is sewn is the only surviving example of Vansommer's work. Presumably, his original output must have been, like Garthwaite's, well over a thousand designs.

DIMENSIONS: *1526 × 610mm each panel.*

PROVENANCE: *Private Collection.*

LITERATURE: *Dr. Norma Perry, John Vansommer of Spitalfields Huguenot, silk-designer and correspondent of Voltaire, in Studies on Voltaire and the Eighteenth Century, LX, 1968, Institut et Musée Voltaire, Les Delices, Geneva, pp. 289–310.*

442 *Bill of John Lamy, handkerchief weaver*
AT THE BLUE BALL IN GUN STREET, SPITALFIELDS, UNDATED BUT BEFORE 1749.

Gun Street in the Old Artillery Ground was one of the older districts in Spitalfields and it may have become one of the streets in which certain specialist weavers congregated, for a rich and controversial handkerchief weaver, Lewis Chauvet, also had premises there.

John Lamy was born *c.* 1706 since he was apprenticed in 1721 to Abraham Carpentier and turned over to Nicholas Lamy in 1723. He should have been free in 1728. Nicholas Lamy (his father?) insured his goods, utensils, and stock in trade in July, 1740 in Duke Street for £1000 (Sun Insurance Company Policy, 84735 Vol. 57). This was twice the average and exceptional for the street. Nicholas died in 1744 and John Lamy went on the Weavers' Company Livery in 1745, perhaps circumstantial evidence that he was the former's son and heir. John offered twelve men to fight the Young Pretender in 1745 (*see page* 98), and by 1749, had moved to Princes Street. Perhaps he had overreached himself, for in 1754, he went bankrupt ('Gentleman's Magazine' XXIV, p. 436). The firm was resurrected the following year as Salmon and Lamy in Kent's 'Directory' and listed for several years afterwards. Although Nicholas was admitted to the Weavers' Company as a journeyman upon his service in France, taking over young John at the same court, it is not recorded from where he had come.

DIMENSIONS: *65 × 195mm.*

PROVENANCE: *Heal Collection, Department of Prints and Drawings, British Museum.*

442

443 *Bill of Andrew Benjamin Guiraud, Weaver*
AT THE SIGN OF THE BLUE BALL AND GOLDEN BELL, ELDER STREET, 4 MAY 1757.

The bill is for 125 ells in all of half yard alamode i.e. half yard wide and narrower than the usual half ell wide. This would almost certainly have been a black silk. At 23d it is remarkably cheap.

Although the bill indicates that the premises are 'Near Spittle Square Norton Falgate', Elder Street was one of the poorer streets by comparison with Spital Square or Princes Street. Guiraud appears in the Weavers' Company lists as a master weaver but not a liveryman, nor does he seem to have been a donor to any of the major charities. He worked, however, in two branches of the silk industry, the Black and the Fancy, which made gauzes and similar fabrics. Guiraud signed the earliest surviving trades union agreements in the silk industry in these branches in 1769. (There was an earlier list of agreed piece rates in 1763 but no copy has come to light.) As the rates had no legal standing and the industry was in severe difficulties, many master weavers continued to cut wages. The journeymen retaliated by cutting or threatening to cut work on the loom. Guiraud may have been sympathetic to their cause or, because he was one of the minor master weavers with, possibly, little capital, he may have signed because he was worried that his silks might be cut if he did not do so.

ILLUSTRATED: *page 289.*
DIMENSIONS: *106 × 211m.*
PROVENANCE: *Heal Collection, Department of Prints and Drawings, British Museum.*

441

444 *Peter Ogier III (1711–1775)*
OIL ON CANVAS, ARTIST UNKNOWN, *c.*1760.

Peter Ogier I of Bas Poitou had 13 children. He died in 1697 and in 1700 his widow came to London with some of them. Their fourth son, Peter Abraham Ogier, born in 1680, was the first to enter the industry. His brother Peter II had a dramatic escape in 1730. In 1725 the Abbé Goued reported to the French authorities, 'Un tres riche marchand encore plus dangereux que . . . son oncle . . . médite de sortir du royaume . . . et qui a envoyé deux de ses enfants agés de dix et de douze ans en Angleterre.' All five of Peter II's sons became master weavers. Peter III, the subject of this portrait, was one of them. He was apprenticed to Daniel Gobbee, his uncle's neighbour and also a weaver of flowered silks. After the death of Peter II in 1740, Peter III, carried on the business at 4 Spital Square. Anna Maria Garthwaite sold 23 designs to Peter Abraham Ogier and to his nephew Peter III for most of the large-scale patterned silks of the time between 1742 and 1749. She sold him no more designs afterwards but he took John Vansommer into partnership (*Catalogue number* 445).

In 1743, Peter III joined the Livery of the Weavers' Company; in 1756 he became an Assistant, in 1758 Renter Bailiff and in 1760 he was elected to the highest office in the Company, Upper Bailiff, a fair achievement for a boy born in France and not even naturalised until 1749. In 1765, both he and his brother Lewis gave evidence to the Select Committee, and a third brother, Thomas Abraham, gave evidence in 1766. His junior partner, Charles Triquet, also gave evidence denouncing those mercers who wanted to import French silks. Several witnesses mentioned that there were only two or three distinguished pattern drawers in Spitalfields and two of these were tied to particular houses. One of these was surely John Vansommer. Ogier had, therefore, good economic reasons for rejecting the argument of the mercers that they needed to see fresh patterns from France. He also had £3,000 worth of stock in a warehouse in the City (Sun Insurance Company Policy Register Vol. 164, p. 432, No. 227851 insurance 1765).

Peter Ogier III was a Director of the French Hospital in 1761, as was his brother, Lewis, in 1771. From 1752 to 1774 he was a regular contributor to the London Hospital. He married Elizabeth Gastineau (1710–1800), a relation of John Gastineau who patented a new method for making silk mourning crape in 1730. Peter III's youngest sister Louisa Perina (1729–1807) married Samuel Courtauld I in 1749. Like many others, Peter Ogier acquired a country house. This was between Sydenham and Lewisham in Kent, but later in life he moved to the Old Artillery Ground where he died in 1775.

It would be impossible to overestimate the importance of the Ogiers in the London silk industry. They came from Chassais-l'Eglise in Bas Poitou, emigrating in successive generations. They entered almost every branch, six Ogier firms offered men to fight the Young Pretender in 1745 (*see page* 98). For a time they dominated the Weavers' Company. They were directly connected with 25 other Huguenot silk families including the Audeer, Bigot, Byas, Courtauld, Duthoit, Gastineau, Giles, Gobbee, Godin, Grellier, Hebert, Lemaître, Levesque, Maillard, Maze, Messman, Merzeau, Mocquette, Nouaille, Rivalins, Rocher, Perigal, Sorel, Triquet, and Vansommer families, and through these with many other master weavers and throwsters.

DIMENSIONS: *820 × 750mm.*

PROVENANCE: *French Hospital.*

LITERATURE: *François Baudry, La Révocation de l'Edit de Nantes et le Protestantisme en Bas Poitou au XVIIIe siècle; 1922; Natalie Rothstein, The Silk Industry in London 1702–1766, unpublished thesis, University of London, 1961; Herbert Sturmer, Some Poitevin Protestants in London, Notes about the families of Ogier from Sigournais and Creuzé from Châtelleraut, 1896.*

445 *Bill of Triquet Van Sommer & Co, Flowered Silk Weavers*
15TH JANUARY 1769.

The bill is for a dress length, '22¼ yards of Rich tiss(ue) in Changes at 16 shillings per yard, costing in all £17 16s.' 'In Changes' signifies that the colours of the bobbins in the weft were changed according to the pattern. This produces transverse bands on the back of the silk but would make it a little cheaper.

Sixteen shillings per yard in 1769 indicates a very expensive silk. [Ogier], Vansommer and Triquet were, possibly, the largest firm of master weavers of their day. It is consistent with their status that they had an address in Pall Mall as well as their headquarters in Spital Square. They announced their intention of setting up a branch in Exeter and insured utensils and stock in Galloways Buildings, Bath, in 1770. (Sun Insurance Company Policy Register 11936 Vol. 203, p. 126. Information supplied by Mr. S.B. Turner.)

Founded by Peter Ogier, one of several brothers from Bas Poitou, they were unique in having a pattern drawer, John Vansommer, as a partner (*Catalogue number* 441). 'Flowered' was the generic name for silks with free drawloom-woven patterns. They supplied, however, both dress silks and furnishings. There are several beds at Petworth hung with the polychrome velvet they supplied to Lord Egremont in 1764. Both Peter Ogier (*Catalogue number* 444) and Charles Triquet gave evidence to the Select Committee of the House of Commons on the silk industry in 1765 and 1766.

No Ogier is mentioned in the 'New Complete Guide' of 1772, when the partners are given as Vansommer, Chavany, Paul and Nicholls of Spital Square. Peter Cheveney was a pattern drawer who gave evidence to the 1765 Parliamentary Committee on the status of pattern drawers in France. He vanished from the list of partners in 1773 and John Vansommer, junior, is listed as a silk throwster in Mason's Court, Spitalfields. This seems to have been the end of the firm.

DIMENSIONS: *190 × 240mm.*

PROVENANCE: *The Lady Monson.*

444

445

446 *Peter Ouvry (1741–1808)*

a. PETER OUVRY'S INDENTURE OF APPRENTICESHIP, 20 OCTOBER 1755.

This form of indenture remained standard for many years.

Peter Ouvry (1741–1808) was apprenticed to his father, John Ouvry (1707–1774), in the Weavers' Company of London. The family was a large one with many branches in the silk industry. According to family tradition, they came from Picardy, possibly from the Dieppe region. James Ouvry I, Peter's grandfather, was born about 1660–1670, emigrated to London, and was naturalised in 1683, two years before the Revocation of the Edict of Nantes. He was not the only man of this name in the industry and it has proved impossible to assign facts to specific members of the family in this generation. He may have been the James Ouvry summoned for the Livery in the drive made by the Weavers' Company in 1740 to recruit all the leading foreign weavers. He may also, therefore, have been the James Ouvry who offered nineteen men to fight the Young Pretender in 1745 (*see page* 98). It is certainly his house which was insured for a modest £300 on the North side of Church Street (Hand in Hand Insurance Company Guildhall Ms 8674/69 fol. 73). He owned the next door house on one side and, his son-in-law, Peter Bourdon, a weaver who offered twenty-six men to fight the Young Pretender, on the other. Another house in the same row was inhabited by his son, John Ouvry. James died in 1748, leaving £1,200 in trust to his widow, Mary, which was then to go to John. Two daughters had married Englishmen, for he mentioned his daughter, Mary Watts, and son-in-law, William Abraham Young as well as Peter Bourdon. The witnesses to the will were James Lardant and Cornelius Dutch, both weavers.

John Ouvry, James's son and heir, was probably born in 1707 and may have been the John Ouvry apprenticed to Thomas Philpot in 1720. It is, however, certain, that John Ouvry of Christ Church, Spitalfields, son of James Ouvry, was admitted a freeman of the Weavers' Company on 28 November 1738. John Ouvry offered thirty-five men to fight the Young Pretender in 1745 (*see page* 98). He was possibly a customer of Anna Maria Garthwaite for she sold three designs for tobines (warp-patterned silks) in 1749 and 1751 to Mr. Ouvry. By 1763, however, he advertised as a weaver of striped and plain lustring, mantua and tabby. Peter Ouvry might, therefore, have been trained in the weaving of patterned silks but much more likely plain ones. John Ouvry married twice, Mary de Beauvar or Bouvar, his first wife, in 1730/1. She died in 1741, 4 days after the birth of her son, Peter. The latter was her third surviving child. He had two elder sisters, Magdalen (1735–55) and Mary (1732–1760). When their father, John Ouvry, died he left his son-in-law, Peter Sauberque (who had married Mary), £20 for mourning and £50 each to the two Sauberque children. Peter Sauberque was a throwster of Princes Street, who, like other successful throwsters, became a silk broker. Until Peter Ouvry moved out of the industry to Acton, it would seem that the family had lived surrounded by their customers, compatriots and relatives in the same house for three generations. The house, now 29 Fournier Street, still exists and a view of the street is illustrated in the 'Survey of London', with details which show how elegant the houses were formerly.

b. PETER OUVRY, PORTRAIT MINIATURE, PENCIL ON PAPER, ARTIST UNKNOWN, *c*.1780. INSCRIBED ON THE REVERSE IN A LATER HAND: PETER OUVRY OF ACTON, MIDDLESEX BORN 2ND AUGUST 1741, DIED 17TH NOVEMBER 1808 BURIED AT ACTON, MARRIED FRANCISCA GARNAULT. FATHER OF FRANCISCA OUVRY.

The miniature is reputed to represent the Peter Ouvry who was apprenticed to his father in 1755 (see *a.* above). The portrait shows a man in the fashions of the 1780s who could be about forty years old. He was the third of his direct family to enter the silk industry but his particular speciality is unknown. When his father died in 1774 he inherited the household goods from one room in the house, no. 20 Church Street (now Fournier Street) in which he was in partnership with his father. He was still listed there in 1777 ('New Complete Guide') but does not appear in the later directories.

He married well. Francisca Garnault (died 1809) was the eldest daughter and co-heiress of Aimé Garnault of Bulls Cross, Enfield, and Lincoln's Inn Fields. Garnault was Governor and sometime Treasurer of the New River Company (*see Catalogue number* 309). They had seven children of whom three boys died in infancy. One was, however, the twin of Peter Aimé, the eldest surviving son. This child, born in 1766, proved healthy and from him came another dynasty of Ouvrys. Peter and his sister both married Huguenots, but Peter and Francisca's children married out of the community and into widely differing professions. Their assimilation into the English professional middle classes was virtually complete by the 1790s. Successive Ouvrys have maintained a connection with the silk industry, however, as members of the Livery and, in the twentieth century, as Clerks to the Worshipful Company of Weavers.

DIMENSIONS: *170 × 155mm.*

PROVENANCE: *Jonathan Ouvry.*

LITERATURE: *Survey of London, Vol. XXVII, Spitalfields and Mile End New Town, p. 220, pl. 65a.*

446*b*

DIMENSIONS: *140 × 112mm.*

PROVENANCE: *Private Collection.*

LITERATURE: *Notes compiled by E.C. Ouvry (1866–1951) and Norman D. Ouvry.*

This Indenture Witnesseth, That Peter Owry son of John Owry Citizen and Weaver of London doth put himself Apprentice to his said Father Citizen and WEAVER of London, and with him (after the Manner of an Apprentice) to serve from the Day of the Date hereof, unto the full End and Term of Seven Years from thence next following, to be fully compleat and ended. During which Term the said Apprentice his said Master faithfully shall serve, his Secrets keep, his lawful Commandments every where gladly do. He shall do no Damage to his said Master, nor see it to be done of others, but that he to his Power shall lett or forthwith give warning to his said Master of the same. He shall not waste the Goods of his said Master, nor lend them unlawfully to any. He shall not commit Fornication, nor contract Matrimony, within the said Term. He shall not play at Cards, Dice, Tables, or any other unlawful Games, whereby his said Master may have any Loss, with his own Goods or others, during the said Term, without Licence of the said Master. He shall neither buy nor sell. He shall not haunt Taverns or Play-houses, nor absent himself from his said Master's Service Day or Night unlawfully. But in all things as a faithful Apprentice he shall behave himself towards his said Master, and all his, during the said Term. And the said Master ——————————— his said Apprentice, in the same Art which he useth, by the best Means that he can, shall teach and instruct, or cause to be taught and instructed, finding to his said Apprentice Meat, Drink, Apparel, Lodging, and all other Necessaries, according to the Custom of the City of London, during the said Term. And for the true Performance of all and every the said Covenants and Agreements, either of the said Parties bindeth himself unto the other by these Presents. In Witness whereof the Parties above named to these Indentures interchangeably have put their Hands and Seals the Twentieth Day of October in the Year of our Lord 1755 and in the Twenty Ninth Year of the Reign of our Sovereign Lord GEORGE the Second, King of Great-Britain, &c.

446a

447 *Bond and Partnership Agreement of Simon Mestayer*

a. BOND FOR £200 GIVEN BY JOHN RUNN OF WILKES STREET IN THE PARISH OF CHRIST CHURCH, SPITALFIELDS, BAKER, AND VALLERIEN PASCAL OF CRISPIN STREET, CHRIST CHURCH, SPITALFIELDS, TO SIMON MESTAYER OF ST. GILES IN THE FIELDS, MIDDLESEX, WEAVER, DATED 21ST DECEMBER 1769.

b. PARTNERSHIP AGREEMENT BETWEEN SIMON MESTAYER, PETER BEAN AND STEPHEN GUIGON 'TO CARRY ON THE TRADE ART AND MYSTERY OF CLOUDING SILKS' FOR TWENTY ONE YEARS.

PROVENANCE: *Huguenot Library, Ms. J.57/1.*

LITERATURE: *Irvine R. Gray, Huguenot Manuscripts: A Descriptive Catalogue of the Remaining Manuscripts in the Huguenot Library, Huguenot Society Quarto Series, Vol. LVI, 1983, p. 76–7. English 'clouded' silks are illustrated in British Textiles Designs in the Victoria and Albert Museum, ed. D. King, 1980, Vol. II, pls. 22,31. There are examples from the late eighteenth century on pls. 214,216,222,224.*

The partners had to agree to pay one third of any 'damages, costs or charges' arising from any case brought against Simon Mestayer by William Sagnier. Mestayer had agreed, in writing, to teach Sagnier this trade, and they seemed to expect him to prosecute them.

'Clouded' or chiné silks were very fashionable in the period. They required a skilled and delicate technique whereby the warp was printed with a pattern before weaving. According to mercers giving evidence to the Select Committee on the Silk Industry in 1765, 'clouds' (an expressive term) were made better in France than in England, a statement which the weavers naturally disputed.

The Mestayer family came from Saintonge, but Simon Mestayer is probably the Simon Mestayer baptised in St Peter's French Church, Dublin.

448 *Loom end*

ENGLISH SILK, WOVEN IN SPITALFIELDS BY OR FOR A MEMBER OF THE DUTHOIT FAMILY, PROBABLY JAMES SENIOR OR JUNIOR, *c.*1770.

This heavily ribbed, brocaded silk may have been intended for ladies' dress or for men's suitings. The stylised flowers are typical of the date, and declined even further in size in the next few years. There is virtually no difference in the colour or style of this and contemporary French silks with which it was competing. It should be emphasised that the Duthoits were master weavers. They are unlikely to have woven silks themselves once out of their apprenticeship. The work would have been done by their journeymen.

The Duthoit family originated from Marq-en-Bareul, near Lille, and according to family tradition, moved to Canterbury in 1614. A branch remained there throughout the eighteenth century. By the 1710s some Duthoits had moved to Spitalfields where two brothers, or cousins, entered the silk industry – those in Canterbury were also weavers.

James Duthoit was fined as overseer of the poor in Christ Church, Spitalfields in 1727/8, and he appears on the Livery of the Weavers' Company in the 1730s. From 1736 onwards, he lived in Princes Street (today Princelet Street) and in later years he is listed in partnership with his son of the same name. Peter Duthoit became free of the Company in 1716 and appears in the 1728 livery list with an address in Mason's Buildings, Brick Lane. He was obviously successful because he later moved to Wood Street, a much better and more highly rated address. He was a member of the 1743 Vestry Committee for the removal of the North Steps of Christ Church. Both Duthoits offered men to serve against the Young Pretender; James offered seven, and Peter twelve.

Peter Duthoit, junior, in partnership with his father, is given in Mortimer's 'Directory' of 1763 as a weaver of black silk, perhaps mourning was a more profitable venture (assuming his father was in the same branch) than the more chancy flowered silks. Some members of the family remained in the industry until the late nineteenth century, a connection which had then lasted for nearly two hundred years.

DIMENSIONS: *180 × 489mm.*

PROVENANCE: *Private Collection.*

449 *Waistcoat*

ENGLISH FIGURED SATIN, WOVEN BY MAZE & STEER, SPITALFIELDS, 1787.

This waistcoat was identified from a pattern book acquired by the Victoria and Albert Museum (T. 384–1972) from the Warner Archive. From 1786–92 there are sample pieces with lower and side borders and a pocket edge. This waistcoat has elegant matching buttons, not in the pattern book.

The firm was prolific for there are several surviving waistcoats from them in the Royal Albert Memorial Museum in Exeter as well as in the Victoria and Albert Museum. Waistcoats with this cut were current from the early 1780s. Embroidery was becoming very fashionable and the woven decoration on this waistcoat deliberately imitates its competitor.

So far it has proved impossible to establish which member of the Maze (or Mase) family was in partnership with Mr. Steer. Throughout the century there were many John and James Mazes (or Mases) in the silk industry.

COLOUR PLATE: *page 16.*

DIMENSIONS: *660 × 444mm (approximate).*

PROVENANCE: *Given to the London Museum by Mrs. Chamberlayne, 1934; Museum of London.*

450 *Peter Nouaille (d.1809)*

PORTRAIT ENGRAVING, T. BLOOD AFTER SIR THOMAS LAWRENCE.

INSCRIBED: PETER NOUAILLE ESQR OF GREATNESS, SEVEN-OAKS, KENT AGED 86, 1809.

Peter Nouaille was the son of a throwster of the same name. The family were said to be from Nîmes and their connection with the industry lasted over one hundred years. Peter I was in partnership with his son-in-law, James Fruchard, from 1736–1749 in a house in Paternoster Row, Spitalfields, insured for £500 in 1745 (Hand in Hand Insurance Company Guildhall Library Ms 8674/68 fol. 87). The house and its attached warehouse was situated between a weaver, George Garret, and Christopher Baudouin's widow. From 1740, Nouaille and Fruchard are listed as 'silkmen', thus progressing on the normal road of the successful throwster from manufacturing to wholesale enterprise. Their working address from 1738 to 1749 was Corbet Court. By 1753, Peter the younger was sufficiently experienced to become his father's partner, and they were both advertising as 'merchants' in Paternoster Row and thus solely wholesalers.

Peter the elder, a Director of the French Hospital from 1760, died in 1763, leaving substantial property in Essex as well as £50 to the French church in Petticoat Lane and £50 to La Soupe.

Peter the younger took up and retained his Livery in the Weavers' Company but is listed as a merchant at St. Mary Axe in the 1770s. He then moved to Sevenoaks in Kent, not to retire but to found a silk mill. While the claim that he had introduced crêpe to England is exaggerated, for every throwster knew how to overtwist thread, he did take out a patent in 1770. The mill flourished.

Peter died in 1809 leaving kindly bequests to his servants and even to his son's servant. Peter III was one of three throwsters to give evidence to the Select Committee on the employment of children in manufactures in 1818. Although his small girls worked a 12-hour day he gave them 'playtime' and meal breaks as well as medical attention and some clothing. His whole family ran a school after work for 47 children, giving Bibles and Prayer Books to the first dozen successful readers. This was in the typical Huguenot spirit, benevolent, industrious, but offering rewards for virtue.

ILLUSTRATED: *page 303.*

DIMENSIONS: *428 × 370mm.*

PROVENANCE: *French Hospital.*

LITERATURE: *D.C.A. Agnew, Protestant Exiles from France, Index volume. 1874, p.74; B. Woodcraft, Abridgements of the Specifications relating to Spinning, London, 1866, p.17 (A.D. 1770, May 25, No. 960, Peter Nouaille for crossing silk in throwing).*

448

449

451 *Cup*

DIMENSIONS: *230mm high.*

PROVENANCE: *Purchased by the Museum of London, 1981.*

LITERATURE: *The Spitalfields Acts; Seven Pamphlets 1818–1828, includes G.E. Justions, William Hale, silk merchant, An Appeal to the Public in defence of the Spitalfields Acts with remarks on the causes . . ., 1822.*

SILVER, POSSIBLY BY WILLIAM BATEMAN, LONDON, 1818.

INSCRIBED ON THE SIDE: THIS CUP IS PRESENTED TO WILLIAM HALE, ESQRE BY A FEW OPERATIVE SILK WEAVERS OF SPITALFIELDS, AS A TOKEN OF GRATITUDE FOR HIS INDEFATIGABLE EXERTIONS IN THE YEAR 1818 BY WHICH THE ACTS OF PARLIAMENT WERE SUPPORTED AND THE PRICES OF THEIR LABOUR SECURED TO THEM (AND ON THE BASE WITH THE NAMES OF OPERATIVE SILK WEAVERS) WILLIAM DEIGHTON, JOHN DAVIS, JOSEPH ROQUEZ, JOSEPH BENSON, THOMAS JENNISON, JOHN OLIVER, JOHN FOSTER, THOMAS FRANCTON, THOMAS COLLIER, JOHN ROBINSON.

William Hale (*d.* 1841) of Wood Street, Spitalfields, was allegedly a descendant of the brother of Sir Matthew Hale, an outstanding Lord Chief Justice of the seventeenth century, whose coat of arms and crest he adopted. William Hale was born in Colchester. He made his fortune in the Spitalfields silk industry, but retired early on account of the duty on imported silk. Hale would not reduce wages, and no doubt lost much money in consequence.

Hale was an active campaigner for the Spitalfields poor; in 1807 he had addressed a pamphlet on their behalf to the M.P. Samuel Whitbread, who was endeavouring to improve the country's poor laws. Of the operative silk weavers above, only Joseph Roquez and John Oliver have Huguenot names.

452 *Silkweaving loom with jacquard apparatus*

PROVENANCE: *Given to the London Museum by J.G. Joicey in 1915 and said to have been used 'for weaving Spitalfields silk by M. Hurable senior'; Museum of London.*

USED IN SPITALFIELDS DURING THE NINETEENTH CENTURY.

This silkweaving loom, like many of the thousands which once supported the industry in Spitalfields, Bethnal Green, Shoreditch and Mile End New Town, is a composite one.

The frame is eighteenth century and may originally have been a drawloom. At some time during the nineteenth century, the batten with flying shuttle mechanism (invented in 1733 by John Kay) was added to help the weaver increase his output. The jacquard apparatus (invented in France by Joseph Marie Jacquard, but not generally introduced to Britain until much later) was made by James Jacquier, 'machinemaker' of Panderston Gardens, Bethnal Green Road, around 1850. The jacquard is essentially a shedding device, activated by a string of punched cards, for selecting and raising warp threads to enable complex figured fabrics to be woven.

453 *Trade card of Claud Guillotte*

DIMENSIONS: *93 × 123mm.*

PROVENANCE: *Heal Collection, Department of Prints and Drawings, British Museum.*

LITERATURE: *Natalie Rothstein, The Introduction of the Jacquard Loom to Great Britain, in Studies in Textile History, ed. by Veronika Gervers, Royal Ontario Museum, 1977, pp. 281–304.*

MACHINE MAKER, 37 CRISPIN STREET, SPITALFIELDS, MID-NINETEENTH CENTURY.

Claud Guillotte was one of the earliest manufacturers of jacquard looms in London. As his trade card specifies, he also made the accessories for the machine, i.e. reading and stamping machines, as well as supplying mails, lingoes (weights) etc. The punching device on the lower left may be compared with the illustrations in 'The Ladies Treasury' which dates from 1857, p. 85. The card cannot be much later since he advertises wooden as well as iron jacquards.

Claud Guillotte gave long evidence to the Select Committee on Arts and Manufactures in 1835. At that time he had only sold a few jacquards to London firms but more to Yorkshire. He then complained bitterly of the duty levied on the cardboard coming in from France which was necessary for the cards (shown on the right of the trade card). At the top right-hand side is a ribbon loom with a jacquard attachment. The Crispin Street address was presumably his show room, while he had his factory in Gun Street.

The eighteenth-century silks in the exhibition were woven on the drawloom which the jacquard superseded. The pattern on the drawloom was controlled by cords, simple and lashes, the last pulled by a drawboy for each line of the pattern. Any carpenter in Spitalfields could make or adapt a loom while the pattern-making mechanism required only string and weights to keep it at the correct tension. The jacquard eliminated the drawboy, but required a new technology and the beginnings of a machine tool industry. Only when there was an extensive demand for large patterns did the jacquard become an economic proposition.

450

453

454 *Vanner & Sons*

a. APPRENTICE INDENTURE OF JOHN VANNER, PARCHMENT, 17 JANUARY 1774.

John Vanner was the son of John Vanner of Coopers Gardens, Hackney Road, weaver.

The earliest known reference to a Vanner as a silk weaver occurs in the Weavers' Company records for 1717, when William Vanner was apprenticed to a silkweaver.

The present firm of Vanners, Silk Weavers of Sudbury, Suffolk, is said to have been founded in about 1730.

b. MEDAL, SILVER, ALBERT BARRE; PRESENTED TO J. VANNER & SONS AT THE PARIS EXHIBITION, 1855; INSCRIBED ON THE OBVERSE: NAPOLEON III EMPEREUR; REVERSE: EXPOSITION UNIVERSELLE. AGRICULTURE. INDUSTRIE. BEAUX. ARTS. PARIS 1855 J. VANNER & SONS. SPITALFIELDS. 1ST CLASS.

A gold medal was awarded to the firm *c.* 1900 on exhibiting their electrically driven looms at Earl's Court.

c. JAMES ENGLEBERT VANNER, 1834–1906
PORTRAIT, OIL ON CANVAS, W.W. OULESS, *c.*1895.

James Englebert Vanner was Director of the Midland Bank, 1898–1906 and Chairman of John Vanners (Silks), 1866–1900.

James Vanner was offered £10,000 for his work in seeing through the merger of the City Bank and the Midland Bank in 1898. He refused the money but asked that it should be distributed among the staff. This portrait in oils was subsequently presented to him by the Midland Bank.

'Resolved that Mr. J.E. Vanner be requested to allow his portrait to be painted for the Board Room of the Bank in consideration of the great services he has rendered to the Bank, and that the following gentlemen be appointed a Committee to give effect on behalf of the City Bank to this resolution:

Sir Thomas Sutherland
Sir G.F. Faudel-Phillips
Mr. J. Howard Gwyther'

Extract from the Board Minutes of the City Bank Ltd., 27 October 1895.

James Vanner had succeeded his father, John, as a Director of the City Bank and the Midland Bank in 1866, and subsequently emerged as the dominant personality on a powerful Board of Directors. The Vanner family's original business was the manufacture of silk in Spitalfields and Coleman Street, London, where they became the leading suppliers of umbrell inilks. Other family interests included underwriting and insurance broking at 32 Great St. Helens.

James Vanner and his brothers owned the John Vanner silk business, which operated from 1 Coleman Street. A plan of their Coleman Streetnilk warehouse (1857) is amongst the Vanner papers at the Midland Bank. The silk business was sold in 1900, the last year in which James Vanner is recorded on the Board of Directors. The firm of Vanners subsequently merged with Fennell Brothers and later moved to Sudbury.

James Vanner was also a major personality in the world of London non-conformism and charity work. He married Maria Early of the blanket manufacturing family of Witney, Oxfordshire.

The firm of John Vanner continues today as Vanners, silk weavers, of Sudbury, Suffolk.

PROVENANCE: *Vanners, Sudbury.*
EXHIBITED: *Silk Centre, 49 Park Lane, W1, April, 1951.*

PROVENANCE: *Vanners, Sudbury.*
EXHIBITED: *Silk Centre, 49 Park Lane, W1, April 1951.*

DIMENSIONS: *1400 × 1650mm.*
PROVENANCE: *Midland Bank plc.*
LITERATURE: *W.F. Crick and J.E. Wadsworth, A Hundred Years of Joint Stock Banking, 1936, 4th edition 1964; E. Green, The Making of a Modern Bank Group, The Midland Bank since 1900, 1979; Peter Thornton and Natalie Rothstein, The Importance of the Huguenots in the London Silk Industry, Proceedings of the Huguenot Society of London, Vol. 20 (1958–1964), pp. 60–88.*

454*b*

454*b*

454*a*

454*c*

455 *Samuel Courtauld (1876–1947)*
BRONZE PORTRAIT BUST, BENNO ELKAN, 1947.

Samuel Courtauld was Chairman of Courtaulds, an art collector and founder of the Courtauld Institute of Art.

He joined the family business, Samuel Courtauld & Co. Ltd, in 1898. He was appointed Mill Manager, Halstead, Essex in 1901, General Manager of the textiles mills in 1908, a Director in 1915 to 1917, and Chairman from 1921 to 1946. Under Samuel Courtauld's leadership the business became a highly respected industrial giant in the artificial silk industry.

The Courtaulds were Huguenot refugees from the vicinity of La Rochelle. Working as outstanding London goldsmiths between 1701 and 1780, the family then entered the silk industry through their connection by marriage with the Ogier family of Spitalfields. Prominent in the development of the black crêpe industry towards the end of the eighteenth century, by 1901 the firm was the largest of its kind in the world.

The industry of artificial silks developed between 1898 and 1905, rayon, the first man-made fibre, being produced in the post war years; by 1940 Courtaulds commanded the viscose and cellulose acetate processes, which produced cellulose yarn and fibre, particularly for women's stockings and underwear.

It was during this period that Samuel Courtauld built up the most remarkable collection of French Impressionist paintings in the country, and within a few years of their acquisition, made them available to the public. In 1931 he created and handsomely endowed the Courtauld Institute of Art in the University of London.

DIMENSIONS: *360mm high.*

PROVENANCE: *The Courtauld Institute.*

LITERATURE: *D.C. Coleman, Courtaulds, An Economic and Social History, Vols. I and II, 1969, Vol. III, 1980.*

455

Andrew Chaigneau

MANUFACTURES

and Sells at his Shop

at the Golden Ball on CORK HILL

All sorts of Gold and Silver Laces for Ladies and Gentlemens wear, and officers Sashes, with every other Article that is Usualy Found in Lace Shops

His Grace Duke of Bedford, Lord Lt &c.
To Andrew Chaigneau Dr

456 *Francis Tayspill (c.1591–1666)*

PORTRAIT, OIL ON CANVAS, ARTIST UNKNOWN.

INSCRIBED: FRANCIS TAYSPILL BAY & SAY MAKER. COLCHESTER. B. AT NIEUWE KIRKE AB. 1591. D.AT COLCHESTER 1669. SON OF GILES TAYSPILL. AETATIS 59. A:O 1650. (AND ON LABEL) FRANCIS TAYSPILL, BAY & SAY MAKER OF COLCHESTER. B. AT NEUVE EGLISE (SON OF GILES TAYSPILL) A 1591 M.ABIGAIL COCQ GRANDFATHER OF SARAH TAYSPILL (WIFE OF SAML PUPPLET) WHOSE DAUGHTER MARRIED SAML CARR & WAS GREAT GRANDFATHER OF MARY CARR (BENTHUSE) OF COLCHESTER (d.1918).

The sitter is shown seated, half-length, facing to the right, wearing a dark coat with a lace collar and cap

Francis Tayspill, cloth merchant, was the son of Giles Tayspill, a refugee weaver from Ypres, Flanders (c.1568) during Alva's persecution. He is mentioned on 29 April 1622 in the 'Complaints of the Inglishe against the Dutch Strangers' as an 'alien borne, bay and say maker (who) buyeth and selleth sayes to Forryners besides those he makes'. He occupied an important position as a cloth merchant in Colchester, and as a deacon and elder of the Dutch church.

By the time of the Civil War, the Tayspills were accounted one of the nine leading families in Colchester. Half of the £12,000 fine demanded in 1648 by Fairfax, on the town's surrender, was assessed on the thriving Dutch community. The Tayspill family subscribed £1,470 of which Francis contributed £250.

In his will, which was proved in 1669, he left 500 guilders to the Dutch Church, and the same amount to local almspeople.

Francis Tayspill was the grandfather of Sir Isaac Rebow, M.P., and an ancestor of several prominent Colchester families.

dimensions: *761 × 635mm.*

PROVENANCE: *Christie's South Kensington, 25 March 1981 (147); Historic House Hotels Ltd from Bodysgallen Hall Hotel, Llandudno.*

LITERATURE: *Joseph J. Green, The Tayspill Family of Ypres and Colchester, The Essex Review Vol. XXVII (1918), pp. 68–71; Victoria County History, Essex, 1907, pp. 396(n) and 398; W.J.C. Moens, Registers of the Dutch Church in Colchester, Huguenot Society Quarto Series, Vol. XII, 1905; Tayspill Pedigrees, Huguenot Library, Ms.T5/11.*

457 *Bill of Andrew Chaigneau, laceman*

AT THE SIGN OF THE GOLDEN BALL ON CORK HILL, DUBLIN, 19TH APRIL, 1760.

This bill is addressed to the 4th Duke of Bedford, Lord Lieutenant of Ireland. An earlier bill dated 1757 from Towers and Chaigneau at the sign of the Hen and Chickens on Cork Hill, Dublin, is in the same collection.

There were three freemen of the City of Dublin of this name in the 1750s and 1760s; a Peter Chaigneau and his two sons, John and Abraham.

DIMENSIONS: *264 × 207mm.*

PROVENANCE: *Marquess of Tavistock and Trustee of the Bedford Estates.*

458 *Trade card of Francis Chassereau, fanmaker*

AT THE SIGN OF THE CROWN AND FAN IN HANOVER STREET, LONG ACRE, c.1740.

Francis Chassereau the elder was admitted to the Worshipful Company of Fanmakers on 4 December 1721. Another Francis Chassereau was admitted to the same Company on 3 November, 1758. Another trade card in the Banks Collection records Honour Chassereau, a Fanmaker and Stationer at the Fan and Crown in Long Acre.

Francis Chassereau was a relative of Peter Chassereau, the Surveyor and Architect who advertised in the 'Gentleman's Magazine', 1741, and Robert Chassereau, watchmaker (*Catalogue number* 373). The family came originally from Niort, Poitou.

DIMENSIONS: *369 × 266mm.*

PROVENANCE: *Banks Collection, Department of Prints and Drawings, British Museum.*

LITERATURE: *B.R. Collins, A Short Account of the Worshipful Company of Fan-Makers, 1950.*

459 *Fan*

ETCHING, COLOURED BY HAND, ON IVORY STICKS, FRANCIS CHASSEREAU, 1741.

INSCRIBED: ACCORDING TO ACT OF PARLIAMENT, 1741 F. CHASSEREAU.

This fan has been painted and gilded by hand to represent a group of people seated or standing in a garden. There are five other etched designs for fans by Chassereau in the British Museum.

DIMENSIONS: *230mm long.*

PROVENANCE: *Schreiber Collection, Department of Prints and Drawings, British Museum.*

LITERATURE: *Lionel Cust, Catalogue of the Collection of Fans presented to the British Museum by Lady Charlotte Schreiber, 1893, p. 81; Peter Thornton, Fans, in Antiques International ed. P. Wilson, 1966, pp.193–205, pl.12.*

456

458

459

460 *George Aufrère*

PORTRAIT, OIL ON CANVAS, ATTRIBUTED TO WILLIAM HOARE, C.1750.

George Aufrère was the younger son of Israel Antoine Aufrère, the Huguenot minister of the Savoy Chapel (*Catalogue number 63*).

He worked as a linen draper and is recorded as supplying the Countess of Exeter with muslin and holland in the 1740s. In 1746, he married the Countess of Exeter's niece, Arabella Bate (*Catalogue number 311*), who had been brought up by her aunt at Burghley. George Aufrère was later elected M.P. for Stamford.

He acquired Walpole House, adjacent to Chelsea Hospital in London, which he filled with an important collection of Old Master paintings (*Catalogue number 461*).

In 1774, his daughter Sophia married the first Lord Yarborough, whom she had met on a visit to Rome with her parents. Her father provided a dress of 'Point d'Angleterre' lace representing 'Spring' which he purchased in Brussels on their return journey. Sophia was painted in this dress by Sir Joshua Reynolds.

DIMENSIONS: *820 × 670mm.*

PROVENANCE: *By family descent to the present Earl of Yarborough.*

461 *Catalogue of Mr Aufrère's pictures at Chelsea, c. 1800*

George Aufrère collected paintings during his travels in France and Italy, and displayed his collection at Walpole House, Chelsea.

On his wife's death in October 1804, the 'Monthly Magazine' noted that Lord Yarborough had inherited 'one of the finest collections of paintings in this country. The late Sir Joshua Reynolds frequently said, that it contained a greater variety of pieces by the first masters of the Italian, Dutch, French and Flemish Schools than any other Private Collection in England.'

George Aufrère also collected sculpture. In 1792, he purchased from the sale of Sir Joshua Reynolds' Collection, the statue of Neptune and Triton by Bernini, which Reynolds had bought from Thomas Jenkins in Rome for £700 in 1786. It was set up in the summer house at Chelsea, and eventually moved to the gardens at Brocklesby, the Yarborough seat in Lincolnshire, before it was sold to the Victoria and Albert Museum in 1950.

PROVENANCE: *By family descent to the present Earl of Yarborough.*

LITERATURE: *Tessa Murdoch, Louis François Roubiliac and His Huguenot Associations, Proceedings of the Huguenot Society of London, Vol. 24 (1983), pp. 26–45.*

462 *Head of Christ*

WOVEN PICTURE, JACQUES CHRISTOPHE LE BLON; INSCRIBED: VERA SALVATORIS NOSTRI EFFIGIES AD IMITATIONEM IMAGINIS SMARAGNO INCISAE IUSSI TIBERII CAESARIS QUO SMARAGNO POSTEA, EX THESAURO CONSTANTINOPOLITANO TURCARUM IMPERATOR INNOCENTIUM VIII PONT.MAX.ROM.DONAVIT PROREDIMENDO FRATRE CHRISTIANIS CAPTIVO.

This picture was woven by a method for which Le Blon was awarded patent no. 492 on 1 May 1727.

There are sixteen different examples of this subject extant; including one in the Victoria and Albert Museum, Pembroke College, Cambridge, the Spalding Society and another in the Mormon Tabernacle in Salt Lake City.

NOT EXHIBITED.

DIMENSIONS: *760 × 510mm.*

PROVENANCE: *Museum of London.*

LITERATURE: *H.C. Marrillier, English Tapestries of the eighteenth century, 1930, pp. 98–100, pl. 39(a).*

463 *George, Prince of Wales*

TAPESTRY WOVEN PORTRAIT, *c.* 1755; SIGNED: DANTHON.

The sitter is shown half-length to the left in a red coat wearing the star and ribbon of the Order of the Garter.

In 1693, Jan Danthon is recorded as a tapestry-weaver, when he married Rachel Cauvin at the French church of St. Jean, Spitalfields. His wife was later buried in the parish of St. Ann, Soho in 1726.

By the 1750s, a member of the Danthon family had set up an independent workshop and was producing tapestry pictures and tapestry woven furnishings and probably also furnishings in knotted pile in the manner of Savonnerie, for a portrait in knotted pile, possibly of George, Prince of Wales, signed Danthon and dated 1755, was seen in London in the 1920s or 1930s.

In 1773, a Pierre Danthon, 'Natif d'Aubusson dans la Haute Marche, agé de 70 ans Refugié pour sa Religion – membre de La Patente et tapissier à Fabrique – fort pauvre et sans ouvrage', was admitted to the French Hospital, where he died in 1774.

DIMENSIONS: *740 × 610mm.*

PROVENANCE: *Her Majesty the Queen.*

LITERATURE: *Wendy Hefford, Soho and Spitalfields: Little-known Huguenot tapestry-weavers in and around London, 1680–1780, Proceedings of the Huguenot Society of London, Vol. 24 (1984), pp. 103–112.*

463

464 *Henriette Le Fanu (1709–1789)*

PORTRAIT, OIL ON CANVAS, PHILIP MERCIER; SIGNED: P. MERCIER, *c.*1747.

The sitter is shown three-quarter length, to the front, in an oval surround.

Henriette Le Fanu (née Raboteau) married in Dublin in 1734. Mercier also painted her husband, William Le Fanu. The portraits were probably executed during Mercier's visit to Ireland in 1747.

DIMENSIONS: *742 × 622mm.*

PROVENANCE: *Private Collection.*

EXHIBITED: *Philip Mercier 1689–1760, City Art Gallery, York and Iveagh Bequest, Kenwood, 1969(46), illustrated.*

LITERATURE: *John Ingamells and Robert Raines, A Catalogue of the Paintings, Drawings and Etchings of Philip Mercier, The Walpole Society, Vol. LXVI, 1976–1978, no 6, p. 26.*

464

NINETEENTH-CENTURY HUGUENOT HERITAGE

By the end of the eighteenth century, the Huguenots were well integrated
into British Society, and most of their churches had ceased to function.
However, many families possessed pedigrees dating back to the Revocation
or even earlier and were aware of their French origins.

In the second quarter of the nineteenth century, popular interest in the
history of the Huguenots was aroused by Meyerbeer's opera, 'Les Huguenots',
which was first performed in Paris, 1836, and centred upon the Massacre of
St. Bartholomew. It was produced in London in 1842, and inspired the young
John Everett Millais to paint 'The Huguenot', which was exhibited at the
Royal Academy ten years later. In 1858, the rebuilt Covent Garden Opera
House opened with 'Les Huguenots', and the opera remained one of the most
popular works in the repertoire until early this century.

The approaching bicentenary of the Revocation of the Edict of Nantes,
1885, inspired the descendants of the original refugees, the Directors of the
French Hospital, to found a Society, which would have for its objects the
exchange and publication of knowledge about the history of the Huguenots in
France, the Huguenot emigrations from France, the refugee settlements
throughout the world, and the effects of these settlements upon the professions,
industry, commerce and social life in Britain. They planned that original
Huguenot records should be rescued and published. The Society was intended
to form a bond of fellowship among those who had inherited or admired the
characteristic Huguenot virtues, or who desired to perpetuate the memory of
their Huguenot ancestors.

The Inaugural Meeting of the Huguenot Society of London was held on
15 April 1885 at the Criterion Restaurant, Piccadilly Circus. Sir Henry Austen
Layard was the first President and the Directors of the French Hospital became
Members of Council and Officers of the Society.

471

465 *Massacre of St Bartholomew*

A TRAGEDY, MANUSCRIPT 30 ff; ANONYMOUS, EIGHTEENTH-CENTURY.

This tragedy, which appears to survive in manuscript only, consists of 30 folios of foolscap, held in a loose cardboard folder.

The scene is set at Lisieux, 25 August, 1572. The Catholic clergy wish to defend the local Protestants from massacre.

DIMENSIONS: *Foolscap.*

PROVENANCE: *Presented to the French Hospital Library by Henry Wagner, 1882; Huguenot Library, Ms.M8.*

LITERATURE: *Irvine R. Gray, Huguenot Manuscripts: A Descriptive Catalogue of the Remaining Manuscripts in the Huguenot Library, Huguenot Society Quarto Series, Vol.LVI, 1983, p.169.*

466

466 *Les Huguenots*

AN OPERA IN FIVE ACTS, MUSICAL SCORE, GIACOMO MEYERBEER, WITH LIBRETTO BY EUGENE SCRIBE.

In October 1832, Meyerbeer signed a contract for an opera entitled 'La St. Barthélemy'. Eventually known as 'Les Huguenots', the opera had its premiere, one of the most memorable in opera history, on 29 February, 1836 under the directorship of Duponchel at the Paris Opera House.

The central episode of the opera is the Massacre of the Protestants by the Catholics on the night of St. Bartholomew, Paris, 24 August 1572 (Acts IV and V).

Giacomo Meyerbeer (1791–1864) came from a wealthy Jewish family in Berlin. He was therefore well placed to maintain a strict impartiality between the Papists and the Huguenots. After 1831, he became the central musical figure in French grand opera.

Eugène Scribe (1791–1861) was a French dramatist and librettist, who was elected to the Academie Française in 1836. As a librettist, he is mainly remembered for his work with Meyerbeer. Scribe drew on Prosper Merimée's 'Chronicles of the Time of Charles the Ninth' for his libretto of 'Les Huguenots'.

PROVENANCE: *British Library.*

LITERATURE: *The New Grove Dictionary of Music and Musicians, 1980, under Meyerbeer; W.L. Crosten, French Grand Opera, an Art and a Business, 1948.*

467 *The Huguenot*

OIL ON CANVAS, JOHN EVERETT MILLAIS, 1852; INSCRIBED: J.M. 1852.

Sir John Everett Millais (1829–1896) was twenty-two when he completed this painting in November, 1851. He was then staying at Worcester Park Farm with Holman Hunt and Charles Allston Collins. Arthur Lemprière sat for the figure of the Huguenot and Anne Ryan, a professional model, for the girl. The painting was exhibited at the Royal Academy, 1852, and its sentimentality immediately appealed to the public of the day.

According to the artist, the painting shows a young Huguenot taking leave of his sweetheart on the eve of the Massacre of St. Bartholomew. She tries unsuccessfully to persuade him to wear the white armband of the Catholic Guise party which would save him from massacre.

The subject was inspired by the recent performance in London of Meyerbeer's opera 'Les Huguenots', Act V, where Valentine tries to persuade her lover, Raoul de Nangis to wear the white scarf in order to protect him from becoming a victim of the massacre. Millais also painted 'Mercy: St. Bartholomew's Day, 1572' (Tate Gallery no.1510).

There is another sketch in oils for this painting, which the artist himself described as 'the only important replica'. A preparatory drawing is in the City Museum and Art Gallery, Birmingham. The painting was engraved in 1856.

DIMENSIONS: *927 × 62mm.*

PROVENANCE: *The Makins Collection.*

EXHIBITED: *Royal Academy, 1852 (478); John Everett Millais, Royal Academy, 1967 (36); The Pre-Raphaelites, The Tate Gallery, 7 March–25 May, 1984 (41).*

LITERATURE: *Frank Davis, 'A Wall of Foreboding', Country Life, 24 August, 1972, p.456; J.G. Millais, The Life and Letters of Sir John E. Millais, 1899, Vol.II, p.468.*

467

469

468

468 *Model of the production of Meyerbeer's 'Les Huguenots'*
COVENT GARDEN, 1858.

The scene in progress appears to be Act II, which takes place in the park of Chenonceaux, not far from Amboise. Margaret of Valois, the betrothed of Henry of Navarre, is receiving the local nobility in order to give them instructions from her brother Charles IX. She also attempts to unite the Catholics and Protestants among them, by proposing that the young Huguenot, Raoul de Nangis, should marry Valentine, the daughter of the Catholic Comte de Saint Bris. Raoul, however, despite his declaration of fealty to the Queen, refuses to do as she wishes.

DIMENSIONS: *305 × 254mm.*

PROVENANCE: *Museum of London.*

469 *Handbill for Meyerbeer's 'Les Huguenots'*
COVENT GARDEN, 15 MAY 1858.

Meyerbeer's opera 'Les Huguenots' was chosen to open the present Covent Garden building in 1858. The previous building had been destroyed by fire in 1856.

From every point of view, 'Les Huguenots' was a crucial work for opera throughout the second half of the nineteenth century. It was first performed at Covent Garden in 1842, and repeated every year from 1847 to 1855, 1860 to 1863, 1865 to 1866, and continuously from 1868 to 1894. The production lingered on till 1912, although it was derided by serious musicians. It was revived in 1927 for a notorious last and worst performance.

More recently, in 1968, a concert performance was held at the Royal Albert Hall.

DIMENSIONS: *755 × 503mm.*

PROVENANCE: *The Theatre Museum.*

LITERATURE: *Harold Rosenthal, Two Centuries of Opera at Covent Garden, 1968.*

470 *Certificate of the Huguenot Society of London*
GIVEN TO SIR AUSTEN HENRY LAYARD, FIRST PRESIDENT, 1885.

Sir Austen Henry Layard (1817–1894) was a Member of Parliament and an Under Secretary for Foreign Affairs. He is best remembered as an archaeologist for his excavation of Nineveh.

DIMENSIONS: *540 × 440mm.*

PROVENANCE: *Huguenot Library.*

LITERATURE: *Irvine R. Gray, Huguenot Manuscripts: A Descriptive Catalogue of the Remaining Manuscripts in the Huguenot Library, Huguenot Society Quarto Series, Vol.LVI, 1983, pp.147, 184.*

471 *Badge of the Huguenot Society of London*
SILVER; INSCRIBED: OBVERSE: L'ETERNEL GARDE LES FIDELES. IN EXERGUE: 1572–1685; REVERSE: THE HUGUENOT SOCIETY OF LONDON FOUNDED 1885.

The obverse shows ships approaching the cliffs of Dover, guided by a flaming beacon, with fleur-de-lys and Tudor rose motifs. The design is based on a die which was presented to the Society in 1890.

An enamelled Presidential badge of the same design was presented to the Society in 1939 by Mr. E.C. Ouvry, on his retirement from the Presidency.

ILLUSTRATED: *page 313.*

DIMENSIONS: *308 × 205mm.*

PROVENANCE: *Huguenot Library.*

LITERATURE: *Proceedings of the Huguenot Society of London, Vol.16 (1937–41), pp.183, 188–9, pl.18; Proceedings of the Huguenot Society of London, Vol.21 (1965–70), p.161.*

MASSACRE OF S⁺ BARTHOLOMEW. 1572.

LANDING IN ENGLAND.

La Sainte Bible

The Huguenot Society of London.

This is to Certify that

The Rt. Hon. Sir Henry A. Layard. G.C.B.

is the First President of

The Huguenot Society of London

HAVING FOR ITS OBJECTS,

The interchange and publication of knowledge relating to:—

A. The History of the Huguenots in France.

B. The Huguenot Emigrations from France and adjoining countries.

C. The Refugee Settlements throughout the world, particularly those in Great Britain, Ireland and the Channel Islands; and the resulting effects of those Settlements upon the professions, manufactures, commerce, and social life of the several places in which they were made.

D. Huguenot genealogy & heraldry & Huguenot Church & other registers.

To form a bond of fellowship among some of those who inherit or admire the characteristic Huguenot virtues, and who desire to perpetuate the memory of their Huguenot ancestors.

Dated this   day of   188

President

Hon: Sec.

REVOCATION OF THE EDICT OF NANTES 1685.

The Church	The Army	The Law	Science & Art	Literature	Commerce
ALLIX	LIGONIER	MASÈRES	DESAGULIERS	DE BOSTAQUET	DE PORTAL
CHENEVIX	RUVIGNY	OUVRY	DOLLOND	MARTINEAU	FOURDRINIER
ROMAINE	SCHOMBERG	ROMILLY	LE SUEUR	RAPIN DE THOYRAS	HOUBLON
SAURIN	TURENNE	SYLVESTRE	VIGNOLES	ROGET	PASSAVANT

470

472 *Banner of the Huguenot Lodge No. 2140*

EMBROIDERED WITH THE INSCRIPTION: THE HUGUENOT LODGE NO.2140 LUX LUCET IN TENEBRIS ANTIQUISSIMA INSIGNIA FOUNDED TO COMMEMORATE THE BICENTENARY OF THE REVOCATION OF THE EDICT OF NANTES 1685–1885.

The banner is embroidered in gold lurex thread on a cotton and man-made fibre and has a gold fringe. It depicts a lighted candle surrounded by seven stars and hangs from a brass pole with fleur-de-lis terminals.

The Lodge was founded in May, 1886 in commemoration of the Bicentenary of the Revocation of the Edict of Nantes.

Its founders and original members were all Directors of the French Hospital or Fellows of the then newly formed Huguenot Society of London. Its first Worshipful Master was W. Brother Richard Hervé Giraud, Deputy Governor of the French Hospital.

Although the Lodge intended essentially to attract representatives of Huguenot families, permission was made from the first for the admission of those interested in HLguenot history or admirers of the character and principles of their ancestors, although they might not necessarily be of Huguenot descent themselves.

DIMENSIONS: *1210 × 840mm.*

PROVENANCE: *Huguenot Lodge No.2140.*

LITERATURE: *Proceedings of the Huguenot Society of London, Vol. 22 (1970–1976), p.282.*

473 *Past Master's Jewel*

HUGUENOT LODGE, 1939; INSCRIBED ON THE RIBBON: LUX LUCET IN TENEBRIS.

Depicting the arms of the Waldenses or Vaudois (Protestant community of the Piedmont valleys): on a shield azure, a candlestick or, with a lighted candle proper surmounted by seven stars, representing the 'Light that shineth in Darkness,' and the Seven Liberal Arts and Sciences.

The jewel is suspended from a special ribbon of red and white symbolising 'the purity of our Protestant martyrdom stained by the blood of the persecution'.

PROVENANCE: *Presented by The Huguenot Lodge No. 2140 to W. Bro. Stanley Abbott-Bonner, W.M. 1938–9; Huguenot Lodge No 2140.*

LITERATURE: *A. Hervé Browning, Notes on the Huguenot Lodge No. 2140, 1935, p. 6.*

474 *'The Huguenot Refugee', four-part song*

WINDHAM RYVES, THE WORDS BY DR. SAMUEL BYLES, NINETEENTH CENTURY.

I tell of the noble Refugee
Who strove in a holy faith,
At the altars of his God to bow,
When the road it was marked with death.

How vain was the flight, in the wild midnight,
To the forest's inmost glade;
Where the holy few, to those altars true,
On the greensward knelt and prayed.

When the despot's sword and the bigot's torch
Had driven him forth to roam
From village, and farm, and city and town,
He sought our Island Home.

And store of wealth, and a rich reward,
He brought in his open hand,
For many a peaceful art he taught,
Instead of the foeman's brand.

And boldly he fought for the land he'd sought,
When the battle storm awoke,
In the tented field, or the guarded fort,
Or on board our hearts of oak.

And dear to him now is the red crossed flag
(His ancient hate and fear),
And well does he love his adopted land,
And the friends who've welcomed him here.

CHORUS

Hey! for our land, our English land,
The land of the brave and free;
Who with open arms in the olden time,
Received the Refugee.

Dr. Samuel Byles (*d.*1856), who wrote these words, was medical officer for 30 years at the French Hospital; he also practised in Hackney Road.

The song was frequently sung at French Hospital Court dinners.

PROVENANCE: *Huguenot Library.*

475 *The Roll of the Huguenots settled in the United Kingdom*

LITHOGRAPH, MARTIN HOOD & CO. BERNARD QUARITCH, *c.*1885.

This includes the names and armorials of some of the most prominent Huguenot families who settled in England.

DIMENSIONS: *765 × 590.*

PROVENANCE: *French Hospital.*

LITERATURE: *Robin D. Gwynn, Huguenot Heritage, 1985, Appendix, Tracing Huguenot Ancestors, pp.176–187.*

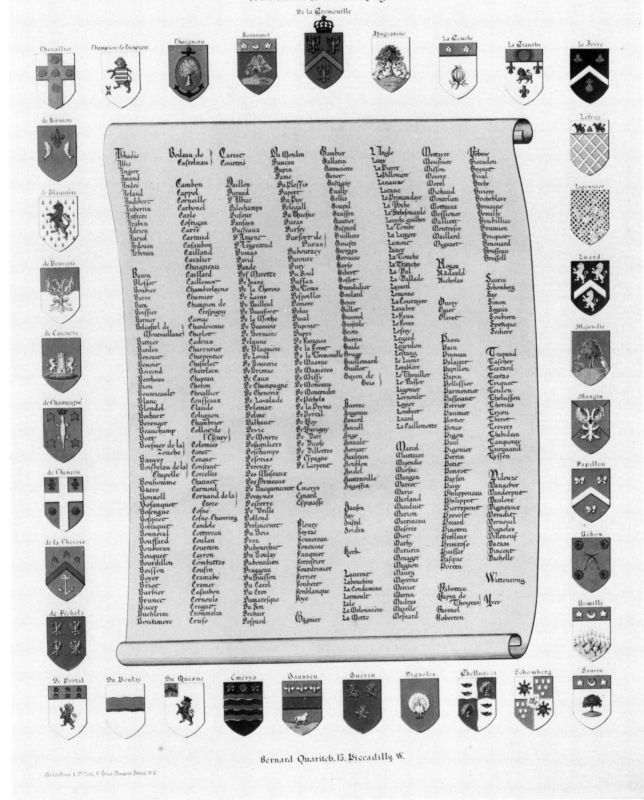

475

List of lenders

We would like to thank the following lenders for their cooperation and kind permission to reproduce copyright photographs in the catalogue.

Her Majesty the Queen   145, 402, 463
His Grace the Duke of Buccleuch and Queensberry   247, 269, 271, 393, 394, 395, 396
His Grace the Duke of Northumberland   207
The Most Hon. The Marquess of Hartington   324, 325
The Most Hon. The Marquess of Tavistock and the Trustees of the Bedford Estates   83, 158, 335, 457
The Right Hon. The Earl of Radnor   1, 423, 424
The Right Hon. The Earl of Yarborough   311, 460, 461
The Lady Monson   445
Sir Westrow Hulse Bt.   222
The Society of Antiquaries   433
The Worshipful Society of Apothecaries   168
Musée de L'Armée, Paris,   20, 21
The Visitors of the Ashmolean Museum, Oxford   340, 345, 347, 362, 368
The Bank of England   412, 414, 415, 417, 418, 419, 420, 421, 422
The Bate Collection, Faculty of Music, Oxford University 211
Major C.J.C. Beckett   138
Dr. David Bindman   291
Museum Boymans-van-Beuningen, Rotterdam   264
The British Architectural Library/RIBA   265, 273
The British Library   18, 27, 42, 46, 49, 71, 124, 130, 175, 179, 183, 198b, 209, 210, 228, 231b, 232, 251, 252, 255, 262, 386, 466
The British Museum   4, 13, 16, 17, 110, 125, 126, 137, 139, 149, 150, 153, 154, 155, 157, 159, 160, 161, 162, 165, 169, 172, 173, 178, 212, 216, 231a, 233, 237, 238, 242, 243, 245, 246, 253, 258, 260, 282, 292, 293, 294, 304, 305, 312, 331, 342, 357, 358, 359, 360, 365, 366, 370, 372, 375, 376, 377, 380, 381, 382, 383, 384, 442, 443, 453, 458, 459
City of Canterbury Museum   374
Cazenove & Co.   427, 428
The Administrative Trustees of the Chevening Estate   316
The Collection of the Worshipful Company of Clockmakers 355, 364, 367, 369
The Worshipful Company of Clothworkers   297
The Courtauld Institute Galleries   455
The Trustees of the Devonshire Collection   276
Dollond and Aitchison Museum   184, 185b, 186, 187, 188, 189, 190
The Trustees of the Fifth Earl of Durham's Picture Settlement   204
Dutch Church, Austin Friars   51
Eton College   330, 338, 349, 350
French Church, Canterbury   77
French Church, Portarlington   82
French Church, Soho Square   11, 54, 56, 57, 58, 59, 61, 66, 68, 70, 80, 121, 193
French Hospital, Rochester   9, 14, 29, 36, 45, 55, 72, 75, 78, 79, 81, 89, 90, 92, 94, 99, 100, 101, 107, 112, 113, 114, 115, 122, 141, 317, 444, 450, 475
Garrick Club   201
Gloucester County Record Office   274
The Worshipful Company of Goldsmiths   332, 334, 385
The Grenadier Guards   146
The Guildhall Library   65, 134, 135, 164, 176, 194, 195, 220, 413, 426, 430
Historic House Hotels Ltd.   456
Museum of the History of Science, Oxford   180, 181
C. Hoare & Co. Bankers   197, 339

The Huguenot Library   5, 7, 8, 12, 19, 24, 26, 28, 37, 40, 43, 44, 48, 67, 73, 84, 85, 86, 87, 88, 93, 95, 96, 97, 98, 103, 104, 105, 108, 117, 123, 132, 133, 140, 156, 163, 215, 320, 327, 432, 435, 447, 465, 470, 471, 474
The Huguenot Lodge   472, 473
The Worshipful Company of Ironmongers   336
Mrs. Jaulmes   31, 32, 60
Kent County Record Office   300
Theodore Landon Esq.   69
Leeds City Art Galleries   289, 296, 348
Leeds District Archives   290
London Library   219
Museum of London   22, 53, 64, 106, 129, 174, 196, 202, 203, 208, 226, 227, 239, 240, 248, 249, 261e, 283, 301, 302, 318, 351, 352, 353, 354, 356, 363, 371, 373, 403, 411, 449, 451, 452, 468
The Makins Collection   467
Musée de la Marine, Paris   41
Midland Bank PLC   454
National Army Museum   143, 147, 148
National Maritime Museum   177
National Museum of Wales   303
National Portrait Gallery   63, 136, 152, 200, 213, 218, 229, 244, 278, 310
National Trust
  Dunham Massey   288
  Knole   287
Colonel Nelthorpe   306
Jonathan Ouvry Esq.   116, 118, 446a
The Worshipful Company of Pewterers   199
Pharmaceutical Society of Great Britain   170, 171
Pilkington Glass Museum   398
Portals Ltd.   50, 257
Private Collections   74, 166, 214, 217, 221, 223, 224, 225, 254, 259, 277, 279, 280, 284, 309, 313, 314, 315, 328, 337, 343, 344, 346, 361, 431, 441, 446b, 448, 464
Musée du Protestantisme, Paris   2, 3, 10, 23, 25, 33, 34
Public Record Office   62, 437
Madame Rosin   30
Michael Riviere Esq.   261
Mrs. F. Roper   119, 120
Royal Academy of Arts, London   281
Royal College of Obstetricians and Gynaecologists   167
Royal Society, London   182
St. Mary's Church, Rye   76
St. Mary's College, Strawberry Hill   378
Science Museum, London   198a
The Shipley Art Galley, Gateshead   206
The Society of Antiquaries   433
Southampton Record Office   256
The Right Hon. The Speaker   268
The Trustees of the Tate Gallery   434
Tessiers Ltd.   387, 388, 389, 390, 391, 392, 393
Theatre Museum   469
H.M. Armouries, Tower of London   321, 322, 323, 326
United Reformed Church   52
University of London Library   416
Vandome & Hart Ltd.   191, 192
Vanners, Sudbury   454
A.J.W. Vaughan Esq.   128
Victoria and Albert Museum   205, 234, 235, 236, 241, 250, 263, 267, 270, 272, 275, 298, 299, 307, 308, 333, 341, 379, 397, 399, 400, 401, 404, 406, 407, 408, 409, 410, 436, 438, 439, 440
The Worshipful Company of Vintners   329
The Wernher Collection, Luton Hoo   405
The Wiltshire County Record Office   425

INDEX

This is a name index of catalogue entries containing all Huguenot names and other names relevant to Huguenot history.
Compound names are arranged mainly following the English form of usage, e.g. under De Lamerie, Paul.
Monarchs are arranged under their forename, e.g. Henry IV.
Nobles under their title, e.g. Marlborough, John Churchill, Duke of.
Numbers refer to catalogue entries.

Abbadie, Jacques (c.1654–1727), *minister*, 130
Allen, John, *smallworker*, 348
Allix, Pierre, *minister*, 65
Ames, Susannah (d.1887), 104
Amman, Jost, *engraver*, 12
André, Major John (1751–1780), 147, 148
Angibaud, Charles, *apothecary*, 171, 172
Angibaud, Marthe, 171, 172
Anne, Queen, 302, 375, 376
Anne of Denmark, 168, 393
Anspach, —, *minister*, 86 b
Antrobus, Jane, 127
Archambo, Peter, *silversmith*, 334
Ardouin, Philip, *schoolmaster*, 123
Arlaud, Benjamin (fl.1701–1731), 396
Arlaud, J.A. (1668–1748), *miniaturist*, 396
Artaud, E., 110
Artois, Comte d', 47
Aubert, —, 57
Aubert, —, *engraver*, 278
Aubertin, Peter, *merchant*, 441
Aubrisset, Jean, *ivory worker*, 301
Audeer family, 444
Audinet, Philip (1766–1837), *engraver*, 241
Audinet, Rev. Samuel, 241
Aufrère, Anthony, 63
Aufrère, Antoine, 63
Aufrère, Arabella (d.1804), 311, 460
Aufrère, George, *draper*, 311, 460, 461
Aufrère, Israel Antoine (1677–1758), *minister*, 63, 311, 460
Aufrère, Sophia, 311, 460, 461

Badcock, Richard, *silk weaver*, 440
Baillie, Hon. George (d.1738), 316 b
Baillie, Lady Grizel (1665–1746), 316 a
Baker, William, *stationer*, 258
Baker & Fourdrinier, *stationers*, 258
Baldero, Elizabeth, 164
Barbaroux, William, *leatherman*, 161
Baril, Louis (1692–1761), 309
Barraud, Francis Gabriel, *watch and clockmakers*, 344, 369, 370
Barraud, Magdalene, 344, 369
Barraud, Paul Philip, 370
Barraud, Philip, *engraver*, 369

Barreau, David, 435
Barrett, C.R.B., *engraver*, 163
Basire, Isaac (1704–1768), *engraver*, 233, 234
Basire, James (1730–1802), *engraver*, 226, 227, 233
Basire, James (1769–1822), *engraver*, 228, 233
Basire, James (1796–1869), *engraver*, 233
Basire, John, *engraver*, 233
Bate, Arabella, 311, 460
Bate, William, 311
Bateman, William, *silversmith*, 451
Bathurst, Allen, 1st Earl, 124
Batoni, Pompeo, *painter*, 202
Baudouin, Christopher, *silk designer*, 437, 438, 450
Baudouin, Rene, 140
Bean, Peter, *silk weaver*, 447
Beard, Charles, *engraver*, 161
Beaufort, Daniel Augustus (1739–1821), *geographer*, 200
Beauvais, Anne, 359
Beauvais, Françoise, 359
Beauvais, Paul, *watchmaker*, 359
Beauvais, Susanne, 359
Bedford, 2nd Duke of, 309, 335
Bedford, 5th Earl of, 83
Bellotti, L.L., *engraver*, 36
Benovad, Stephen, 132
Berchère, Jaques Louis (1670–1753), *banker*, 57, 309, 348
Berchère, Suzanne Judith, 348
Berchet, Pierre (1659–1720), *painter*, 277
Bernard, Elie, *watchmaker*, 363
Bernardeau, Daniel, *woodturner*, 294
Berthon, Isaac, 57
Besombes, Samuel, *minister*, 133
Betambeau, Peter, 104
Beteilhe, Francis, 132
Bigot, Peter, 439, 444
Binning, Lady Rachel (1696–1773), 316 d
Bion, Jean, *pastor*, 42
Bloodworth, John, 438
Bloodworth, Sarah, 438
Boisragon, Louis Chevalleau de, Chevalier de la Chenaye (1666–1736), 138
Boissier, Guillaume, 348
Boissier, Jean Daniel, 348
Boissonet, Jacques, *deacon*, 176
Boitard, —, *playing cards designer*, 178
Bonneau, Jacob, *engraver*, 237, 244, 294
Bonneau, Peter, 294
Bonneau, Pierre, *engraver*, 294
Bordier, James (1616–1684), *painter*, 395
Bosanquet, Claude, 57
Bosanquet, David, 80
Boucher, Joseph, *tailor*, 269
Bouchet, James, *wine merchant*, 155
Boujet, —, 273, 288
Bourdon, Peter, *silk weaver*, 446

Bouttats, Gaspard, *engraver*, 14
Bouveries, Edward des, 423
Bouveries, Sir Edward des (1621–1694), 423
Bouveries, Sir Edward des (1688–1731), 424
Bouveries, Sir Jacob des, 425
Bouveries, Laurens des (1563–1610), 423
Bouveries, William des, 423
Bouveries, Sir William des (1656–1717), 424
Bouveries, *see also* Radnor, Earls of
Boyer, Abel (1667–1729), 124, 269
Brevint, M., *diarist*, 170
Briot, François, 399
Brockedon, William, *painter*, 218
Brodrick, Thomas (1654–1730), 305
Brooks, John, 408
Brousson, Claude (1647–1698), *lawyer*, 37
Browning, A.H.G., 107, 119
Bulteel, Jean, *pastor*, 75
Bulteel, Mary, 75
Burrell, Sir Merrick, 422
Burrell, Peter, 422
Busher, Sarah, 123
Butty, Francis, *goldsmith*, 350
Byas family, 444
Byles, Dr. Samuel (d.1856), 474

Cabibel, Peter, 45
Cahusac, Thomas, *musical instrument maker*, 211, 212
Cahusac, William, 212
Cailleau, Pierre (d.1760), *gunsmith*, 327
Caillouel, Isaac, *merchant*, 19
Calas, Anne Rose, 45
Calas, Donat, 45
Calas, Jean, *linen merchant*, 45, 46, 47
Calas, Marc Antoine, 45
Calvin, John (1509–1564), 1, 3, 7, 51
Campart, Mary, 439
Campart, Peter, *silk weaver*, 439
Carbonnel, Delilers, 57
Caroline, Princess of Wales, 82
Carpentiers, Adrien, *painter*, 205
Castaing, John, 426
Catherine de Medici, 11
Cauvin, Rachel, 463
Cavalier, Jean (d.1698 or 1699), *sculptor*, 296–300
Cavalier, Jean (1681–1740), *soldier*, 40
Cazenove, Edward, *stockbroker*, 428
Cazenove, Henry junior, *stockbroker*, 428
Cazenove, Phillip (1798–1880), *stockbroker*, 427, 428
Cazenove & Co., *stockbrokers*, 427–9
Chaigneau, Andrew, *laceman*, 457
Chamberlen, Hugh, *physician*, 167
Chamberlen, Peter, *physician*, 167
Chambers, Margaret, 311
Chambers, Thomas, 311
Chambers, Sir William, *architect*, 235, 236
Chamier, Anthony (1725–1780), 217

Sabourin & Marchant, *cabinet makers*, 165
Sagnier, William, 447
Sanxay, Daniel (*d.*1739), *headmaster*, 127
Sanxay, James, *headmaster*, 127
Sanxay, Robert, *druggist*, 127
Sarasin, Jean, 67
Sartor, James, *engraver*, 384
Sauberque, Peter, *throwster*, 446
Saurin, Jacques, *minister*, 54, 55, 79
Savage, J., *engraver*, 178
Savigny, J.H., *instrument maker*, 173, 174
Savigny, John Tessier, *razormaker*, 173
Savigny, Paul, 173
Scalé, Bernard, 246
Scarlett, William, *silversmith*, 99
Schnebbelie, R.B., *painter*, 64, 227
Schomberg, Frederick, 1st Duke of (1615–1690), 18, 125, 130, 136–40, 266
Scotin, G., *engraver*, 153, 407
Scribe, Eugène (1791–1861), 466
Segalas, Israel, *gunsmith*, 151
Seignoret, Stephen, 435
Serces, Jacques (1695–1762), 44, 67
Serces, Moise, 44
Settle, Elkanah (1648–1724), *poet*, 413
Shakespeare, William (1564–1616), 204, 205
Shepherd, Thomas H. (*fl.*1815–*c.*1860), 150
Sherrard, William, 435
Simon, Pierre, *pastor*, 61
Simonin, Claude, 322
Simonin, Jacques, 322
Six, James (1731–1793), 198
Smith, I., *engraver*, 136
Sorel family, 444
South, J.C.B., 109
Sprimont, Nicholas, *goldsmith*, 344, 402–5
Stanhope, Countess Grisel (1719–1811), 316e
Stanhope, Philip, 2nd Earl (1714–1786), 316g
Stanhope family, 316; *see also* Chesterfield
Stapleton, Canon H.C.E., 109
Stone, René, *framemaker*, 292
Stonyer, William, 53
Storni, J.J., *painter*, 36
Stretes, William, 52
Stukeley, William, *antiquary*, 306, 310
Subleyras, Pierre, *painter*, 344
Sufflee, —, 439
Suffolk, Catherine, Countess of (1566–1633), 393

Sympson, Joseph (*c.*1730–*c.*1747), *engraver*, 282

Talman, William, *architect*, 274, 275
Tanqueray, Anne, 335, 341
Tanqueray, David, 335, 341
Taudin, James, *pewterer*, 199
Tayspill, Francis (*c.*1591–1666), *cloth merchant*, 456
Tayspill, Giles, *weaver*, 456
Tessier, H. & E., *jewellers*, 387
Tessier, Henry, *jeweller*, 388, 389
Tessier, Henry Alexander, 392
Tessier, Lewis de (*d.*1811), 387, 392
Tessier, Louis Edward (1841–1895), *jeweller*, 392
Tessier & Sons, *jewellers*, 391
Thornhill, Sir James (1676–1734), *painter*, 277
Tijou, Jean, *ironsmith*, 117, 262, 263
Tijou, Thomas, *worker in gold*, 117, 262
Toms, W.H., *engraver*, 195
Tookey, J., *engraver*, 152
Toutin, Jean, *goldsmith*, 394
Tregent, James, *watchmaker*, 371, 372
Triquet, Charles, *silk weaver*, 444, 445
Triquet, Vansommer & Co., 445
Trotter, —, *engraver*, 55
Tuttell Thomas (*c.*1674–1702), *instrument maker*, 177–9

Utenhove, John, 51

Vaillant, Adam, 254
Vaillant, Frances (1776–1845), 254
Vaillant, François, *bookseller*, 253
Vaillant, Isaac (1679–1753), *bookseller*, 253
Vaillant, Letitia (1770–1852), 254
Vaillant, Paul (1671–1739), *bookseller*, 45, 72, 253, 254
Vaillant, Paul (1716–1802), *bookseller*, 253, 254
Vaillant, Suzanne (1669–1749), 253
Vaillant family, 72
Van der Erve, Egidus, *printer*, 68
Van Neck, —, 57
Van Somer, Paul, *engraver*, 63
Vandome, Richard, *scalemaker*, 191, 192
Vanner, James Englebert, *banker*, 454
Vanner, John, *weaver*, 454
Vanner, William, *weaver*, 454
Vansommer, John (1706–1774), *pattern drawer*, 441, 444, 445, 448
Vauloué, James, *engineer*, 150, 195
Vautier, Daniel, 439
Vautrollier, Thomas, *printer*, 251

Vaux, Gerard de, *papermaker*, 50, 256
Vaux, John de, 257
Verbeck, —, 439
Vertue, George, 206, 214, 271, 277, 278, 291, 310, 315, 320
Verzelini, Jacob, *glass maker*, 397
Viet, Claude, *clockmaker*, 384
Viet, Marie Anne, *jeweller*, 384
Vigne, J.R., 109
Vigne, Louis Ferdinand, *watchmaker*, 441
Villette family, 49
Vintimille, Charles Gaspard William de, Archbishop of Paris, 29
Vivares, Francis (1709–1780), *engraver*, 237, 239, 243–5
Vivares, John, 244
Vivares, Thomas, 244
Voltaire, François-Marie Arouet de, 45–7, 441

Walpole, Sir Robert, 422
Wagner, Joseph (1706–1780), *engraver*, 244
Wale, S., 240
Warrington, George Booth, 2nd Earl of, 273, 288, 333, 334, 340
Watteau, Jean Antoine, *painter*, 172, 207
Watts, Mary, 446
Weatherhead, —, 385
Webb, Aston (1849–1930), *architect*, 59, 60
Whichcote, Theodosia (1735–1827), 254
White, R., *engraver*, 237
Whood, Isaac (1688–1752), *painter*, 412
Willaume, Adam, *goldsmith*, 82
Willaume, Anne, 335, 341
Willaume, David, *goldsmith*, 82, 335, 338, 341
William III, 63, 90, 117, 130, 136, 214, 264, 300;
   arrival in London, 129;
   pair of pistols for, 322;
   portraits, 137, 299, 318o, 354;
   Royal Approbation, 54;
   state coach for, 322;
   Victory of Namur, 229
William IV, 128
Wren, Sir Christopher (1632–1723), *architect*, 62, 131, 262, 308, 310

Yarborough, Charles Anderson Pelham, Lord, 311, 460, 461
Young, Canon G.M., 109
Young, William Abraham, 446

Zoffany, Johann, *painter*, 204